D1070057

AXIOMATIC
ANALYSIS:

An Introduction to Logic
and the Real Number System

Under the general editorship of

DAVID VERNON WIDDER

Harvard University

AXIOMATIC ANALYSIS:

An Introduction to Logic and the Real Number System

ROBERT KATZ

Tufts University

D. C. HEATH AND COMPANY • BOSTON

This book, the last of three class-tested versions, was
written with the assistance of Mr. Michael P. Grossman,
one of the author's students. It is hoped that this
collaboration has resulted in an exposition which will
appeal to students who seek a simple, clear, and orderly
treatment of elementary logic and analysis.

Preface

The knowledge gained from studying an axiomatic development of the real number system provides the essential foundation for calculus and an appropriate background for modern algebra. Because students should study such a development as early as possible, this self-contained book was designed in such a manner that only high school algebra is a formal prerequisite.

The development is based on the conception of the real number system as a complete ordered field, although no modern algebra is required or included. The axioms concern a set and three functions (addition, multiplication, and max) and reveal interesting algebraic connections between these functions. Among the topics covered are extrema of number sets, inductive proofs, completeness, irrational powers, real functions, $\sum$, and many useful tools such as the Bernoulli Inequalities for real powers.

As a suitable preliminary to the real number system, there is included an introduction to logic, sets, ordered pairs, and functions.

The treatment of logic rests on the notion of *similar statements* (statements that express the same thought). There are semiformal developments or informal discussions of the following items:

> the logic of *and, or, not, if ... then, if and only if;*
> entailment, logical truth, and logical falsity;
> quantified statements and their negations;
> existence and nonexistence;
> deductive truth, deductive falsity, and undecidability;
> justification of various methods of proof;
> systems, consistency, and completeness;
> and sundry foundational issues.

The material on sets includes Russell's paradox and a few basic axioms of set theory. Ordered pairs are so defined that no ordered pair is a singleton, a feature that has some pedagogical advantage.

v

The book is divided into sixty-five lessons, which fall into three relatively independent parts: logic (thirteen lessons); sets, ordered pairs, functions (eight lessons); and the real number system (forty-four lessons). A student may start at Lesson 1 or Lesson 14 or Lesson 22, referring back if necessary. Throughout the text are interspersed over six hundred exercises, most of which are essential to the development.

The lessons are divided into numbered sections, and all references in the text are to sections rather than to pages.

For example, "216" refers to Lesson 2, 16th section.

Some sections are divided into alphabetically designated parts.
For example, "1205b" refers to Lesson 12, section 5, part b.

The author wishes to extend his gratitude to

Professor H. Ronald Rouse and Mr. Charles K. Wilkinson for their penetrating, critical analyses and invaluable improvements;

Professor and Mrs. David V. Widder, Dr. Yiannis N. Moschovakis, and Dr. David F. Isles for their helpful comments and suggestions;

Miss Barbara B. Betts and Mrs. Matilda C. Young for their fine editorial work;

Mr. David A. Reed, Mr. Wendell W. Wilkinson, and Mr. Richard A. Dudman for their expert technical assistance;

Mrs. Edith A. Wilkinson, Mrs. Doris M. Rushton, and Mrs. A. Hope Baltzer for their excellent transcriptions;

his father, Louis F. Katz, for encouragement and financial assistance;

and lastly, to his dear wife, Rosalie, for her patience and devotion.

Criticism and suggestions are cordially invited.

ROBERT KATZ
51 Mt. Vernon Street
Boston, Massachusetts

Contents

AXIOMATIC
ANALYSIS:

*An Introduction to Logic
and the Real Number System*

Things, Symbols, and Statements

101. In the early lessons of this book the author *attempts* to provide a simple philosophy of mathematics that will be understandable by undergraduates and acceptable to working mathematicians.

All prescriptions set forth here for the use of language apply to mathematical discourse and may be contrary to customary usage. In the author's opinion, however, mathematics is not a language but rather a highly refined concept game created and played by the human mind.

102. By a *thing* we mean any actual or fictitious object, attribute (trait), relationship, event, concept, or process. Furthermore, each collection of things is deemed to be a thing.

A fictitious thing is a figment, a creation of the mind. For example, a major portion of this book is devoted to the study of certain fictitious things inappropriately called *real* numbers.

103. Example. Here is a diversified list of things:

the planet Neptune,
the word *Neptune*,
the blob of ink NEPTUNE,
the Greek god Neptune,
the city of San Francisco,
Mozart's manuscript of his opera *Don Giovanni*,
the Boston performance of *Don Giovanni* by the Metropolitan Opera in 1958,
Virgil's conception of the underworld as described in his epic *Aeneid*,
Leibniz's concept of monad,
the sound of the first note of *The Messiah* as first imagined by Handel,
the sound of the first note of *The Messiah* as first heard by Handel,

1

Adam Smith's concept of a free market,
the American Revolutionary War,
the attribute of being the first President of the United States of America,
George Washington,
the relationship *less than* between real numbers,
the first sentence of *Moby Dick*,
the process of manufacturing a 1964 Corvette automobile,
the collection of eighteen things described above.

104. Symbols.

a. Symbols are written or printed marks and are used for many different purposes. Symbols may be chosen or designed at one's pleasure but should be easily recognizable and readily reproducible. Ideally each symbol should have a name so that sentences containing the symbol may be rendered into speech.

b. Some symbols are used permanently to denote (stand for, refer to) particular things. E.g. (this means *for example*), the symbol 3 permanently denotes a certain real number; the letter e permanently denotes the real number called Euler's number; the symbol $+$ permanently denotes the operation of addition of real numbers; the symbol $\neq$ permanently stands for the expression *is not equal to* (*is not identical to*). In the study of complex numbers the letter i is used as a permanent symbol for a certain complex number; however, since we shall not deal with complex numbers in this book, we shall consider the letter i to be "available." Later, however, we shall adopt the letter I as a permanent symbol.

c. Permanent symbols are introduced by conventions; the author uses the caption **Notation** (or NOTATION) to indicate such conventions.

d. To determine the thing (if there is one) that is denoted by a symbol, one must refer to the convention where the symbol is introduced; it does no good to stare at the symbol, hoping that its meaning will be revealed in some mystical manner.

e. Some symbols are used temporarily to denote things; this is often called *ad hoc usage*. E.g., if one is discussing Tufts University, he may say "Let the symbol T denote Tufts University" or simply "Let T denote Tufts University."

f. Appropriate choice of symbols often simplifies an otherwise complicated discussion. Only an obscurantist would begin a discussion thus: "Let H denote Tufts University and let T denote Harvard University."

g. A symbol that denotes a thing is not the same as the thing. E.g., the symbol 3 is not the same as the real number that it denotes. Disregard of this principle may lead to serious confusion.

h. Different things should be denoted by different symbols; howe[...]
ent symbols are often used to denote the same thing. E.g., the
symbols are different but denote the same real number:

$$3, \quad \text{III}, \quad 1 + 2, \quad 7 - 4, \quad 6/2.$$

The use of two or more different symbols does not necessarily mean that
we are referring to different things.

i. Some symbols are used only as part of other symbols or expressions and
do not denote anything. E.g., in this book we shall use the symbol Σ only
as part of another symbol; by itself the symbol Σ does not denote anything. This kind of usage is often referred to as *contextual usage*. In
most books, the symbols ∞, $-\infty$, $+\infty$ are only used contextually, and it
is futile to maintain that they denote things.

j. Symbols often enable us to express complicated thoughts clearly and
simply. E.g., the thought expressed by the sentence

Each real number whose square is one less than twice itself equals one

may be expressed in the following ways.

No matter what real number we consider, say t,
if $t^2 = 2t - 1$, then $t = 1$.

No matter what real number y we consider,
if $y^2 = 2y - 1$, then $y = 1$.

For any real number u: if $u^2 = 2u - 1$, then $u = 1$.

For each real number b such that $b^2 = 2b - 1$: $b = 1$.

NOTE I. It is understood here that none of the letters t, y, u, b has been
or is being chosen as a permanent symbol; furthermore, any available
symbol could be used here equally well in place of t, y, u, b.

NOTE II. The author uses the symbol $\vdots$ as a punctuation mark to separate
certain parts of mathematical sentences.

NOTE III. *Such that* means *which have* (or *has*) *the property that.*

105. The words *each*, *every*, *all* are used synonymously. The word *any* is often
used as a synonym for *each*, *every*, *all*. E.g., the following sentences
express the same thought.

Any person who studies will acquire knowledge.
Each person who studies will acquire knowledge.
Every person who studies will acquire knowledge.
All persons who study will acquire knowledge.

The word *any* is also used in other ways; however, *any* should never be
used as a synonym for *some*, which means *at least one* (*one or more*).

106. Unless there is a special qualification to the contrary, the use of the plural in mathematical discourse indicates a *possible* plurality rather than an *actual* plurality.

E.g., the sentence
For any real numbers x, y: if 3x = y − x, then x = y/4
as well as the sentence
For any two real numbers x, y: if 3x = y − x, then x = y/4
means
For any possibly equal real numbers x, y: if 3x = y − x, then x = y/4.

Note that even the use of the word *two* does not indicate an actual plurality.

To indicate an actual plurality we may use the special qualifier *distinct* (or *different*). E.g., the following expressions are synonymous and indicate that we are considering an actual plurality of real numbers:

For any *distinct* real numbers x, y
For any two *distinct* real numbers x, y.

NOTE. In mathematical discourse the word *distinct* means *different* and does not mean *plain, clear, definite, unmistakable*.

107. In formulating mathematical sentences one should *quantify* (*suitably introduce*) all symbols used. Of course permanent symbols such as 3, =, + need not be explained each time they are used.

The author rejects as meaningless an expression that contains an unquantified symbol. E.g., he considers the expression $(x + x = 2x)$ to be meaningless; if one claims that it means (For each real number x: $x + x = 2x$), then it should be so written. As another example, the expression $(x + 2 = 5)$ is meaningless; if one claims that it means (There exists a real number x such that $x + 2 = 5$), then let it be so written.

When a professional mathematician omits quantifiers (suitable introductions), he knows what quantification is missing, but his readers may founder in a sea of ambiguity. Therefore, in this book we shall provide all necessary quantification, except in the case of notational conventions where quantifiers will often be omitted. During his first exposure to rigorous mathematics the student should cultivate the habit of providing all necessary quantification in his written work.

In Lessons 8 and 9 we shall discuss quantifiers in greater detail.

NOTE. *Meaningless* does not mean *false*; *meaningful* does not mean *true*.

108. In mathematical discourse the expressions *there exists, there is* are synonymous; the word *there* always indicates existence rather than location. When following these expressions, the articles *a, an* always mean *at least* *one* (*one or more*). To illustrate the use of these words, we point out that the following sentences express the same thought.

> There is a real number x such that $x = x^2$.
> There is a real number that equals its square.
> There is at least one real number that equals its square.
> At least one real number equals its square.
> Some real number equals its square.
> There exists a real number x such that $x = x^2$.
> There exists a real number that equals its square.
> There exists at least one real number that equals its square.

109. Definition. A *statement* is any meaningful, unambiguous, declarative sentence.

NOTE. This definition means the following:

each statement is a meaningful, unambiguous, declarative sentence
and
each meaningful, unambiguous, declarative sentence is a statement.

110. Example. The following are not statements.

> Rain hopes rainfully. (*meaningless*)
> John told Jack that his sister admires him. (*ambiguous*)
> Love thy neighbor. (*not declarative*)

111. Example. Each of the following is a statement.

> Snow is white.
> Snow is not white.
> Snow is white or grass is blue.
> Snow is white and grass is blue.
> If snow is white, then grass is blue.
> Each horse is brown or some tiger is lame.
> No man is mortal.
> No man is immortal.
> Some man is unwise
> At most one man is wise.
> Precisely one man is wise.
> The nonzero real number that equals its square is well-known.

NOTE I. *At most one* means *not more than one*. Thus, the following statements are true:

> At most one man has eight eyes.
> At most one man is President of the United States of America.

NOTE II. *Precisely one* means *at least one and at most one* and is synonymous with *exactly one, just one, uniquely one, one and only one*.

NOTE III. In mathematical discourse *the* means *the one and only*. E.g., since there is more than one real number that equals its square, the following sentence is meaningless:

The real number that equals its square is well-known.

112. Among other things, logic is concerned with statements, with various methods of combining statements, and with certain relationships between statements.

In explaining a point of logic we often use simple illustrative statements such as *Snow is white*, *Grass is black*. Because the student knows that the first statement is true and that the second is false, he may fail to understand the logical point being explained; in other words, the student's knowledge may actually impede his understanding. Accordingly, the author often uses the word *Zilch* as the name of a thing whose nature is unknown to the student. Thus, the student does not know whether the statement *Zilch is white* is true or false, and this will aid rather than hinder him.

113. Each statement expresses precisely one thought, which nevertheless may consist of several parts. The thought expressed by a statement is called a *proposition*.

Some logicians consider the notion of a proposition to be a dispensable metaphysical abstraction; however, this notion is a useful pedagogical device.

114. Different statements may express the same proposition; e.g., the following statements are different but express the same proposition.

Zilch is white.
White is the color of Zilch.
The color of Zilch is white.

115. Definition. Statements that express the same proposition are said to be *similar*.

NOTATION. To indicate that a statement B is similar to a statement C we shall write B **sim** C, rendered as B *is similar to* C or simply as B *sim* C.

NOTE I. In Lesson 4 the student will learn why he **must not** render the symbol **sim** as *if and only if*.

NOTE II. In place of the word *similar* many logicians use *equivalent*; however, the word *equivalent* is already overworked in mathematics.

116. Example.

(For each real number x such that $x^2 = 2x - 1$: $x = 1$) **sim**
(For each real number y: if $y^2 = 2y - 1$, then $y = 1$).

117. Notation.

(A **sim** B **sim** C) stands for $[(A$ **sim** $B)$ and $(B$ **sim** $C)]$.

(A **sim** B **sim** C **sim** D) stands for
$$[(A \text{ sim } B) \text{ and } (B \text{ sim } C) \text{ and } (C \text{ sim } D)].$$
And so forth.

NOTE. As was mentioned in 107, we shall often omit quantifiers when formulating notational conventions. E.g., in the above convention it is understood that the letters A, B, C, D stand for any statements whatsoever.

118. Fundamental properties of sim.

a. *Reflexivity*

For each statement G: G **sim** G.

I.e. (this means *that is to say*),
each statement is similar to itself.

b. *Symmetry*

For any statements G, H such that G **sim** H: H **sim** G.

I.e., no matter what statements G, H we consider,
if (G **sim** H), then (H **sim** G).

c. *Transitivity*

For any statements G, H, J such that G **sim** H **sim** J: G **sim** J.

I.e., no matter what statements G, H, J we consider,
if (G **sim** H) and (H **sim** J), then (G **sim** J).

d. *Substitutability*

The replacement of a statement S that is part of a statement G
by any statement that is similar to S
yields a statement that is similar to G.

119. In Lesson 12 we shall discuss the terms *theorem* and *proof* in considerable detail; for the present we shall assume that the student has at least a passing acquaintance with these terms. Of course the words *prove, show, demonstrate* are synonymous.

120. Theorem.

For any statements A, B, C, D such that A **sim** B **sim** C **sim** D: A **sim** D.

PREFATORY REMARK. We shall present three proofs.

Tedious Proof.

Consider any statements A, B, C, D such that A **sim** B **sim** C **sim** D.
Then, by 117, (A **sim** B) and (B **sim** C) and (C **sim** D).
Since (A **sim** B) and (B **sim** C), we know by 118c that A **sim** C.
Since (A **sim** C) and (C **sim** D), we may conclude by 118c that A **sim** D.
Q.e.d.

NOTE I. Tedious proofs such as this should be abhorred.

NOTE II. The expression Q.e.d. abbreviates *Quod erat demonstrandum* (meaning *that which was to be proved*) and is often used to indicate the end of a proof. The author seldom uses this abbreviation.

Brief Proof.

For any statements A, B, C, D such that A **sim** B **sim** C **sim** D:
A **sim**$_1$ C and so A **sim**$_1$ D. (*Reference.* 1.118c)

NOTE III. Throughout this book small numerals to the lower right of symbols such as **sim** allude to the references listed after the proof. E.g., in the previous proof the statement (A **sim** C) is justified by 118c, and the statement (A **sim** D) is also justified by 118c. When references are omitted, and this will happen often, the student should assure himself that he can supply the missing references, perhaps on the basis of his memory of previous facts.

NOTE IV. The expression *and so* means *and hence in view of prior facts we may assert that* and does not mean *implies*.

Condensed Proof.: A **sim**$_1$ C and so A **sim**$_1$ D. (*Ref.* 1.118c)

NOTE V. The symbol : at the beginning of this proof indicates the convenient omission of the clause (For any statements A, B, C, D such that A **sim** B **sim** C **sim** D).

NOTE VI. In general the symbol : occurring at the beginning of a proof indicates the omission of the clause that precedes the first occurrence of the symbol : in the statement of the theorem. This device substantially simplifies the writing of proofs because it spares us the chore of repeating the hypotheses when we begin the proofs.

NOTE VII. Although the student perhaps prefers tedious proofs, the author prefers condensed proofs because, among other things, they make greater demands on the student. Nevertheless, proofs should consist of fully quantified statements. Observe that the Condensed Proof above consists of one complete statement, the quantification being provided by the symbol : at the beginning of the proof.

121. It is clear that Theorem 120 may be extended, e.g., as follows:

For any statements A, B, C, D, E such that A **sim** B **sim** C **sim** D **sim** E :
A **sim** E.

122. Exercise.

For any statements A, B, C such that $(A$ **sim** $C)$ and $(B$ **sim** $C)$: A **sim** B.

NOTE I. Unless instructed otherwise, the student is expected to write out fully quantified proofs of the propositions expressed in the exercises. His task will be greatly eased by exploiting the device explained in 120(NOTE VI).

NOTE II.
The obviousness of a proposition does not obviate a proof therefor.

123. To avoid circumlocution we shall frequently fail to distinguish between a proposition and the statements that express it.

Not, And, Or

201. The following two statements are not similar.

> Zilch is white.
> (Zilch is white) is true.

Indeed, the first statement expresses the proposition that Zilch is white, whereas the second statement expresses the proposition that the statement (Zilch is white) is true. Thus the first statement is about Zilch, but the second statement is about the statement (Zilch is white).

Accordingly, if in a given context a letter, say *H*, stands for a statement, then we **must refrain** from rendering the letter *H* as *H is true*.

202. A *negation* of a statement *B* is any statement that denies the proposition expressed by *B*.

E.g., each of the following statements is a negation of (Zilch is white).

Zilch is not white.
White is not the color of Zilch.

Each of the following statements is a negation of (Zilch is not white).

Zilch is white.
White is the color of Zilch.

CAUTION. The statement (Zilch is blue) is not a negation of the statement (Zilch is white).

203. All negations of a statement are deemed to be similar; accordingly, it is convenient to adopt the fiction that for each statement *B* there is precisely one negation, called *the* negation of *B*.

204. Notation. The negation of a statement *B* will be denoted by the expression (∼*B*), perhaps without the parentheses.

NOTE. The symbol ∼ is called *tilde*; the expression (∼*B*) should be read as *negation B* or as *not B*, but never as *B is false*.

205. Examples.

If *G* stands for (Zilch is white),
then (∼*G*) stands for (Zilch is not white).

If *H* stands for (Zilch is not white),
then (∼*H*) stands for (Zilch is white).

206. The following statements are not similar.

∼(Zilch is white).
(Zilch is white) is false.

The first statement, (Zilch is not white), is about Zilch, whereas the second statement is about the statement (Zilch is white).

This explains why we **must refrain** from rendering an expression such as ∼*H* as *H is false*.

207. Notation. ∼∼*B* stands for ∼(∼*B*).

208. The *conjunction* of two statements *B*, *C* is the statement (*B* and *C*) and means *both B and C*.

NOTE I. The expression (*B* and *C*) should be rendered as *B and C* and not as *B is true and C is true*.

NOTE II. The following words are often used instead of *and*: *but, yet, although, nevertheless, however*.

NOTE III. The student is reminded that *two statements* means *two possibly identical statements*.

NOTE IV. The expression (neither *B* nor *C*) means [(∼*B*) and (∼*C*)].

209. The *disjunction* of two statements *B*, *C* is the statement (*B* or *C*). The following are deemed to be similar: (*B* or *C*), (*B* or *C*, possibly both), (Either *B* or *C*), (Either *B* or *C*, possibly both).

The word *or* probably causes more trouble than any other word. In ordinary discourse (*B* or *C*) often means *B or C, but not both*; the Romans used (*B* aut *C*) for this purpose. In mathematical discourse (*B* or *C*) means *B or C, possibly both*; the Romans used (*B* vel *C*) for this purpose.

CAUTION. The expression (*B* or *C*) should be rendered as *B or C* and not as *B is true or C is true*.

210. Notations.

a. $(\sim B$ and $C)$ stands for $[(\sim B)$ and $C]$;
$(B$ and $\sim C)$ stands for $[B$ and $(\sim C)]$;
$(\sim B$ and $\sim C)$ stands for $[(\sim B)$ and $(\sim C)]$.

b. $(\sim B$ or $C)$ stands for $[(\sim B)$ or $C]$;
and so on.

NOTE. We shall frequently omit parentheses and brackets.

211. Next we adopt eight basic rules that will govern our use of $\sim$, *and, or.*
These basic rules prescribe that certain kinds of statements are similar.
With the aid of 118 and 120 we shall then derive many other rules.

212. Basic rules.

a. *Reciprocity*
For any statements G, H such that G **sim** $\sim H$: $\sim G$ **sim** H.

b. *Idempotency* (and)
For each statement B: $(B$ and $B)$ **sim** B.

c. *Commutativity* (and)
For any statements B, C: $(B$ and $C)$ **sim** $(C$ and $B)$.

d. *Associativity* (and)
For any statements B, C, D: $[B$ and $(C$ and $D)]$ **sim** $[(B$ and $C)$ and $D]$.

e. *Absorption* (or, and)
For any statements A, B: $[A$ or $(A$ and $B)]$ **sim** A.

f. *Distributivity* (and, or)
For any statements A, B, C: $[A$ and $(B$ or $C)]$ **sim** $[(A$ and $B)$ or $(A$ and $C)]$.

g. *DeMorgan's rule* ($\sim$, and)
For any statements A, B: $\sim(A$ and $B)$ **sim** $(\sim A$ or $\sim B)$.

h. *Disjunctive syllogism*
For any statements G, H: $[G$ and $(\sim G$ or $H)]$ **sim** $(G$ and $H)$.

NOTE I. If these basic rules do not harmonize with the student's use of
the words *not, and, or,* he should reread the second paragraph of 101.

NOTE II. The author is indebted to Mr. Michael P. Grossman for eliminat-
ing many redundant rules from a previous list.

213. It can be proved that our eight basic rules are consistent in the sense that for each statement P, it is impossible to derive the similarity of P to $\sim P$.

Principle. No further rules may be adopted that would enable us to derive the similarity of a statement to its negation.

214. In 228e, we shall see why the above principle must not be violated.

215. Derived rule. *Double Negation*
For each statement H ⋮ $\sim\sim H$ **sim** H.

Derivation. ⋮ $\sim H$ **sim**$_1$ $\sim H$, and so $\sim(\sim H)$ **sim**$_2$ H.

References. 1.118a; 2.212a with $\sim H$ for G.

NOTE. The significance of the symbol ⋮ after the caption *Derivation* is the same as that explained in 120(NOTE VI). E.g., in our situation here, the symbol ⋮ indicates the omission of the expression (For each statement H).

216. Derived rule. Similar statements have similar negations; i.e.
for any statements G, B such that G **sim** B ⋮ $\sim G$ **sim** $\sim B$.

Derivation. ⋮ G **sim** B **sim**$_1$ $\sim(\sim B)$, and so G **sim**$_2$ $\sim(\sim B)$, and hence $\sim G$ **sim**$_3$ $\sim B$.

References. 1.215; 2.118c; 3.212a.

NOTE. We shall progressively provide fewer and fewer references; in particular we shall usually omit references to 118, 120, 122, 212a, 215, 216.

217. Derived rule. *Idempotency* (or)
For each statement P ⋮ $(P$ or $P)$ **sim** P.

Derivation. ⋮
$(P$ or $P)$ **sim**$_1$ $(\sim\sim P$ or $\sim\sim P)$ **sim**$_2$ $\sim(\sim P$ and $\sim P)$ **sim**$_3$ $\sim(\sim P)$ **sim** P, and so $(P$ or $P)$ **sim** P.

References. 1.215,118d; 2.212g; 3.212b,216.

NOTE I. Henceforth we shall omit "cleanup" clauses such as the last line of this derivation. Furthermore we shall frequently write our derivations vertically rather than horizontally. E.g., the above derivation may be written as follows:

P or P **sim**$_1$
$\sim\sim P$ or $\sim\sim P$ **sim**$_2$
$\sim(\sim P$ and $\sim P)$ **sim**$_3$
$\sim(\sim P)$ **sim**
P.

NOTE II. We shall often skip trivial steps which the student can fill in.

218. Derived rule. *Commutativity* (or)
For any statements M, P: $(M$ or $P)$ **sim** $(P$ or $M)$.

Derivation.:
M or P **sim**
$\sim\sim M$ or $\sim\sim P$ **sim**
$\sim(\sim M$ and $\sim P)$ **sim**$_1$
$\sim(\sim P$ and $\sim M)$ **sim**
$\sim\sim P$ or $\sim\sim M$ **sim**
P or M.

Reference. 1.212c.

219. Derived rule. *Associativity* (or)
For any statements M, N, P: $[M$ or $(N$ or $P)]$ **sim** $[(M$ or $N)$ or $P]$.

Derivation.:
M or $(N$ or $P)$ **sim**
$\sim\sim M$ or $(\sim\sim N$ or $\sim\sim P)$ **sim**
$\sim\sim M$ or $\sim(\sim N$ and $\sim P)$ **sim**
$\sim[\sim M$ and $(\sim N$ and $\sim P)]$ **sim**$_1$
$\sim[(\sim M$ and $\sim N)$ and $\sim P]$ **sim**
$\sim(\sim M$ and $\sim N)$ or $\sim\sim P$ **sim**
$(\sim\sim M$ or $\sim\sim N)$ or $\sim\sim P$ **sim**
$(M$ or $N)$ or P.

Reference. 1.212d.

220. Derived rule. *Absorption* (and, or)
For any statements G, H: $[G$ and $(G$ or $H)]$ **sim** G.

Derivation.:
G and $(G$ or $H)$ **sim**$_1$
$(G$ and $G)$ or $(G$ and $H)$ **sim**
G or $(G$ and $H)$ **sim**$_2$
G.

References. 1.212f; 2.212e.

221. Derived rule. *Distributivity* (or, and)
For any statements L, M, P: $[L$ or $(M$ and $P)]$ **sim** $[(L$ or $M)$ and $(L$ or $P)]$.

Derivation.:
L or $(M$ and $P)$ **sim**$_1$
$[L$ or $(L$ and $P)]$ or $(M$ and $P)$ **sim**
$[L$ or $(P$ and $L)]$ or $(P$ and $M)$ **sim**
L or $[(P$ and $L)$ or $(P$ and $M)]$ **sim**$_2$

L or $[P$ and $(L$ or $M)]$ **sim**$_3$
$[L$ and $(L$ or $M)]$ or $[P$ and $(L$ or $M)]$ **sim**
$[(L$ or $M)$ and $L]$ or $[(L$ or $M)$ and $P]$ **sim**$_2$
$(L$ or $M)$ and $(L$ or $P)$.

References. 1.212e; 2.212f; 3.220.

222. Derived rule. *DeMorgan* $(\sim,$ or$)$
For any statements G, H: $\sim(G$ or $H)$ **sim** $(\sim G$ and $\sim H)$.

Derivation.:
$\sim(G$ or $H)$ **sim**
$\sim[\sim\sim G$ or $\sim\sim H]$ **sim**
$\sim\sim[\sim G$ and $\sim H]$ **sim**
$\sim G$ and $\sim H$.

223. Notations.

a. $(B$ and C and $D)$ stands for $[B$ and $(C$ and $D)]$;
$(A$ and B and C and $D)$ stands for $[A$ and $(B$ and C and $D)]$;
and so on.

b. $(B$ or C or $D)$ stands for $[B$ or $(C$ or $D)]$;
$(A$ or B or C or $D)$ stands for $[A$ or $(B$ or C or $D)]$;
and so on.

224. Exercises.

a. For any statements A, B, C: $(A$ and B and $C)$ **sim** $(C$ and B and $A)$.
NOTE. See 122(NOTE II).

(*Extensions of DeMorgan's Rules*)

b. For any statements G, H, K: $\sim[G$ and H and $K]$ **sim** $[\sim G$ or $\sim H$ or $\sim K]$.

c. For any statements A, B, C: $\sim[A$ or B or $C]$ **sim** $[\sim A$ and $\sim B$ and $\sim C]$.

225. Derived rule. For any statements M, P: $[M$ or $(\sim M$ and $P)]$ **sim** $(M$ or $P)$.

Derivation.:
M or $(\sim M$ and $P)$ **sim**
$\sim\sim M$ or $\sim(M$ or $\sim P)$ **sim**
$\sim[\sim M$ and $(M$ or $\sim P)]$ **sim**
$\sim[\sim M$ and $(\sim\sim M$ or $\sim P)]$ **sim**$_1$
$\sim[\sim M$ and $\sim P]$ **sim**
M or P.

Reference. 1.212h.

226. Derived rule. For any statements R, S: $[R$ and $(S$ or $\sim S)]$ **sim** R.

Derivation.:
R and $(S$ or $\sim S)$ **sim**
$(R$ and $S)$ or $(R$ and $\sim S)$ **sim**
$[(R$ and $S)$ or $R]$ and $[(R$ and $S)$ or $\sim S]$ **sim**₂
$[R]$ and $[\sim S$ or $(\sim\sim S$ and $R)]$ **sim**₂
R and $[\sim S$ or $R]$ **sim**
R.

NOTE. The subscript question marks indicate that the student should be particularly conscientious in justifying these steps.

227. Derived rule. For any statements A, B: $(A$ or $\sim A)$ **sim** $(B$ or $\sim B)$.

Derivation.:
A or $\sim A$ **sim**₁
$(A$ or $\sim A)$ and $(B$ or $\sim B)$ **sim**
$(B$ or $\sim B)$ and $(A$ or $\sim A)$ **sim**₂
B or $\sim B$.

Reference. 1.226 with $(A$ or $\sim A)$ for R, and B for S.

228. Exercises.

a. For any statements R, S: $[R$ or S or $\sim S]$ **sim** $(R$ or $\sim R)$.

b. For any statements G, H: $(G$ and $\sim G)$ **sim** $(H$ and $\sim H)$.

c. For any statements A, B: $[A$ or $(B$ and $\sim B)]$ **sim** A.

d. For any statements R, S: $[R$ and S and $\sim S]$ **sim** $(R$ and $\sim R)$.

e. Assuming that there is a statement A such that A **sim** $\sim A$, prove that all statements are similar. HINT. Prove that for each statement B: B **sim** A. NOTE. See 214.

If . . . then . . .

301. A *conditional* is any statement of the form (If A, then B); its premise (or hypothesis) is the statement A and its conclusion is the statement B.

To deny a conditional (If A, then B) amounts to affirming A and denying B; i.e., we deem the statement $\sim$(If A, then B) to be similar to (A and $\sim B$). Accordingly, we deem (If A, then B) to be similar to $\sim$(A and $\sim B$).

These informal remarks suggest the next basic rule.

302. Basic rule. For any statements A, B: (If A, then B) **sim** $\sim$(A and $\sim B$).

303. Notation. ($A \Rightarrow B$) stands for (If A, then B).

NOTE. The expression ($A \Rightarrow B$) may be rendered as *A arrow B* or as *if A, then B*. After we have completed our treatment of logic, the student may render ($A \Rightarrow B$) as *A implies B*.

CAUTION. The expressions ($A \Rightarrow B$), (If A, then B) should not be rendered as *if A is true, then B is true*.

304. Derived rule. For each statement H: ($\sim H \Rightarrow H$) **sim** H.

Derivation.:
$\sim H \Rightarrow H$ **sim**$_?$
$\sim(\sim H$ and $\sim H)$ **sim**
$\sim(\sim H)$ **sim**
H.

305. In ordinary discourse the conditional (If A, then B) is deemed to express some sort of connection or relationship between A, B. In mathematical discourse no connection or relationship is intended: (If A, then B) is merely similar to $\sim(A$ and $\sim B)$. The following discussion will help the student to see the point.

Let W stand for (Zilch is white).
Surely the statement W is about Zilch and not about statements.
So the statement W does not express a relationship between two statements.
But, by 304, W **sim** (If $\sim W$, then W).
Therefore the statement (If $\sim W$, then W) does not express a relationship between two statements.

306. Exercise.

For any statements J, K: $(J \Rightarrow K)$ **sim** $(\sim J$ or $K)$.

307. Derived rule. For any statements G, H: $[G$ and $(G \Rightarrow H)]$ **sim** $(G$ and $H)$.

Derivation.:
G and $(G \Rightarrow H)$ **sim**
G and $(\sim G$ or $H)$ **sim**
G and H.

308. Derived rule. For any statements A, B: $(A \Rightarrow B)$ **sim** $(\sim B \Rightarrow \sim A)$.

Derivation.:
$A \Rightarrow B$ **sim**
$\sim A$ or B **sim**
B or $\sim A$ **sim**
$\sim(\sim B)$ or $\sim A$ **sim**
$\sim B \Rightarrow \sim A$.

309. Derived rule.
For any statements G, H: $[\sim H$ and $(G \Rightarrow H)]$ **sim** $(\sim H$ and $\sim G)$.

Derivation.:
$\sim H$ and $(G \Rightarrow H)$ **sim**
$\sim H$ and $(\sim H \Rightarrow \sim G)$ **sim**$_1$
$\sim H$ and $\sim G$.
Reference. 1.307.

310. Derived rule.
For any statements G, H, K: $[G \Rightarrow (H \Rightarrow K)]$ **sim** $[(G$ and $H) \Rightarrow K]$.
Derivation.:
$G \Rightarrow (H \Rightarrow K)$ **sim**
$\sim G$ or $(H \Rightarrow K)$ **sim**
$\sim G$ or $(\sim H$ or $K)$ **sim**

$(\sim G$ or $\sim H)$ or K **sim**
$\sim(G$ and $H)$ or K **sim**
$(G$ and $H) \Rightarrow K$.

NOTE. Now it is clear that for any statements A, B, C:
$[A \Rightarrow (B \Rightarrow C)]$ **sim** $[B \Rightarrow (A \Rightarrow C)]$. (Why?)

311. Derived rule. For any statements H, S: $[(H \Rightarrow S)$ and $(\sim H \Rightarrow S)]$ **sim** S.

Derivation.:
$(H \Rightarrow S)$ and $(\sim H \Rightarrow S)$ **sim**
$(S$ or $\sim H)$ and $(S$ or $H)$ **sim**
S or $(\sim H$ and $H)$ **sim**₂
S.

312. Derived rule. For any statements M, N, P:
$(M \Rightarrow N)$ **sim** $\big[(M \Rightarrow N)$ and $[M \Rightarrow (N$ or $P)]\big]$.

Derivation.:
$M \Rightarrow N$ **sim**
$\sim M$ or N **sim**
$\sim M$ or $[N$ and $(N$ or $P)]$ **sim**
$(\sim M$ or $N)$ and $[\sim M$ or $(N$ or $P)]$ **sim**
$(M \Rightarrow N)$ and $[M \Rightarrow (N$ or $P)]$.

313. Derived rule. For any statements G, H, K:
$[(G \Rightarrow H)$ and $(H \Rightarrow K)]$ **sim** $[(G \Rightarrow H)$ and $(H \Rightarrow K)$ and $(G \Rightarrow K)]$.

Derivation.:
$[G \Rightarrow H]$ and $(H \Rightarrow K)$ **sim**₁
$\big[(G \Rightarrow H)$ and $(G \Rightarrow (H$ or $K))\big]$ and $(H \Rightarrow K)$ **sim**
$\big[(G \Rightarrow H)$ and $(G \Rightarrow (\sim H \Rightarrow K))\big]$ and $(H \Rightarrow K)$ **sim**₂
$(G \Rightarrow H)$ and $(\sim H \Rightarrow (G \Rightarrow K))$ and $[H \Rightarrow K]$ **sim**₁
$(G \Rightarrow H)$ and $(\sim H \Rightarrow (G \Rightarrow K))$ and $\big[(H \Rightarrow K)$ and $(H \Rightarrow (K$ or $\sim G))\big]$ **sim**₂
$(G \Rightarrow H)$ and $(H \Rightarrow K)$ and $\big[(\sim H \Rightarrow (G \Rightarrow K))$ and $(H \Rightarrow (G \Rightarrow K))\big]$ **sim**₃
$(G \Rightarrow H)$ and $(H \Rightarrow K)$ and $[G \Rightarrow K]$
References. 1.312; 2.310NOTE; 3.311.

314. Derived rule. For any statements G, H, K:
$[(G$ or $H)$ and $(G \Rightarrow K)$ and $(H \Rightarrow K)]$ **sim** $[(G$ or $H)$ and $K]$.

Derivation.:
$(G$ or $H)$ and $(G \Rightarrow K)$ and $(H \Rightarrow K)$ **sim**
$(G$ or $H)$ and $(K$ or $\sim G)$ and $(K$ or $\sim H)$ **sim**
$(G$ or $H)$ and $[K$ or $(\sim G$ and $\sim H)]$ **sim**
$(G$ or $H)$ and $[K$ or $\sim(G$ or $H)]$ **sim**
$(G$ or $H)$ and K.

315. Exercises.

a. For any statements G, H, K:
$[G$ and $(G \Rightarrow H)$ and $(H \Rightarrow K)]$ **sim** $(G$ and H and $K)$.

b. For each statement G: $(G \Rightarrow \sim G)$ **sim** $\sim G$.

c. For any statements G, H, K: $[(G \Rightarrow H)$ or $(G \Rightarrow K)]$ **sim** $[G \Rightarrow (H$ or $K)]$.

d. For any statements A, B: $(A \Rightarrow B)$ **sim** $[(A$ and $\sim B) \Rightarrow B]$.
NOTE. This is interesting indeed.

e. For any statements G, H: $[\sim G \Rightarrow (H$ and $\sim H)]$ **sim** G.

f. For any statements E, H: $[E \Rightarrow (H$ and $\sim H)]$ **sim** $\sim E$.

g. For any statements G, H: $[(H$ or $\sim H) \Rightarrow G]$ **sim** G.

h. For any statements A, B, C: $[A \Rightarrow (B$ or $C)]$ **sim** $[(A$ and $\sim B) \Rightarrow C]$.

i. For any statements A, B, C: $[(A \Rightarrow C)$ and $(B \Rightarrow C)]$ **sim** $[(A$ or $B) \Rightarrow C]$.

316. Definition. The *contrapositive* of a conditional $(A \Rightarrow B)$ is the conditional $(\sim B \Rightarrow \sim A)$.

317. Derived rules.

a. Each conditional is similar to its contrapositive.
Derivation. 308.

b. Contrapositives of similar conditionals are similar.
Derivation. For any similar conditionals $(C \Rightarrow D)$, $(G \Rightarrow K)$:
$(\sim D \Rightarrow \sim C)$ **sim** $(C \Rightarrow D)$ **sim** $(G \Rightarrow K)$ **sim** $(\sim K \Rightarrow \sim G)$.

318. Definition. The *converse* of a conditional $(A \Rightarrow B)$ is the conditional $(B \Rightarrow A)$.

319. Students who erroneously believe that each conditional is similar to its converse should scrutinize the following example.

Let W stand for (Zilch is white).
Then, $(\sim W \Rightarrow W)$ **sim** W.
And, $(W \Rightarrow \sim W)$ **sim** $\sim W$.
By 213, W is not similar to $\sim W$.
Hence, $(\sim W \Rightarrow W)$ is not similar to its converse $(W \Rightarrow \sim W)$.

320. Surprise. Converses of similar conditionals are not necessarily similar.
Proof. Let W stand for (Zilch is white).
Let G stand for $(W$ or $\sim W)$.
Then the conditionals $[G \Rightarrow (\sim G \Rightarrow G)]$, $[(G$ and $\sim G) \Rightarrow G]$ are similar (310), but their converses are not similar because they are respectively similar to $\sim(W$ and $\sim W)$, $(W$ and $\sim W)$. (Why?)

321. Notation.

$(B \Rightarrow C \Rightarrow D)$ stands for $[(B \Rightarrow C)$ and $(C \Rightarrow D)]$;

$(A \Rightarrow B \Rightarrow C \Rightarrow D)$ stands for $[(A \Rightarrow B)$ and $(B \Rightarrow C)$ and $(C \Rightarrow D)]$;

and so on.

322. We may now express 313 as follows.

For any statements G, H, K:

$(G \Rightarrow H \Rightarrow K)$ **sim** $[(G \Rightarrow H \Rightarrow K)$ and $(G \Rightarrow K)]$.

323. The following ways of rendering $(A \Rightarrow B)$ tend to confuse students and so will seldom be used in this book:

A only if B,

A is sufficient (or is a sufficient condition) for B,

B is necessary (or is a necessary condition) for A.

324. Notation. $(B \Leftarrow A)$ stands for $(A \Rightarrow B)$.

NOTE I. The author renders $(B \Leftarrow A)$ as B *if* A.

NOTE II. We shall see later that this notation is quite useful.

If and only if

401. Notation. $(A \Leftrightarrow B)$ stands for $[(A \Rightarrow B) \text{ and } (B \Rightarrow A)]$.

NOTE I. The symbol $\Leftrightarrow$ is read *if and only if*.

NOTE II. *Iff* also stands for *if and only if*.

NOTE III. Statements of the form $(A \Leftrightarrow B)$ are called *biconditionals*.

NOTE IV. $(A \Leftrightarrow B)$ **sim** $(B \Leftrightarrow A)$. (Why?)

NOTE V. For now, let us not render the symbol $\Leftrightarrow$ as *is equivalent to*.

NOTE VI. Surely the student will not render the expression $(A \Leftrightarrow B)$ as *A is true if and only if B is true.*

402. There is a vital difference between our use of the symbols $\Leftrightarrow$, **sim**.

The symbol $\Leftrightarrow$ is used to form a new statement $(A \Leftrightarrow B)$ out of two given statements A, B; it is not used to express a relationship between statements. The expression $(A \Leftrightarrow B)$ merely stands for $[(A \Rightarrow B)$ and $(B \Rightarrow A)]$. It makes no sense to say that A is "if and only if" to B, and it makes no sense to say that A, B are "if and only if."

The symbol **sim** is used to express the fact that two statements are related in a special way. It makes sense to say that A is similar to B, and it makes sense to say that A, B are similar.

Perhaps the following analogy will be helpful. The symbol $(6/2) + 3$ denotes a certain real number associated with the real numbers $(6/2)$, 3; the symbol $+$ is not used to express a relationship between real numbers; it makes no sense to say that $(6/2)$ is "plus" to 3. On the other hand, the expression $(6/2 = 3)$ stands for an assertion that the real numbers $(6/2)$, 3 are related in a very special way, namely that they are the same real number.

22

In a subsequent lesson we shall obtain results that dramatically reveal the connection between ⇔ and **sim**.

NOTE. The failure to distinguish between ⇔ and **sim** has caused many people to miss the whole point of logic.

403. Exercises.

a. For any statements G, H: $[G$ and $(G \Leftrightarrow H)]$ **sim** $(G$ and $H)$.

b. For any statements G, H: $(G \Leftrightarrow H)$ **sim** $[(G$ and $H)$ or $(\sim G$ and $\sim H)]$.

c. For any statements A, B: $\sim(A \Leftrightarrow B)$ **sim** $(\sim A \Leftrightarrow B)$.

d. For each statement G: $[G \Leftrightarrow (G$ or $\sim G)]$ **sim** G.

404. Let us agree that the statement (Snow is white) is *not similar* to the statement $[(Snow$ is white) or (snow is not white)$]$.

405. The following discussion is for the benefit of students who still do not see the difference between ⇔ and **sim**.

Let B stand for (Snow is white).
The statement $[B \Leftrightarrow (B$ or $\sim B)]$, being similar to B by 403d, is true in the ordinary sense.
However, by 404, B is not similar to $(B$ or $\sim B)$.
We summarize: the statement $[B \Leftrightarrow (B$ or $\sim B)]$ is true in the ordinary sense, but B is not similar to $(B$ or $\sim B)$.

This apparent paradox will be resolved in Lesson 6 where we shall learn that, although true in the ordinary sense, the statement $[B \Leftrightarrow (B$ or $\sim B)]$ is not logically true.

406. Definition. The *contrapositive* of a biconditional $(A \Leftrightarrow B)$ is the biconditional $(\sim B \Leftrightarrow \sim A)$.

407. Derived rule. Each biconditional is similar to its contrapositive.

Derivation. For any statements M, N:
$M \Leftrightarrow N$ **sim**
$(M \Rightarrow N)$ and $(N \Rightarrow M)$ **sim**
$(\sim N \Rightarrow \sim M)$ and $(\sim M \Rightarrow \sim N)$ **sim**
$\sim N \Leftrightarrow \sim M$.

408. Notation.
$(B \Leftrightarrow C \Leftrightarrow D)$ stands for $[(B \Leftrightarrow C)$ and $(C \Leftrightarrow D)]$;
$(A \Leftrightarrow B \Leftrightarrow C \Leftrightarrow D)$ stands for $[(A \Leftrightarrow B)$ and $(B \Leftrightarrow C)$ and $(C \Leftrightarrow D)]$;
and so on.

409. Derived rule.

For any statements G, H, K: $(G \Rightarrow H \Rightarrow K \Rightarrow G)$ sim $(G \Leftrightarrow H \Leftrightarrow K)$.

Derivation.:

$G \Rightarrow H \Rightarrow K \Rightarrow G$ **sim**

$(G \Rightarrow H)$ and $(H \Rightarrow K)$ and $(K \Rightarrow G)$ **sim**

$[(K \Rightarrow G) \text{ and } (G \Rightarrow H)]$ and $[(H \Rightarrow K) \text{ and } (K \Rightarrow G)]$ **sim**

$[(K \Rightarrow G) \text{ and } (G \Rightarrow H) \text{ and } (K \Rightarrow H)]$ and
$$[(H \Rightarrow K) \text{ and } (K \Rightarrow G) \text{ and } (H \Rightarrow G)] \text{ sim}_?$$

$(G \Rightarrow H)$ and $(H \Rightarrow K)$ and $[(K \Rightarrow H) \text{ and } (H \Rightarrow G) \text{ and } (K \Rightarrow G)]$ **sim**

$(G \Rightarrow H)$ and $(H \Rightarrow K)$ and $[(K \Rightarrow H) \text{ and } (H \Rightarrow G)]$ **sim**

$[(G \Rightarrow H) \text{ and } (H \Rightarrow G)]$ and $[(H \Rightarrow K) \text{ and } (K \Rightarrow H)]$ **sim**

$(G \Leftrightarrow H)$ and $(H \Leftrightarrow K)$ **sim**

$G \Leftrightarrow H \Leftrightarrow K$.

410. Exercises.

a. For any statements G, H, K:
$(G \Leftrightarrow H \Leftrightarrow K)$ sim $[(G \Rightarrow H \Rightarrow K) \text{ and } (K \Rightarrow H \Rightarrow G)]$.

b. For any statements G, H, K:
$(G \Leftrightarrow H \Leftrightarrow K)$ sim $[(G \Leftrightarrow H \Leftrightarrow K) \text{ and } (G \Leftrightarrow K)]$.

411. We have adopted certain basic rules governing our use of $\sim$, *and*, *or*, $\Rightarrow$. Next we should adopt basic rules to govern our use of *each*, *some*, and other related words and expressions. E.g., one such rule would legitimatize the claim that the following statements are similar:

$\sim$(Each wise man is kind)
Some wise man is not kind.

However, we shall defer to Lessons 8 and 9 our discussion of some (but not all) of the basic rules governing *each*, *some*, and other related words and expressions.

Entailment

501. So far we have studied the relationship of similarity between statements; in this lesson we shall study the relationship of entailment between statements.

502. What does it mean to say that a statement *A* entails a statement *B* (i.e., that *B* is a logical consequence of *A*)? For hundreds of years philosophers had the marvelous idea that this means that *B* is already contained in *A*, but they were apparently unable to express this idea with suitable precision. With our stock of concepts this is easy to do.

503. Definition. A statement *A* *entails* a statement *B* provided that (*A* and *B*) is similar to *A*.

NOTATION. *A* **ent** *B*, read as *A entails B* or as *B is entailed by A*.

NOTE. *Provided that* (as well as *provided*) means *when and only when* and will often be used in definitions.

504. The distinction between ⇒ and **ent** is analogous to the distinction between ⇔ and **sim**, (see 402). The symbol ⇒ is used to form a new statement out of two statements; it is not used to express a relationship between two statements. It makes no sense to say, "*A* if-then's *B*." On the other hand, the symbol **ent** is used to express the idea that two statements are related in a very special way.

The following discussion vividly points up one difference between ⇒ and **ent**.

Let *B* stand for (Snow is white).
The statement (∼*B* ⇒ *B*), being similar to *B* by 304, is true in the ordinary sense.

Now we shall demonstrate that $\sim B$ does not entail B.

By 404, $(B$ or $\sim B)$ is not similar to B.

Hence, $\sim(B$ or $\sim B)$ is not similar to $\sim B$.   (?)   [See NOTE below.]

So, $(\sim B$ and $B)$ is not similar to $\sim B$.   (?)

Therefore, $\sim B$ does not entail B. See 503.

We summarize: the statement $(\sim B \Rightarrow B)$ is true in the ordinary sense, but the statement $\sim B$ does not entail the statement B.

This apparent paradox will be resolved in the next lesson where we shall learn that, although true in the ordinary sense, the statement $(\sim B \Rightarrow B)$ is not logically true. We shall also obtain results that reveal the connection between $\Rightarrow$ and **ent**.

NOTE. When the student sees a question mark in parentheses, he is expected to supply a justification for the preceding statement.

505. Theorem. Each statement entails itself.

Proof. For each statement G: $(G$ and $G)$ **sim** G, and so G **ent** G.

NOTE. This theorem could, of course, be called a derived rule.

506. Theorem. For any statements A, B: $(A$ and $B)$ **ent** A.

Proof.: $[(A$ and $B)$ and $A]$ **sim** $(A$ and $B)$.

NOTE. Surely the student can prove that $(A$ and $B)$ **ent** B.

507. Theorem. For any statements G, H: G **ent** $(G$ or $H)$.

Proof.: $[G$ and $(G$ or $H)]$ **sim** G.

NOTE. Surely the student can prove that G **ent** $(H$ or $G)$.

508. Exercises.

  a. For any statements C, D: $(C$ and $D)$ **ent** $(C$ or $D)$.
  NOTE. The student may not yet use 515.

  b. Show that the converse of 508a violates 213; i.e., assuming that for any statements C, D: $(C$ or $D)$ **ent** $(C$ and $D)$, produce a statement similar to its negation.

509. Theorem. For any statements G, H: $[G$ and $(G \Rightarrow H)]$ **ent** H.

Proof.:
$[G$ and $(G \Rightarrow H)]$ and H **sim**
$(G$ and $H)$ and H **sim**
G and H **sim**
G and $(G \Rightarrow H)$.

510. Theorem. For any statements G, H, K: $(G \Rightarrow H \Rightarrow K)$ **ent** $(G \Rightarrow K)$.

Proof.: $[(G \Rightarrow H \Rightarrow K)$ and $(G \Rightarrow K)]$ **sim**$_1$ $(G \Rightarrow H \Rightarrow K)$. (*Ref.* 1.322)

511. Exercises.

   a. For any statements A, B: B **ent** $(A \Rightarrow B)$.

   b. For any statements G, H: $\sim G$ **ent** $(G \Rightarrow H)$.

   c. For any statements A, B, C: $(A \Rightarrow C)$ **ent** $[(A \text{ and } B) \Rightarrow C]$.

   d. For any statements A, B, C: $[(A \text{ or } B) \Rightarrow C]$ **ent** $(A \Rightarrow C)$.

   e. For any statements A, B, C: $[(A \text{ or } B) \text{ and } (\sim A \text{ or } C)]$ **ent** $(B \text{ or } C)$.

512. Next we prove two theorems that collectively tell us what we have suspected: similar statements are statements that entail each other.

513. Theorems.

   a. Similar statements entail each other, i.e.,
for any statements B, C such that B **sim** C: $(B$ **ent** $C)$ and $(C$ **ent** $B)$.

   Proof.: $(B$ and $C)$ **sim** $(B$ and $B)$ **sim** B, and so B **ent** C;
$(C$ and $B)$ **sim** $(C$ and $C)$ **sim** C, and so C **ent** B.

   b. Statements that entail each other are similar, i.e.,
for any statements B, C such that $(B$ **ent** $C)$ and $(C$ **ent** $B)$: B **sim** C.

   Proof.: B **sim** $(B$ and $C)$ **sim** $(C$ and $B)$ **sim** C.

514. Theorem. For any statements G, H, K such that $(G$ **ent** $H)$ and $(G$ **ent** $K)$: G **ent** $(H$ and $K)$.

   Proof.:
G and $(H$ and $K)$ **sim**
$(G$ and $H)$ and $(G$ and $K)$ **sim**
G and G **sim**
G.

515. Theorem.
For any statements G, H, K such that $(G$ **ent** $H)$ and $(H$ **ent** $K)$: G **ent** K.

   Proof.:
G and K **sim**
$(G$ and $H)$ and K **sim**
G and $(H$ and $K)$ **sim**
G and H **sim**
G.

516. Exercises.

   a. For any statements G, H such that G **ent** H: $\sim H$ **ent** $\sim G$.

   b. For any statements A, B, M, N such that $(A$ **ent** $B)$ and $(M$ **ent** $N)$: $(A$ and $M)$ **ent** $(B$ and $N)$.

c. For any statements G, H, J, K such that $(G$ sim $H)$ and $(H$ ent $J)$ and $(J$ sim $K)$: G ent K.

QUERY. In 506NOTE did the student prematurely use 516c or a variant thereof?

517. Next we come to an important theorem that will provide many shortcuts.

518. The Deduction Theorem.

For any statements P, A, B such that $(P$ and $A)$ **ent** B: P **ent** $(A \Rightarrow B)$.

Proof.:
P and $(A \Rightarrow B)$ **sim**
P and $(\sim A$ or $B)$ **sim**
$(P$ and $\sim A)$ or $(P$ and $B)$ **sim**$_2$
$(P$ and $\sim A)$ or $[(P$ and $B)$ and $(A$ or $\sim A)]$ **sim**
$(P$ and $\sim A)$ or $[(P$ and B and $A)$ or $(P$ and B and $\sim A)]$ **sim**$_1$
$(P$ and $\sim A)$ or $[(P$ and $A)$ or $(P$ and B and $\sim A)]$ **sim**$_?$
P and $[\sim A$ or A or $(B$ and $\sim A)]$ **sim**$_?$
P and $(\sim A$ or $A)$ **sim**$_2$
P.

References. 1.hypothesis; 2.226.

519. Exercise.

Prove the converse of the Deduction Theorem; i.e., prove that for any statements P, A, B such that P **ent** $(A \Rightarrow B)$: $(P$ and $A)$ **ent** B.

520. The expression $(B$ **ent** $C)$ may also be rendered as follows:

From B follows C,
C follows from B,
C logically follows from B,
C is deducible from B,
C is logically deducible from B,
C is a consequence of B,
C is a logical consequence of B.

NOTE. The student should not render $(B$ **ent** $C)$ as B *implies* C.

521. Notations.

a. $(B$ **ent** C **ent** $D)$ stands for $[(B$ **ent** $C)$ and $(C$ **ent** $D)]$; etc.

b. A mixed expression such as $(A$ **ent** B **ent** C **sim** $D)$ stands for $[(A$ **ent** $B)$ and $(B$ **ent** $C)$ and $(C$ **sim** $D)]$.

522. When we say that two or more statements entail a statement P, we mean that their conjunction entails P.

Contradictions, Tautologies

601. Definition. A *contradiction* is any statement that entails its negation.

NOTE I. Accordingly, a contradiction is any statement P such that $(P$ and $\sim P)$ **sim** P.

NOTE II. This definition is not standard; hopefully, logicians will forgive the author for using some well-established terminology in a new way.

NOTE III. *Contradiction* and *logically false statement* are synonymous.

602. Theorem. For each statement G: $(G$ and $\sim G)$ is a contradiction.

Proof.:
$(G$ and $\sim G)$ and $\sim(G$ and $\sim G)$ **sim**
$(G$ and $\sim G)$ and $(G$ or $\sim G)$ **sim**$_1$
G and $\sim G$.
Reference. 1.226.

603. Theorems.

a. All contradictions are similar.
Proof. For any contradictions A, B:
A **sim** $(A$ and $\sim A)$ **sim** $(B$ and $\sim B)$ **sim** B.

b. Each statement similar to a contradiction is a contradiction.
Proof. For any statement G that is similar to a contradiction H:
$(G$ and $\sim G)$ **sim** $(H$ and $\sim H)$ **sim** H **sim** G, and so G is a contradiction.

604. Theorems.

a. For any statement H and contradiction C: $(H$ and $C)$ **sim** C.
Proof.: $(H$ and $C)$ **sim** $[H$ and $(C$ and $\sim C)]$ **sim**$_1$ $(H$ and $\sim H)$ **sim**$_2$ C.
References. 1.228d; 2.602,603a.

b. For any statement H and contradiction C: $(H$ or $C)$ **sim** H.
Proof.: $(H$ or $C)$ **sim** $[H$ or $(C$ and $\sim C)]$ **sim**$_1$ H. (*Ref.* 1.228c)

605. Theorems.

    a. Each contradiction entails every statement.

    Proof. For any contradiction C and any statement H:
$(C$ and $H)$ **sim** C, and so C **ent** H.

    b. Each statement that entails a contradiction is a contradiction.

    Proof. For any statement H that entails a contradiction C:
H **sim** $(H$ and $C)$ **sim** C, and so H is a contradiction.   (?)

    NOTE. Surely a statement that entails every statement is a contradiction.

606. Exercise. For each statement P: $(P \Leftrightarrow {\sim}P)$ is a contradiction.

607. Theorem. For any statements A, B such that $(A$ and ${\sim}B)$ entails a contradiction: A **ent** B.

    Proof.: $(A$ and ${\sim}B)$ **ent** $(B$ and ${\sim}B)$,   (?)
and so A **ent**$_1$ $\big[{\sim}B \Rightarrow (B$ and ${\sim}B)\big]$ **sim**$_2$ B. (*Ref.* 1.518; 2.315e)

608. Exercise. For any statements A, B such that A **ent** B:
$(A$ and ${\sim}B)$ is a contradiction.

609. Let us say that two statements are *contradictory* provided their conjunction is a contradiction.

610. Definition. A *tautology* is any statement that follows from its negation.

    NOTE I. Accordingly, a tautology is any statement P such that
$({\sim}P$ and $P)$ **sim** ${\sim}P$.

    NOTE II. See 601(NOTE II).

    NOTE III. *Tautology* and *logically true statement* are synonymous.

611. Exercises.

    a. For each statement G: $(G$ or ${\sim}G)$ is a tautology.

    b. All tautologies are similar.

    c. Each statement similar to a tautology is a tautology.

    d. For any statement H and tautology T: $(H$ and $T)$ **sim** H.

    e. For any statement H and tautology T: $(H$ or $T)$ **sim** T.

    f. The negation of each contradiction is a tautology.

    g. The negation of each tautology is a contradiction.

    h. Each statement entails every tautology.

    i. Each statement that follows from a tautology is a tautology.

    j. For any statements G, H: $\big[(G$ and $(G \Rightarrow H)) \Rightarrow H\big]$ is a tautology.

612. Let B stand for (Snow is white).

B is true in the ordinary sense; however, in view of 404, B is not logically true; i.e., B is not tautological. Now reread 405 and 504.

613. The next two theorems reveal the connection between $\Leftrightarrow$ and **sim**.

614. Theorems.

a. For any statements A, P such that A **sim** P: $(A \Leftrightarrow P)$ is tautological.

Proof.: $(A \Leftrightarrow P)$ **sim** $(A \Leftrightarrow A)$ **sim** $[(A \Rightarrow A)$ and $(A \Rightarrow A)]$ **sim** $(A \Rightarrow A)$ **sim** $(\sim A$ or $A)$.

b. For any statements A, P such that $(A \Leftrightarrow P)$ is tautological: A **sim** P.

Proof.:
A **sim**$_1$
A and $(A \Leftrightarrow P)$ **sim**$_2$
A and P **sim**
P and A **sim**$_2$
P and $(P \Leftrightarrow A)$ **sim**
P and $(A \Leftrightarrow P)$ **sim**$_1$
P.

References. 1.611d; 2.403a.

615. The next two theorems reveal the connection between $\Rightarrow$ and **ent**.

616. Theorems.

a. For any statements A, P such that A **ent** P: $(A \Rightarrow P)$ is tautological.

Proof.: $(A \Rightarrow P)$ **sim** $[\sim A$ or $P]$ **sim**$_1$ $[\sim(A$ and $P)$ or $P]$ **sim** $[\sim A$ or $(\sim P$ or $P)]$.   (*Ref.* 1.hypothesis)

b. For any statements A, P such that $(A \Rightarrow P)$ is tautological: A **ent** P.

Proof.: $[A$ and $P]$ **sim** $[A$ and $(A \Rightarrow P)]$ **sim**$_?$ A.

617. Exercise.

For any statements A, B such that A is tautological and $(A \Rightarrow B)$ is tautological: B is tautological.

618. If we had already presented a complete set of basic similarity rules for *each* and *some*, then we could prove that the following statements are tautological.

Each person is wise or unwise.
Each wise person is wise.
Each person is a person.

The negations of these statements would then be contradictions.

Existence, Nonexistence

701. Recall (108) that the expressions *there exists, there is* are synonymous.

702. Empirical existence. When we assert that there exists a horse (or that horses exist), we mean that a certain thing which zoologists call a horse may now be observed somewhere in nature. When we assert that Pericles existed, we mean that according to historical evidence there once lived a man called Pericles. When we assert that there existed an ancient city called Troy, we mean that according to archeological evidence there once was an actual city called Troy. We shall refer to these kinds of existence as empirical existence. Empirical existence is established by factual evidence of the sort acceptable to scientists or historians.

In mathematics we are *not* concerned with empirical existence.

703. Empirical nonexistence. Unicorns do not and did not exist empirically; this is an example of empirical nonexistence. When we assert that real numbers exist, we do not mean that an actual thing has been found which mathematicians call a real number. Real numbers are empirically nonexistent; indeed, all mathematical things (e.g., points, lines, spheres, functions, sets, ordered pairs) are empirically nonexistent.

704. Definitional existence. When we assert that there exists a real number, we merely mean that our definition of the real number system stipulates that there exists a real number. This is an example of definitional existence. Definitional existence is established by appealing to definitions rather than to factual evidence.

Definitions of mathematical systems usually stipulate the existence of certain things. Mathematicians are free to define into existence anything whatsoever; however, if the system turns out to be inconsistent (self-

32

contradictory) then it is rejected as worthless. In 1010, we shall give a simple example of an inconsistent system, and in Lessons 11 and 12 we shall more fully discuss these matters.

It is an interesting fact that outside of mathematics one seldom encounters definitions that stipulate the existence of things.

NOTE. Certain statements in the definition of a mathematical system are   ←
called *axioms* (or *postulates*).

705. Definitional nonexistence. Infrequently a definition of a mathematical system stipulates the nonexistence of certain things. For example, in defining a Euclidean system of points, lines, and planes, David Hilbert set forth various axioms, one of which stipulates the nonexistence of a more extensive system satisfying the other axioms. This unusual situation is discussed by Raymond L. Wilder in his excellent book *Introduction to*   ←
the Foundations of Mathematics, page 37. (See Bibliography.)

706. Deductive existence. The existence of a real number whose square is 5 is neither a matter of empirical existence nor of definitional existence; it is an example of deductive existence. We shall discuss this in 1118.

707. Deductive nonexistence. The nonexistence of a real number whose square is -1 is not a matter of definitional nonexistence; it is an example of deductive nonexistence. We shall discuss this in 1118.

708. Where prudence requires, one should carefully indicate the kind of existence he is talking about.

709. An *existential* statement is one that asserts the existence of a thing or things.

710. Example. The following statements are existential.

There exists a horse. (*empirical*)
There exists a real number. (*definitional*)
There exists a real number that equals its square. (*deductive*)

711. Examples.

a. The statement (There exists no kind person who is unwise) is not existential because it does not assert the existence of a thing; indeed, it denies the existence of certain things.

b. The statement (At most one man has eight eyes) is not existential because it means *There is not more than one man with eight eyes* and does not assert the existence of a thing.

c. The statement (At most one man is President of the United States of America) is not existential.

d. [This one will startle the student.] The statement (Each kind person is wise) is not existential because it means *There exists no kind person who is unwise*. See 711a. We shall discuss this further in Lessons 8 and 9.

712. A *general* statement is one whose negation is existential.

713. Examples.

a. The statement (Each kind person is wise) is general because its negation is the existential statement (There exists a kind person who is unwise).

b. The statement (No kind person is unwise) is general because its negation is the existential statement (There exists a kind person who is unwise).

c. The statement (The square of each nonzero real number is positive) is general because its negation is the existential statement (There exists a nonzero real number whose square is not positive).

NOTE. We shall discuss these matters further in Lessons 8 and 9.

714. An *empirically true* statement is one that is true in the ordinary sense of being in accord with the facts of nature. E.g., the following statements are empirically true.

Snow is white.
There exists a horse.
The Earth revolves around the Sun.
The blood of each living person circulates through his body.
Handel composed the oratorio *Judas Maccabaeus*.
There are no unicorns.

715. An *empirically false* statement is one whose negation is empirically true.

NOTE. Except where noted, the empirical truth or falsity of illustrative statements is irrelevant to the discussion. In mathematics we are concerned with neither empirical truth nor empirical falsity.

Each, Some

801. We shall not present a complete set of similarity rules governing the words *each* and *some*; instead we shall explain their use by submitting a wide variety of examples.

802. In ordinary discourse the statement (Each man is mortal) is usually taken to mean *There is a man, and there is no man who is immortal.*

Mathematicians have found this usage to be inconvenient, and so they have adopted a different viewpoint that we shall now explain.

803. The statement (Each man is mortal) means *There is no man who is immortal*; surely this statement is empirically true.

The statement (Each man is immortal) means *There is no man who is mortal*; surely this statement is empirically false.

The statement (Each unicorn is happy) means *There is no unicorn that is unhappy*; this statement is empirically true because there is no unicorn of any kind.

The statement (Each unicorn is unhappy) means *There is no unicorn that is happy*; this statement is also empirically true.

804. The words *each, every, all* are used synonymously and are used to express generality in the sense described above; we shall characterize our use of these words by saying that they have no existential import.

805. We always use the words *each, every, all* in the individual sense rather than in the collective sense; e.g., to a mathematician, the statement (All tools in this box weigh two pounds) means that each individual tool in the box weighs two pounds.

no!

806. Exercise.

Which of the following statements are empirically true?

    i.   Each immortal human is immortal.
    ii. Each immortal human is mortal.
    iii. Each immortal human is human.
    iv. Each immortal human is inhuman.
    v. Each immortal human is an elephant.
    vi. Each unicorn is happy and unhappy.

807. We use the word *any* in many different ways.

   a. We use the word *any* as a synonym for *each, every, all,* e.g., as in the statement (Any student who studies acquires knowledge).

   b. We use *any* in a sentence such as (Consider any honest man *x*); this sentence means *No matter what honest man one considers, say x, the following remarks pertain.*

   c. We use *any* in formulating definitions such as (A Bostonian is any person who lives in Boston); this definition is deemed to be similar to the following conjunction: (Each Bostonian is a person who lives in Boston) and (each person who lives in Boston is a Bostonian).

   d. Unfortunately some mathematicians occasionally use *any* as a synonym for *some*; e.g., in the following sentence *any* means *some.*

   If any pupil locked Miss Grumble in the closet, then the Christmas party will be cancelled.

   NOTE I. The author never uses *any* to mean *some.*

   NOTE II. *Any* has no existential import.

808. Exercise.

Does any real number equal its negative? (Yes or no.)

NOTE. This question is intentionally expressed to elicit the wrong answer from students who read too fast.

809. We use the articles, *a, an* in many different ways.

   a. In the following statements the article *a* means *at least one.*
There is a positive real number.
The collection of all real numbers contains a number greater than 3.
5 is less than a positive real number.

   NOTE. Recall (108) that when following the expressions *there exists, there is,* the articles *a, an* mean *at least one.*

b. In the following sentences the article *a* expresses generality.

A positive real number is greater than 0.
If a real number is positive, then it is greater than 0.

These sentences both mean that every positive real number is greater than 0.

c. In the following definition the article *a* expresses generality.

A triangle is equilateral provided that its sides have the same length.

This definition is similar to the following conjunction:

(Each equilateral triangle has sides of the same length) and
(each triangle whose sides have the same length is equilateral).

d. The sentence (John is a student) means that John belongs to the collection of all things called students.

e. The article *a* may be used in different ways within the same sentence.

E.g., the sentence (A man who has graduated from a college is better educated than a man who is not a college graduate) means *Each man who has graduated from at least one college is better educated than every man who does not belong to the collection of all things called college graduates.*

810. A symbol is said to be *available* in a given context provided that it is not permanently used to denote a particular mathematical thing and does not occur earlier in the context, except possibly as part of a word.

NOTE I. A symbol that is available in a given context is called a dummy because any other available symbol would serve equally well.

NOTE II. In this book the following letters are available in no context: $e, \pi, I, Q, R, Z, \Sigma, \Pi$. In some books, but not this one, the letters i, j, k, z are available in no context.

NOTE III. All letters used henceforth in this lesson are dummies.

811. We recall (104g) that a symbol is not the thing it refers to.

Disregard of this maxim has caused serious misunderstandings. E.g., many people erroneously believe that high school algebra is the study of certain symbols and manipulations thereof. High school algebra is the study of certain parts of the real number system and is concerned with real numbers rather than symbols; the symbols are merely used to convey ideas about real numbers.

812. The following nine general statements are similar.

Each kind person is wise.
No kind person is unwise.

For each kind person u: u is wise. (See NOTE II below.)
There is no kind person u such that u is unwise. (See NOTE III below.)

Each person who is kind is wise.
No person is kind and unwise.

For each person v such that v is kind: v is wise.
For each person v: v is kind $\Rightarrow$ v is wise.
There is no person v such that v is kind and v is unwise.

NOTE I. None of these general statements is existential. Indeed, no general statement is existential.

NOTE II. The author calls this statement the *standard form* (abbreviated, s.f.) of these nine statements.

NOTE III.   The author calls this statement the *affiliated standard form* (abbreviated, a.s.f.) of these nine statements.

813. Exercise.   Formulate the s.f. and a.s.f. of the following statements.

   i.   Each mortal unicorn is happy.
   ii. No happy unicorn is mortal.
   iii. Each unicorn that is immortal is unhappy.
   iv. No unicorn is unhappy and mortal.
   v. For each unicorn t: t is happy $\Rightarrow$ t is mortal.

814. The trivial (and relatively useless) way of writing the negation of a statement P is to write $\sim P$.

E.g., the trivial negation of (Each kind person is wise) is
$\sim$(Each kind person is wise).

A nontrivial negation of (Each kind person is wise) is
(Some kind person is unwise).

The student must learn how to formulate nontrivial negations of general statements; the easiest way to do this is to replace the first *no* by *an* (or *a*) in the a.s.f. of the general statement.

E.g., a nontrivial negation of statements 812 is
(There is a kind person u such that u is unwise);
this version will be called the s.f. negation of statements 812.

We summarize: to formulate the s.f. negation of a general statement P, replace the first *no* by *an* (or *a*) in the a.s.f. of P.

815. The following four existential statements are nontrivial negations of statements 812.

Some kind person is unwise.
There is a kind person u such that u is unwise. **(s.f.)**
Some person is kind and unwise.
There is a person v such that v is kind and v is unwise.

816. Exercises.

    a. Formulate the s.f. negations of the five statements in 813.

    b. Express your answers to 816a in simple English.

817. Caution. Many students erroneously believe that the negation of (Each kind person is wise) is (No kind person is wise); this belief is shattered by the fact that both statements are empirically false. The negation of the former statement is the empirically true statement (Some kind person is unwise).

Accordingly, the statement (Each kind person is unwise) is not the negation of (Each kind person is wise). (?)

818. The following nine general statements are converses of statements 812 and happen to be similar. (However, see 320.)

Each wise person is kind.
No wise person is unkind.

For each wise person u: u is kind. **(s.f.)**
There is no wise person u such that u is unkind. **(a.s.f.)**

Each person who is wise is kind.
No person is wise and unkind.

For each person v such that v is wise: v is kind.
For each person v: v is wise $\Rightarrow$ v is kind.
There is no person v such that v is wise and v is unkind.

819. Exercise. Formulate four different negations of statements 818.

820. The following nine general statements are contrapositives of (and hence similar to) statements 812.

Each unwise person is unkind.
No unwise person is kind.

For each unwise person u: u is unkind. **(s.f.)**
There is no unwise person u such that u is kind. **(a.s.f.)**

Each person who is unwise is unkind.
No person is unwise and kind.

For each person v such that v is unwise: v is unkind.
For each person v: v is unwise $\Rightarrow$ v is unkind.
There is no person v such that v is unwise and v is kind.

821. Exercises.
   a. Formulate nine different contrapositives of statements 818.
   b. Formulate four different negations of statements 820.
   c. Formulate nine different converses of statements 820.

822. Review.
   i.   For each kind person u: u is wise. (s.f.)
   ii.   There is no kind person u such that u is unwise. (a.s.f. of i)
   iii. There is a kind person u such that u is unwise. (s.f. negation of i)
   iv.   For each wise person u: u is kind. (converse of i)
   v.   For each unwise person u: u is unkind. (contrapositive of i)
   vi.   There is no wise person u such that u is unkind. (a.s.f. of iv)
   vii. There is a wise person u such that u is unkind. (s.f. negation of iv)
   viii. For each unkind person u: u is unwise. (contrapositive of iv)
   ix.   There is no unwise person u such that u is kind. (a.s.f. of v)
   x.   There is an unwise person u such that u is kind. (s.f. negation of v)
   xi.   There is no unkind person u such that u is wise. (a.s.f. of viii)
   xii. There is an unkind person u such that u is wise. (s.f. negation of viii)

823. Exercise. For the s.f. statement (For each happy unicorn v: v is immortal), do what is done in 822.

824. Review.
   i.   Some human is immortal.
   ii.   There is a human x such that x is immortal. (s.f. of i)
   iii. There is no human x such that x is immortal. (negation of ii)
   iv.   For each human x: x is mortal. (s.f. of iii)
   v.   For each mortal x: x is human. (converse of iv)
   vi.   For each inhuman thing x: x is immortal. (contrapositive of v)
   vii. There is no inhuman thing x such that x is mortal. (a.s.f. of vi)
   viii. Some inhuman thing is mortal. (negation of vii)

825. Exercise. For the statement (Some mortal is a unicorn), do what is done in 824.

826. The following general statements are similar.

Each unicorn is happy.
For each unicorn x: x is happy. **(s.f.)**
There is no unicorn x such that x is unhappy. **(a.s.f.)**
There is no unhappy unicorn.
Each thing that is a unicorn is happy.
For each thing x such that x is a unicorn: x is happy.
For each thing x: x is a unicorn $\Rightarrow$ x is happy.

The s.f. negation of these statements is (There is a unicorn x such that x is unhappy).

827. The following statement is tautological.

(There is an unhappy unicorn) ⟹ (there is a unicorn).

Accordingly the following statement, being the contrapositive of the previous statement, is also tautological.

(There is no unicorn) ⟹ (each unicorn is happy).

828. The following general statements are similar.

Each person likes every person.
For each person u: u likes every person.
For any person u and person v: u likes v.
There is no person u and person v such that u dislikes v.
For any persons u, v: u likes v. **(s.f.)**
There are no persons u, v such that u dislikes v. **(a.s.f.)**

NOTE. From these statements it follows that each person likes himself and that each person likes every other person; but it does not follow that there exists a person.

829. The following existential statements are negations of statements 828 and hence are similar.

Some person dislikes some person.
There is a person u such that u dislikes some person.
There is a person u and a person v such that u dislikes v.
There are persons u, v such that u dislikes v. **(s.f.)**

NOTE I. It does not follow from these statements that some person dislikes himself.

NOTE II. The following are not negations of statements 828.

Each person dislikes each person.
Some person dislikes each person.
Each person dislikes some person.

830. The following general statements are similar.

Each person likes every other person.
For each person u: u likes every person different from u.
For any different persons u, v: u likes v. **(s.f.)**
There are no different persons u, v such that u dislikes v. **(a.s.f.)**

NOTE. From these statements it does not follow that each person likes himself and it does not follow that there is a person.

831. The following existential statements are negations of statements 830 and hence are similar.

Some person dislikes some other person.
There is a person u such that u dislikes some person different from u.
There are different persons u, v such that u dislikes v. **(s.f.)**
There is a person u and a person v such that u is different from v and u dislikes v.

NOTE. The following are not negations of statements 830.

Each person dislikes every other person.
Each person dislikes some other person.
Some person dislikes every other person.

832. The following general statements are similar.

Each man likes each woman.
For any man x and woman y: x likes y. **(s.f.)**
There is no man x and woman y such that x dislikes y. **(a.s.f.)**

833. The following existential statements are negations of statements 832 and hence are similar.

Some man dislikes some woman.
There is a man x and a woman y such that x dislikes y. **(s.f.)**

834. The following general statements are similar.

Each person was born of some woman.

For each person x:
there is a woman y such that x was born of y. **(s.f.)**

There is no person x such that
$\sim$(there is a woman y such that x was born of y).

There is no person x such that
for each woman y: x was not born of y. **(a.s.f.)**

NOTE. These statements are empirically true.

835. The following existential statements are negations of statements 834 and hence are similar.

Some person was born of no woman.

There is a person x such that
for each woman y: x was not born of y. **(s.f.)**

NOTE. These statements are empirically false.

836. The following existential statements are similar.

Some woman bore each person.

Some woman is the mother of all persons.

There is a woman y such that
for each person x: x was born of y. **(s.f.)**

NOTE. These empirically false statements should be compared with the empirically true statements in 834.

837. Caution. Many students erroneously believe that the following statements are similar.

Each person was born of some woman. (empirically true)
Some woman bore each person. (empirically false)

838. The following general statements are negations of statements 836 and hence are similar.

No woman bore each person.

No woman is the mother of all persons.

For each woman y:
there is a person x such that x was not born of y. **(s.f.)**

NOTE. These statements are empirically true and hence are not similar to statements 835.

839. Exercises.

  a. Formulate the s.f. of the following statements.
    i.   Each man dislikes each woman.
    ii. Each man dislikes some woman.
    iii. Each woman is disliked by some man.
    iv. Some man dislikes each woman.
    v. Some man dislikes some woman.
    vi. Some woman is disliked by some man.
    vii. Some woman is disliked by every man.

  b. Formulate the s.f. negations of statements 839a.

  c. In simple English formulate negations of statements 839a.

840. Review.

    i.   Each worm inhabits some apple.

    ii.   For each worm x:
        there is an apple y such that x inhabits y. (s.f. of i)

    iii. Each apple is inhabited by some worm.

    iv. For each apple u:
        there is a worm v such that u is inhabited by v. (s.f. of iii)

    v.   Some apple is inhabited by no worm. (negation of iii)

    vi. There is an apple x such that
        for each worm y: x is not inhabited by y. (s.f. of v)

    vii. No worm inhabits every apple.

    viii. For each worm x:
        there is an apple y such that x does not inhabit y. (s.f. of vii)

    ix. Some worm inhabits every apple.

    x.   There is a worm x such that
        for each apple y: x inhabits y. (s.f. of ix)

841. Exercises.

  a. Formulate the s.f. negations of statements 840ii,iv,vi,viii,x.

  b. In simple English formulate your answers to 841a.

Each, Some (continued)

901. Recall (107) that *quantified* means *suitably introduced*, and *unquantified* means *not suitably introduced*.

902. Definition. A *condition* is any expression that contains precisely one unquantified letter and becomes a statement when all occurrences of that unquantified letter are replaced by a suitable noun or name.

If the unquantified letter is x, we speak of a condition in x;
if the unquantified letter is y, we speak of a condition in y;
and so on.

903. Example. Each of the following is a condition in x:

x is a man,
x is mortal,
x is mortal and x is green,
x is mortal $\Rightarrow x$ is happy,
x likes each person,
each person likes x,
for each person y: y likes x,
x is the father of Aristotle,
the father of x is not a logician,
there is a person z who likes x,
$x + x = 2x$.

904. For the remainder of this lesson the symbols A_x, B_x, C_x stand for any given conditions in x. The symbol A_x is read *A sub x*.

905. The following are conditions in x and it should be reasonably clear what they signify: $\sim A_x$, $(A_x \text{ and } B_x)$, $(A_x \text{ or } B_x)$, $(A_x \Rightarrow B_x)$, $(A_x \Leftrightarrow B_x)$.

We shall assume that all our similarity rules for statements apply equally well to conditions; e.g., $\sim(A_x \text{ or } B_x)$ **sim** $(\sim A_x \text{ and } \sim B_x)$.

906. Notation. The vertical stroke | stands for *such that*.

NOTE. The symbol | is also used for other purposes.

907. By prefixing a quantifier to a condition we obtain a statement.

E.g., if G_x stands for (x is green), then the following are statements:

for each thing x ⫶ G_x,
for each unicorn x ⫶ G_x,
there is a thing $x \mid G_x$,
there is a unicorn $x \mid G_x$,
there is at most one dog $x \mid G_x$,
there is precisely one dog $x \mid G_x$.

908. Basic rule.
[For each so-and-so x ⫶ $(A_x$ and $B_x)$] **sim**
[(for each so-and-so x ⫶ A_x) and (for each so-and-so x ⫶ B_x)].

909. Example. The following statements are similar.

Each thing is blue and wet.
For each thing x ⫶ x is blue and x is wet.
(For each thing x ⫶ x is blue) and (for each thing x ⫶ x is wet).
(Each thing is blue) and (each thing is wet).

910. The following are not necessarily similar.

i. For each so-and-so x ⫶ A_x or B_x.
ii. (For each so-and-so x ⫶ A_x) or (for each so-and-so x ⫶ B_x).

E.g., the following two statements are not similar.

For each thing x ⫶ x is blue or x is not blue.
(For each thing x ⫶ x is blue) or (for each thing x ⫶ x is not blue).

Indeed, the former statement is tautological and means *Each thing is blue or not blue*, whereas the latter statement is empirically false and means *Each thing is blue or each thing is not blue*.

NOTE. 910ii entails 910i, but 910i does not entail 910ii.

911. Basic rule.
[There is a so-and-so $x \mid (A_x$ or $B_x)$] **sim**
[(there is a so-and-so $x \mid A_x$) or (there is a so-and-so $x \mid B_x$)].

912. Example. The following are similar.

Something is blue or wet.
There is a thing $x \mid (x$ is blue or x is wet).
(There is a thing $x \mid x$ is blue) or (there is a thing $x \mid x$ is wet).
Something is blue or something is wet.

913. The following are not necessarily similar.

    i. There is a so-and-so $x \mid (A_x$ and $B_x)$.
    ii. (There is a so-and-so $x \mid A_x$) and (there is a so-and-so $x \mid B_x$).

E.g., the following statements are not similar.

There is a thing $x \mid (x$ is blue and x is not blue).
(There is a thing $x \mid x$ is blue) and (there is a thing $x \mid x$ is not blue).

Indeed, the former statement is a contradiction and means *Something is blue and not blue*, whereas the latter statement is empirically true and means *Something is blue and something is not blue*.

NOTE. 913i entails 913ii, but 913ii does not entail 913i.

914. Basic rule.
    $\sim$(For each so-and-so $x \colon A_x$) **sim** (there is a so-and-so $x \mid \sim A_x$).

915. Example.
    $\sim$(For each person $x \colon x$ is kind $\Rightarrow x$ is wise) **sim**
    there is a person $x \mid \sim (x$ is kind $\Rightarrow x$ is wise) **sim**
    there is a person $x \mid (x$ is kind and x is unwise).

QUERY. Can the student show that 911 is redundant by deriving it from 908 and 914?

916. Derived rule.
    $\sim$(There is a so-and-so $x \mid B_x$) **sim** (for each so-and-so $x \colon \sim B_x$).

    Derivation.
    $\sim$[There is a so-and-so $x \mid B_x$] **sim**
    $\sim$[there is a so-and-so $x \mid \sim\sim B_x$] **sim**$_1$
    $\sim$[$\sim$(for each so-and-so $x \colon \sim B_x$)] **sim**
    for each so-and-so $x \colon \sim B_x$.

    Reference 1.   914 with $\sim B_x$ for A_x.

917. Example.
    $\sim$(There is a wise person $x \mid x$ is kind) **sim**
    for each wise person $x \colon \sim(x$ is kind) **sim**
    for each wise person $x \colon x$ is unkind.

918. Let W stand for the statement
    [There is a logician $x \mid (x$ is kind $\Rightarrow x$ is wise)].

Although in mathematics we seldom encounter statements that have the structure of W, it is instructive to note that the following statements are similar.

W.

$\sim[\sim W]$.

$\sim[$For each logician $x\colon$ $\sim(x$ is kind $\Rightarrow x$ is wise)$]$.

$\sim[$For each logician $x\colon$ x is kind and x is unwise$]$.

$\sim[$(For each logician $x\colon$ x is kind) and (for each logician $x\colon$ x is unwise)$]$.

$\sim[$(Each logician is kind) and (each logician is unwise)$]$.

$\sim$(Each logician is kind) or $\sim$(each logician is unwise).

$\sim$(Each logician is kind) or (some logician is wise).

(Each logician is kind) $\Rightarrow$ (some logician is wise).

Accordingly, W is similar to the following statement.

If each logician is kind, then some logician is wise.

919. Exercises.

   a. Formulate the s.f. negation of statement W in 918.

   b. In simple English formulate the negation of W.

   c. $[($For each so-and-so $x\colon$ $A_x \Rightarrow B_x)$ and (for each so-and-so $x\colon$ $B_x \Rightarrow C_x)]$
ent
for each so-and-so $x\colon$ $A_x \Rightarrow C_x$.

920. Example. The following are similar.

   $\sim[$Each married man is liked by some friend of his wife$]$.

   $\sim[$For each married man $x\colon$
there is a friend y of x's wife $\mid y$ likes $x]$.

   There is a married man $x \mid$
$\sim[$there is a friend y of x's wife $\mid y$ likes $x]$.

   There is a married man $x \mid$
for each friend y of x's wife$\colon$ y dislikes x.

   Some married man is disliked by every friend of his wife.

921. Example. The following are similar.

   $\sim[$Some married man is liked by all friends of his wife$]$.

   $\sim[$There is a married man $x \mid$
for each friend y of x's wife$\colon$ y likes $x]$.

   For each married man $x\colon$
$\sim[$for each friend y of x's wife$\colon$ y likes $x]$.

   For each married man $x\colon$
there is a friend y of x's wife $\mid y$ dislikes x.

   Each married man is disliked by some friend of his wife.

922. Example. The following are similar.

   $\sim[$Some married man's wife is liked by all of his sisters$]$.

~[There is a married man x |
for each sister z of x: z likes x's wife].

For each married man x:
~[for each sister z of x: z likes x's wife].

For each married man x:
there is a sister z of x | z dislikes x's wife.

Each married man's wife is disliked by a sister of his.

923. Example. The following are similar.

~[For any man x and woman y who married x:
there is a sister z of x | z dislikes y].

There is a man x and a woman y who married x |
~[there is a sister z of x | z dislikes y].

There is a man x and a woman y who married x |
for each sister z of x: z likes y.

924. Let P stand for the following general statement.

Each sewing club contains all the mothers of all the members of some biology club.

P means that no matter what sewing club be considered, say x, there exists a biology club, say y, such that all the mothers of all the members of y are members of x.

P has structural features that are found in many important mathematical statements.

The standard form of P is as follows.

For each sewing club x:
[there is a biology club y |
   for each member z of y: the mother of z is a member of x].

Working with this standard form, we may obtain a nontrivial negation of P as follows.

~P **sim**

There is a sewing club x |
~[there is a biology club y |
   for each member z of y: the mother of z is a member of x] **sim**

There is a sewing club x |
for each biology club y:
   ~[for each member z of y: the mother of z is a member of x] **sim**

There is a sewing club x |
for each biology club y:
   there is a member z of y | the mother of z is not a member of x.

Thus we have obtained a nontrivial negation of P.

925. If the student is amazed that he is expected to master these involved linguistic manipulations, he should recall that mathematics is the most intricate concept game created by the mind of man.

926. Exercise. Formulate a nontrivial negation of the following.

For each positive real number p: there is a positive real number h such that for each real number x less than h: $x + 1$ is less than p.

927. Let

 D stand for (There is at least one unicorn),
 E stand for (There is at most one unicorn),
 F stand for (There is precisely one unicorn),
 G stand for (There is more than one unicorn),
 H stand for (There is no unicorn).

The following facts should be scrutinized by the student.

F **sim** (D and E).
$\sim D$ **sim** H.
$\sim E$ **sim** G.
$\sim F$ **sim** (H or G).
$\sim G$ **sim** E.
$\sim H$ **sim** D.
D **sim** (F or G).
E **sim** (F or H).

928. In the next section the author uses a device that he invented to test the student's grasp of quantifiers.

929. Exercises.

The chart below consists of five rows labeled A, B, C, D, E and five columns labeled G, H, I, J, K. Each row contains five numerals and each column contains five numerals.

	G	H	I	J	K
A	1	3	4	2	5
B	6	7	8	5	8
C	7	9	3	4	2
D	8	0	10	3	7
E	5	4	0	1	6

We shall use the symbol ϵ (epsilon) to stand for *is in*, and we shall use the symbol $\notin$ to stand for *is not in*.

E.g., the expression (3 ϵ H) stands for the true statement (3 is in H); the expression (3 $\notin$ H) stands for the false statement (3 is not in H).

Determine the truth or falsity of the following statements.

a. For each numeral x in B: $x \epsilon G$.

b. For each numeral x: $(x \epsilon G) \Rightarrow (x \epsilon B)$.

c. There is a numeral $x \mid x \epsilon B$ and $x \notin G$.

d. For each numeral x: $(x \epsilon G) \Rightarrow (x \notin B)$.

e. Each numeral in D is in I.

f. No numeral in A is in C.

g. Some numeral in A is not in K.

h. Some numeral not in A is in K.

i. For each numeral x: $(x \epsilon B) \Rightarrow (x \epsilon G$ and $x \epsilon K)$.

j. For each numeral x: $(x \epsilon B$ and $x \epsilon G) \Rightarrow (x \epsilon K)$.

k. For each numeral x: $(x \epsilon B) \Leftrightarrow (x \epsilon K)$.

l. For each numeral z in D: $z \epsilon I$ or $z \epsilon K$.

m. (For each numeral z in D: $z \epsilon I$) or (for each numeral z in D: $z \epsilon K$).

n. There is at least one numeral in A that is in B.

o. There is at most one numeral in A that is in B.

p. There is precisely one numeral in A that is in B.

q. No numeral in C is in I and G.

r. There is a numeral x in $A \mid$ for each column y: $x \notin y$.

s. For each numeral x in A: there is a column $y \mid x \epsilon$ y.

t. Some numeral is in each column.

u. There is a numeral $y \mid$ for each column x: $y \epsilon x$.

v. For each column x: there is a numeral $y \mid y \epsilon x$.

w. There is a column $x \mid$ for each numeral y in A: $y \notin x$.

x. For each column x: there is a numeral y in $x \mid$ for each column z different from x: $y \notin z$.

y. There is a column $x \mid$ for each numeral y in x: there is a column z different from $x \mid y \epsilon z$.

z. For each row x: there is a column $y \mid$ each numeral in x is in y.

aa. For each row x: there is a column $y \mid$ some numeral in x is in y.

bb. There is a row $x \mid$ for each column y: some numeral in x is in y.

cc. For any row x and column y: each numeral in x is in y.

dd. For any row x and column y: some numeral in x is in y.

ee. There is a row x and a column $y \mid$ no numeral in x is in y.

ff. There are rows x, $y \mid$ for each column z: z contains a numeral that is in x and y.

gg. For any rows x, y: there is a column $z \mid z$ contains a numeral that is in x and y.

hh. For any rows x, y and column z:
there is a numeral in z that is in x and y.

Definition

see 1241

→ **1001.** The theory of definitions is very complex, e.g., see *Introduction to Logic* by Patrick Suppes. For our purpose it suffices to say that certain (suitably formulated) statements may be called definitions.

NOTE. It is convenient to treat notational conventions as definitions.

1002. For example, let us formally adopt the following definition; i.e., let us agree to call the following statement a definition.

1003. Definition. A *unicorn* is any horse-like animal having one horn.

NOTE I. We deem this definition to be similar to the following conjunction.

(Each unicorn is a horse-like animal having one horn) and
(each horse-like animal having one horn is a unicorn).

NOTE II. The definition may also be expressed thus:

A thing is a unicorn provided it is a horse-like animal having one horn.
(Recall that *provided* means *when and only when*.)

NOTE III. This definition is not existential; it does not stipulate the existence of unicorns, animals, horns, or horse-like animals.

NOTE IV. Very few definitions are existential.

1004. Statements that readily follow from a definition will be listed under the caption **Immediate consequences.**

1005. Immediate consequences.

Each unicorn is horse-like.
Each unicorn is an animal.

Each unicorn is a horse-like animal.
Each unicorn has one horn.
Each unicorn is horse-like and has one horn.
Each unicorn is an animal having one horn.

NOTE. The fact that these statements follow from Definition 1003 is a simple matter of logic and depends neither on the existence of unicorns nor on our understanding of the expressions *unicorn, horse-like, animal, having one horn.*

1006. Let us agree that the statement (Each unicorn is horse-like) is not similar to [(Each unicorn is horse-like) or ~(each unicorn is horse-like)].

1007. Definition. A *psychiatrist* is any person who has received special training in psychoanalysis and has a medical degree.

NOTE I. This definition is similar to the following conjunction.
(Each psychiatrist is a person who has received special training in psychoanalysis and has a medical degree) and
(each person who has received special training in psychoanalysis and has a medical degree is a psychiatrist).

NOTE II. This definition is not existential.

1008. Immediate consequences.

Each psychiatrist is a person.
Each psychiatrist has received special training in psychoanalysis.
Each psychiatrist has a medical degree.
And so on.

1009. It is convenient to deem any conjunction of definitions to be a definition. E.g., the conjunction of Definition 1003 with Definition 1007 is a definition.

Accordingly, the statement (Each unicorn is horse-like and each psychiatrist has a medical degree) follows from a definition. See 516b.

1010. Suppose that the following axioms occur in the definition of a system:

    i. Each gimlet is blue.
    ii. There is a gimlet that is not blue.

These axioms clearly entail the contradiction (There is a gimlet that is blue and not blue), and hence they entail every statement. Since this is undesirable, we consider the system to be worthless. Of course, a mathematical idiot might choose to while away his time by grinding out theorems about gimlets.

1011. Principle of mathematical creativity. Any suitably formulated statement may be adopted as a definition until such time that we discover that in conjunction with previously adopted definitions it entails a contradiction.

1012. The axioms of plane Euclidean geometry entail the following incompletely formulated statement:

I. There exist two different lines that do not intersect.

The axioms of plane projective geometry entail the following incompletely formulated statement:

II. Every two different lines intersect.

For this reason many mathematicians gleefully assert that the axioms of the former system contradict those of the latter. This alleged contradiction is no contradiction at all. Statement I should be expressed as *There exist two different plane Euclidean lines that do not intersect,* and statement II should be expressed as *Every two different plane projective lines intersect,* and these statements are not contradictory.

We must not be deceived by our habit of abbreviating statements.

1013. The axioms of the real number system are so involved that no one has yet conclusively proved that they do not entail a contradiction. Of course it is possible, but not likely, that they do entail a contradiction. Later we shall investigate the real number system in great detail.

Truth, Falsity

1101. In Lesson 6 we discussed logical truth and logical falsity, and in Lesson 7 we discussed empirical truth and empirical falsity. In this lesson we shall introduce the ideas of deductive truth and deductive falsity.

1102. We recall (714) that an empirically true statement is one that is true in the ordinary sense of being in accord with the facts of nature. To establish that a statement is empirically true, one must make observations, conduct experiments, or investigate history.

1103. We also recall (715) that an empirically false statement is one whose negation is empirically true. E.g., the statement (Unicorns exist) is empirically false. A statement that is empirically false today may be empirically true tomorrow; e.g., tomorrow a unicorn may appear. Many years ago the statement (The Earth does not revolve about the Sun) was deemed to be empirically true; today we believe differently.

1104. Words of caution.

a. The expressions *not empirically true* and *empirically false* are not synonymous. Although each statement is surely either empirically true or not empirically true, it is a mistake to believe that each statement is either empirically true or empirically false. E.g., the statement (There is a real number whose square is 5) is not empirically true and not empirically false.

b. *Not empirically false* and *empirically true* are not synonymous.

1105. It is a fundamental assumption of science that no statement is simultaneously empirically true and empirically false. Another fundamental assumption is that any statement that follows from an empirically true statement is empirically true. Indeed, if an alleged empirically true statement entails a statement that turns out to be empirically false, then scientists immediately restudy the data that led them to believe the former statement to be empirically true.

In mathematics we are not concerned with empirical truth or empirical falsity.

1106. Definition. A *deductively true statement* is any statement that follows from a definition.

NOTE I.   Any conjunction of definitions is deemed to be a definition.

NOTE II.   *Theorem* means *deductively true statement*.

NOTE III.   Each definition is deductively true. (Why?)

1107. Examples.

a. The statement (Each unicorn is horse-like) is deductively true.

b. The statement (Some unicorn is horse-like) is not deductively true because no definition presented (or to be presented) entails the existence of a unicorn.

c. We shall see later that the following statements are deductively true:
The square of each nonzero real number is positive.
There exists precisely one nonzero real number that equals its square.

1108. By suitable rigging, an empirically true statement may turn out to be deductively true. E.g., the empirically true statement (The Earth revolves about the Sun) will be deductively true if we define the Earth to be, among other things, a planet that revolves about the Sun.

On the other hand, no rigging can cause the deductively true statement (There exists a real number whose square is 5) to be empirically true.

1109. Theorem. Each tautology is deductively true.

Proof. Consider any tautology T.
Since T follows from every statement (611h), T follows from Definition 1003, and so T is deductively true.

1110. Are all deductively true statements tautological?

ANSWER.   No. Many deductively true statements are not tautological. E.g., the statement (Each unicorn is horse-like) is deductively true but not tautological. See 1006.

1111. Mathematicians are primarily interested in deductively true statements that are not tautological.

Surely we are not interested in the tautology (Each real number is positive or some real number is not positive). The tautological nature of this statement can be established without referring to mathematical definitions, and it is this fact that accounts for our disdain.

NOTE. The view that each deductively true statement is tautological yields the outrageous result that all theorems are similar.

1112. We know that every tautology follows from each statement. See 611h.

Does every deductively true statement follow from each statement?

No. E.g., the deductively true statement (Each unicorn is horse-like), not being tautological, does not follow from its negation.

1113. The deductive truth of a statement is independent of the facts of nature and depends solely on our definitions and rules of logic.

1114. Theorem. Each statement that follows from a deductively true statement is deductively true.

Proof. Consider any statement K that follows from a deductively true statement H.

Since H follows from a definition, say G, we know by 515 that K follows from G, and so K is deductively true.

NOTE. Surely then, each statement that is similar to a deductively true statement is deductively true.

1115. Definition. A *deductively false statement* is any statement whose negation is deductively true.

1116. Examples.

a. The statement (Some unicorn is unhorse-like) is deductively false because its negation (Each unicorn is horse-like) is deductively true.

b. The statement (Each unicorn is unhorse-like) is not deductively false because its negation (Some unicorn is horse-like) is not deductively true. See 1107b.

c. The statement (There exists a nonzero real number whose square is not positive) is deductively false because its negation (The square of each nonzero real number is positive) is, as we shall see later, deductively true.

1117. Words of caution.

a. The expressions *not deductively true* and *deductively false* are not synonymous. When we assert that a statement P is not deductively true we mean that P does not follow from a definition, and this surely differs from the assertion that $\sim P$ follows from a definition.

b. *Not deductively false* and *deductively true* are not synonymous.

c. A statement that follows from a deductively false statement is not necessarily deductively false.

1118. Now we return to concepts of existence.

The statement (There exists a real number that equals its square) is, as we shall see, deductively true; however this statement will not appear in our definition of the real number system. Accordingly, we have here an example of deductive existence.

The statement (There exists no real number whose square equals -1) is deductively true but does not appear in our definition of the real number system. This, then, is an example of deductive nonexistence.

1119. For the remainder of this lesson, *d-true* abbreviates *deductively true* and *d-false* abbreviates *deductively false*.

1120. Theorems.

a. The negation of each d-true statement is d-false.

Proof. For each d-true statement P: $(\sim P)$ is d-false because its negation, being similar to P, is d-true.

b. The negation of each d-false statement is d-true.

Proof. Immediate from 1115.

1121. The results in 1120 are neatly summarized in the following chart called a d-truth table.

B	$\sim B$
d-true	d-false
d-false	d-true

NOTE. d-truth tables should be read only from left to right.

1122. Exercises.

a. Each contradiction is d-false.

b. Each statement that entails a d-false statement is d-false.

1123. The statement (Some unicorn is unhorse-like) is d-false but is not a contradiction. (?)
Accordingly, d-false statements are not necessarily contradictions.

1124. Because each contradiction entails every statement (605a), perhaps the student erroneously believes that each d-false statement entails every statement. The d-false statement (Some unicorn is unhorse-like), not being a contradiction, does not entail its negation.

1125. Now the author is ready to discuss some intriguing questions.

1126. Might there be a statement about whole numbers that is both d-true and d-false?
Yes, but it seems unlikely.

1127. Definition. A system is said to be *consistent* provided that no statement within the system is both d-true and d-false.

A system is said to be *inconsistent* provided there is a statement within the system that is both d-true and d-false.

1128. In the year 1931, Kurt Gödel, then but a young man, in an article of unprecedented imagination and ingenuity, astounded the mathematical world by demonstrating that

> *if a system of logic and whole numbers is consistent,*
> *then any proof of its consistency must employ methods of*
>   *reasoning that transcend those in the system.*

Or in more appealing, anthropomorphic terms: *no consistent system of logic and whole numbers can prove its own consistency.*

1129. Might there be a statement about whole numbers that is neither d-true nor d-false?
Yes.

1130. Definition. A system is said to be *complete* provided that each statement within the system is either d-true or d-false.

A system is said to be *incomplete* provided there is a statement within the system that is neither d-true nor d-false.

1131. Basing his work on the astonishing results of Kurt Gödel, J. B. Rosser proved in the year 1936 that *each consistent system of logic and whole numbers is incomplete;* i.e., within any assumed consistent system of logic and whole numbers there is a statement that is neither d-true nor d-false.

1132. Definition. An *undecidable statement* is any statement that is neither d-true nor d-false.

1133. Immediate consequence. Each statement is either d-true or d-false or undecidable.

1134. Word of caution. The author's expedient definitions of *d-true statement*, *d-false statement*, and *undecidable statement* do not meet the currently accepted standards of logic, according to which these notions are not absolutist in kind but significant only relative to a given system.

1135. Contrary to the belief of some people, Gödel's results do not invalidate case proofs or indirect proofs, which will be discussed in the next lesson. Even though a statement P may be undecidable, the statement $(P \text{ or } \sim P)$ is nevertheless d-true because it is a tautology. If the student is confused by this, perhaps he is (contrary to previous warning) interpreting $(P \text{ or } \sim P)$ to mean *P is true or P is false*.

1136. Exercise.

The negation of each undecidable statement is undecidable.

1137. Can a systematic method be devised that will determine the d-truth, d-falsity, or undecidability of all mathematical statements?

No. In the year 1936 Alonzo Church proved that no such systematic method can be devised.

1138. Theorems.

    a. The conjunction of any two d-true statements is d-true.

    Proof. For any d-true statements B, N: B follows from a definition, say A; N follows from a definition, say M; so by 516b, $(B \text{ and } N)$ follows from the definition $(A \text{ and } M)$.

    b. The conjunction of any two statements, at least one of which is d-false, is d-false.

    Proof. For any statements J, K such that J is d-false:
$(\sim J)$ is d-true, and $(\sim J)$ **ent**$_?$ $\sim (J \text{ and } K)$,
and hence $\sim (J \text{ and } K)$ is d-true;   (?)
therefore $(J \text{ and } K)$ is d-false.

    NOTE. Surely $(K \text{ and } J)$ is also d-false.

1139. The results in 1138 are summarized in the following d-truth table.

A	B	A and B
d-true d-false	d-true d-false	d-true d-false d-false

NOTE I. A blank space in a d-truth table indicates that nothing is assumed there; e.g., in the second line, A is d-false, and B may be d-true or d-false or undecidable.

NOTE II. If (A and B) is d-true, then so are A, B because they follow from (A and B). This fact is not reflected in the above d-truth table which should only be read from left to right.

1140. Theorems.

a. The disjunction of any two statements, at least one of which is d-true, is d-true.

Proof. For any statements J, K such that J is d-true: J **ent** (J or K), and so (J or K) is d-true.

b. The disjunction of any two d-false statements is d-false.

Proof. For any d-false statements G, H: (G or H) is similar to ~(~G and ~H) which is d-false. (?)

1141. The results in 1140 are summarized in the following d-truth table.

A	B	A or B
d-true d-false	 d-true d-false	d-true d-true d-false

1142. If a disjunction (A or B) is d-true, may we conclude that at least one of A, B is d-true?

No. E.g., let A stand for a particular undecidable statement, and let B stand for ~A. Then B is also undecidable. Thus, (A or B) is d-true (because it is a tautology), but A is not d-true and B is not d-true.

NOTE. If the student is confused by this, perhaps he is erroneously interpreting (G or H) as G *is true or H is true.*

1143. Exercise.

For any statements A, B such that A is d-true and (A ⟹ B) is d-true: B is d-true.

62   LSSSON 11

1144. Exercises.

   a. For any statements G, H such that H is d-true: $(G \Rightarrow H)$ is d-true.

   b. For any statements G, H such that G is d-false: $(G \Rightarrow H)$ is d-true.

   c. For any statements G, H such that G is d-true and H is d-false:
   $(G \Rightarrow H)$ is d-false.

1145. The results in 1144 are summarized in the following d-truth table.

A	B	$A \Rightarrow B$
	d-true	d-true
d-false		d-true
d-true	d-false	d-false

1146. Exercises.

   a. For any d-true statements G, H: $(G \Leftrightarrow H)$ is d-true.

   b. For any d-false statements G, H: $(G \Leftrightarrow H)$ is d-true.

   c. For any statements G, H, one of which is d-true and one of which is
   d-false: $(G \Leftrightarrow H)$ is d-false.

1147. The results in 1146 are summarized in the following d-truth table.

A	B	$A \Leftrightarrow B$
d-true	d-true	d-true
d-false	d-false	d-true
d-true	d-false	d-false
d-false	d-true	d-false

Proofs, Disproofs

1201. We started with the fundamental relationship of similarity between statements; in terms of this relationship we defined the entailment relationship; using the entailment relationship we defined *tautology* and *contradiction*.

We then distinguished three kinds of truth:

> empirical (in accord with the facts of nature),
> logical (tautological),
> deductive (following from a definition).

When a mathematician asserts that a mathematical statement is true, he means that it is *deductively true*; when he asserts that it is false, he means that it is *deductively false*. Unless there is an indication to the contrary, the word *true* henceforth means *deductively true* and the word *false* means *deductively false*.

A theorem is any true statement.

In this lesson we shall define the relationship *follows by*; this relationship is used by mathematicians more often than the relationship *follows from*. First we informally explain what is meant by a proof of a statement.

1202. Roughly, a *proof* of a statement is any orderly discussion (or argument) that establishes the statement to be true.

NOTE I. *To prove means to establish as true.*

NOTE II. *Prove, show, demonstrate* are synonymous.

1203. Usually there are many different proofs of a true statement; some proofs are more elegant than others because they more clearly reveal the reasons underlying the truth of the statement.

Creating proofs is an art that cannot be reduced to a mechanical procedure and may require the exercise of considerable imagination and ingenuity. One learns to create proofs by scrutinizing proofs in rigorous books and by submitting his own proofs for inspection by competent mathematicians. The student is reminded of John Stuart Mill's remark: "Mathematicians are notoriously difficult to convince."

NOTE. "An incomplete proof is no proof at all." *Henri Lebesgue*

1204. A *proved* statement is one whose truth has been established earlier in the text.

1205. Examples.

a. In view of 1005, the statement (Each unicorn is horse-like) is proved.

b. Although the statement (There is no real number whose square is -1) is true, we may not at this point say that it is proved.

1206. By 1138a, any conjunction of proved statements may be considered as proved.

1207. Any statement similar to a proved statement may be considered as proved. (Why ?)

1208. A *provable* statement is one that can be proved.

1209. Definition. A statement B *follows by* a statement A provided there is a proved statement P such that $(P$ and $A)$ **ent** B.

NOTATIONS. B follows by A; by A follows B.

NOTE. Of course, P may be a conjunction of proved statements.

1210. Exercises.

a. For any statements A, B such that A is true and by A follows B: B is true.

b. For any statements G, H such that G **ent** H: by G follows H.

1211. Let H stand for (Each unicorn is horse-like).

Since H is proved and $(H$ and $\sim H)$ **ent** H,
we may conclude that by $\sim H$ follows H.

But $\sim H$ does not entail H because H is not a tautology. (1006)

Now the student knows that he may not use the converse of 1210b.

1212. One way to prove a statement B is to find a proved statement A and then to prove $(A \Rightarrow B)$. By 1143, we can then conclude that B is true.

1213. Theorem. For any statements B, F such that F is false and F follows by $\sim B$: B is true.

Proof.: there is a proved statement P such that $(\sim B$ and $P)$ **ent** F;
hence, $\sim B$ **ent**$_?$ $(P \Rightarrow F)$;
therefore, $\sim (P \Rightarrow F)$ **ent** B;   (516a)
but, $\sim (P \Rightarrow F)$ is true because it is similar to $(P$ and $\sim F)$ which is true; so B is true.

NOTE. We do not require F to be a contradiction.

1214. Indirect proof of a statement. The previous theorem provides a useful method of proving a statement B: we establish that a false statement follows by $\sim B$. This is called an *indirect proof* of B.

We repeat: an indirect proof of a statement B consists in establishing that by the negation of B follows a false statement.

Indirect proofs are often shorter and clearer than direct (not indirect) proofs; frequently it is impossible to prove a statement except indirectly.

NOTE I. The author almost always starts an indirect proof of a statement B with the cryptic remark *Suppose not*; this advises the reader that the proof will consist in establishing that by $\sim B$ follows a false statement. At the end of an indirect proof it is customary to write *Contradiction*. This may be misleading because we often establish that a false statement (rather than a contradiction) follows by $\sim B$.

NOTE II. Students who believe that indirect proofs are not "real" proofs obviously do not understand that Theorem 1213 justifies indirect proofs.

1215. Next we turn to proof methods that are applicable only to conditionals.

1216. One way to prove a conditional $(G \Rightarrow K)$ is to establish that G entails K, for then we may conclude that $(G \Rightarrow K)$ is a tautology (616a) and hence true.

This method is of little use to mathematicians because it only works when $(G \Rightarrow K)$ is a tautology, and, as we know, mathematicians are not really interested in tautologies.

1217. Theorem. For any statements G, K such that by G follows K: $(G \Rightarrow K)$ is true.

Proof.: there is a proved statement P such that $(P$ and $G)$ **ent** K, and so P **ent** $(G \Rightarrow K)$, and hence $(G \Rightarrow K)$ is true.

NOTE. Compare 616a.

1218. Exercises.

   a. Prove the converse of 1217.

   b. For any statements G, H, K such that by G follows H, and by H follows K: by G follows K.

1219. Methods of proving a conditional $(G \Rightarrow K)$.

   a. Establish that by G follows K. Justification: 1217.

   b. Find a statement H and prove $(G \Rightarrow H \Rightarrow K)$. Justification: 322.

   c. Prove $(\sim K \Rightarrow \sim G)$. Justification: 308.

   NOTE. This is called a contrapositive proof of $(G \Rightarrow K)$.

   d. Prove $[(G$ and $\sim K) \Rightarrow K]$. Justification: 315d.

   e. Prove $[(G$ and $\sim K) \Rightarrow \sim G]$.

   f. Find a false statement F and prove $[(G$ and $\sim K) \Rightarrow F]$.

1220. Exercises.

   a. Justify method 1219e.

   b. Justify method 1219f.

1221. Methods of proving a biconditional $(A \Leftrightarrow B)$.

   a. Prove $(A \Rightarrow B)$ and prove $(B \Rightarrow A)$.

   b. Find a statement H and prove $(A \Leftrightarrow H \Leftrightarrow B)$. See 410b.

   c. Prove $(\sim B \Leftrightarrow \sim A)$.

   NOTE. This is called a contrapositive proof of $(A \Leftrightarrow B)$.

1222. Round-robin proof of $(G \Leftrightarrow H \Leftrightarrow K)$. We prove $(G \Rightarrow H \Rightarrow K \Rightarrow G)$ and then conclude by 409 that $(G \Leftrightarrow H \Leftrightarrow K)$ is true.

1223. "Bungler" Bob, wishing to prove a certain statement B, manages to establish that by $\sim B$ follows B. He then argues as follows.

Either B is true or B is false.
In case B is true, I am done.
In case B is false, then $(\sim B)$ is true, and so B is true (1210a).
Thus, in every case, B is true.

"Notorious" Ned is unconvinced; he points out that since B may be undecidable, "Bungler" Bob is unjustified in claiming that either B is true or B is false. Whereupon, the Bungler comes up with another "proof."

Since by $\sim B$ follows B, $(\sim B \Rightarrow B)$ is a tautology.
But B is similar to $(\sim B \Rightarrow B)$.
Hence B is true.

1224. Exercises.

   a. Find the flaw in the Bungler's latter proof.

   b. Convince "Notorious" Ned that B is true.

1225. The student must not rashly conclude that case proofs are unsound. Next we prepare for a discussion of properly formulated case proofs.

1226. Theorem. For any statements G, H, K such that $(G$ or $H)$ is true, by G follows K, and by H follows K: K is true.

   Proof.: $[(G$ or $H)$ and $(G \Rightarrow K)$ and $(H \Rightarrow K)]$ is true,   (?) and so K is true (314).

1227. Two-case proof. The previous theorem provides another way of proving a statement K: we find statements G, H such that $(G$ or $H)$ has been proved, and then we establish that by G follows K, and that by H follows K. Such a proof is called a *two-case proof* of K; the statements G, H are referred to as the two cases to be investigated. One should always start such a proof with a proved statement $(G$ or $H)$.

   CAUTION. If $(G$ or $H)$ is not true, then we have no proof at all.

1228. Exercise.

   "Hopeful" Harry wishes to prove a statement K. After much fumbling, he manages to establish that by B follows K and that by $\sim B$ follows K. He suspects that B is undecidable. Convince "Notorious" Ned that K is true.

1229. Exercise.

   For any statements A, B, C, K such that $(A$ or B or $C)$ is true, by A follows K, by B follows K, and by C follows K: K is true.

1230. A **three-case proof** of a statement K works this way: we find statements A, B, C such that $(A$ or B or $C)$ has been proved, and then we establish that K follows by each of A, B, C.

   The statements A, B, C are referred to as the three cases to be investigated. One should start such a proof with a proved statement $(A$ or B or $C)$.

1231. A statement B is said to *follow by two or more statements* provided that B follows by their conjunction.

1232. According to 1115, a false statement is one whose negation is true. Therefore, *to disprove* (establish as false) a statement, we must prove its negation. A *disproof* of a statement B is a proof of $\sim B$. A *disproved* statement is one whose negation has been proved. A *disprovable* statement is one that can be disproved.

1233. Example. To disprove the statement (For each real number x: x is less than x^2) we must prove its negation (There is a real number x such that x is not less than x^2). To prove the latter statement it suffices to produce an example of a real number (e.g., $\frac{1}{2}$) that is not less than its square. Such an example is called a *counterexample* for the original statement.

Our disproof of the original statement may be condensed as follows:

Counterexample. $\frac{1}{2}$.

1234. Example. To disprove the statement (For each real number x: if x is less than x^2, then $x < 1$), we must prove its negation (There is a real number x such that x is less than x^2 and x is not less than 1). To prove the latter statement it suffices to produce a real number (e.g., 3) that is less than its square but not less than 1.

Our disproof of the original statement may be condensed as follows:

Counterexample. 3.

1235. To disprove the statement (There is a real number x such that $x^2 = -1$), we must prove its negation (For each real number x: $x^2 \neq -1$). Of course the latter statement cannot be proved simply by producing an example (or ten billion examples) of a real number whose square differs from -1.

1236. A *lemma* is any statement proved for the purpose of simplifying proofs of subsequent theorems; a *corollary* is any statement that readily follows by previously proved statements.

After a definition the author will often list various statements under the caption **Immediate consequences**; such statements are true and readily follow by the definition.

1237. When we claim that a statement is obvious (clear, evident, plain), we mean that it can be proved by a simple but perhaps long argument which the reader should be able to provide.

1238. By a *pitfall* the author means a false statement that students are apt to believe is true.

1239. Now that the student has patiently studied these twelve lessons, he will be surprised to learn that we shall henceforth write out proofs in the conventional, informal manner and that we shall fail to make the fine distinctions which would be necessary for a purely formal treatment. Nevertheless, the author believes that the level of rigor sustained in the ensuing pages is unimpeachable.

1240. Henceforth the student may render the expression $(A \Rightarrow B)$ as *A implies B*, and he may render the expression $(A \Leftrightarrow B)$ as *A is equivalent to B*.

1241. Summary.   *See also 1001ff*

We create a system by defining it.

We shall refer to the definition of a system as the *primary definition*. Certain statements in the primary definition are called *axioms* (or *postulates*). The axioms usually stipulate that certain things possess certain properties and bear certain relationships to one another. Of these things, properties, and relationships, those that have not arisen in previously defined systems are said to be *primitives* and the words used in referring to them are called *primitive terms* (or less aptly, *undefined terms*). Usually at least one of the axioms asserts the existence of certain primitives, which are said to be *definitionally existent*.

Subsequently we make various *secondary* definitions (and notational conventions) that serve to simplify our investigation of the system. The secondary definitions are nonexistential; i.e., they do not assert the existence of things.

Statements within the system are of three types:

(1) Those that follow from the definitions (primary or secondary) are called *theorems*, are said to be *deductively true* (or simply *true*), and are *proved* by an orderly discussion which establishes that they do follow from the definitions.

(2) Those whose negation follows from the definitions are said to be *deductively false* (or simply *false*), and are *disproved* by proving their negation.

(3) Those that are neither of type (1) nor of type (2) are said to be *undecidable*. Methods of establishing undecidability are not discussed in this book.

An *existence theorem* is one that asserts the existence of a thing whose existence is not specifically indicated in the axioms; such things are said to be *deductively existent*.

A system is *consistent* provided that no statement within the system is both true and false. A system is *inconsistent* provided that some statement within the system is both true and false. Obviously, each system is either consistent or inconsistent.

If a system is inconsistent, then at least one of its theorems is a contradiction.

Proof. Consider any inconsistent system. Then there is a statement P within the system that is both true and false. Hence $\sim P$ is a theorem, and so (P and $\sim P$), which is a contradiction, is a theorem. Q.e.d.

Conversely, if at least one theorem of a system is a contradiction, then the system is inconsistent.

Proof. Consider any system at least one of whose theorems T is a contradiction. Then $\sim T$ is a tautology and hence is a theorem. Thus, T is both true and false, and so the system is inconsistent. Q.e.d.

Now it is clear why an inconsistent system is said to be *contradictory* (or *self-contradictory*). A system that is known to be inconsistent is deemed to be worthless. It has not yet been proved (1964) that the real number system is consistent, although it has been proved that if the system of whole numbers is consistent, then so is the real number system.

A system is *complete* provided that each statement within the system is either true or false. A system is *incomplete* provided that some statement within the system is undecidable, i.e., neither true nor false. Obviously, each system is either complete or incomplete.

1242. Note. Although we have used the word *similar* in a special technical way (115), we shall, henceforth, often use it in the customary manner to mean *analogous*.

Equal, Unequal

1301. Two or more different symbols are often used to denote the same thing.

1302. Notation. $(x = y)$ stands for
(the thing referred to by the symbol x is the same as the thing referred to by the symbol y).

NOTE I. The symbol $=$ is rendered as *equals* or as *is equal to*.

NOTE II. The expressions *equal, identical, the same* are synonymous.

NOTE III. We also use the word *is* to mean *equals*; e.g., $2 + 3$ is 5.

1303. Although we render the expression $(x = y)$ as *x equals y*, we must refrain from interpreting it to mean that the symbols x, y are equal (indeed, they are not); this expression is appropriately interpreted to mean that the things referred to by the symbols x, y are equal.

NOTE. Recall the maxim that *a symbol is not the thing it denotes*.

1304. Fundamental properties of equality.

a. *Reflexivity*
For each thing x: $x = x$.

b. *Symmetry*
For any things x, y such that $x = y$: $y = x$.

c. *Transitivity*
For any things x, y, z such that $x = y$ and $y = z$: $x = z$.

d. *Substitution*
Symbols that refer to the same thing may replace each other wherever they are used to refer to that thing.

1305. Notation.

$(x = y = z)$ stands for $(x = y$ and $y = z)$;
$(w = x = y = z)$ stands for $(w = x$ and $x = y$ and $y = z)$;
and so on.

1306. Exercises. (Use 1304.)

a. For any things a, b, c, d such that $a = b = c = d$: $a = d$.

b. For any things a, b, c such that $a = c$ and $b = c$: $a = b$.

c. Find what is wrong with the following argument.

Let the symbols x, y stand for Mark Twain.
Then $x = y$.
The symbol x is the 24th letter of the alphabet.
Hence, by 1304d, the symbol y is the 24th letter of the alphabet.

d. Find what is wrong with the following argument.

Let the symbols Ike, x stand for General Eisenhower.
Then $x = $ Ike.
Ike is a former President.
Hence the symbol x is a former President.

e. Is something wrong with the following argument?

Let the symbols Ike, x stand for General Eisenhower.
Then $x = $ Ike.
Ike is a former President.
Hence x is a former President.

f. Is something wrong with the following argument?

By (Bach = Handel) follows
[(Bach = Handel) and (Bach = Handel)].

By the statement on the previous line follows
[(Bach = Handel) and (Handel = Bach)]. (1304b)

By the statement on the previous line follows
(Bach = Bach). (1304c)

Therefore the following conditional is true:
(Bach = Handel) $\Rightarrow$ (Bach = Bach). (1217)

g. Create a simple proof of [(Bach = Handel) $\Rightarrow$ (Bach = Bach)].

1307. Notation. $(x \neq y)$ stands for $\sim(x = y)$.

NOTE I.   We render the symbol $\neq$ as *is not equal to*.

NOTE II.   *Not equal, unequal, different, distinct* are synonymous.

CAUTION.   In mathematics, *distinct* does not mean *clear, plain, unmistakable, definite*.

1308. Although we render the expression $(x \neq y)$ as *x is not equal to y*, we must refrain from interpreting it to mean that the symbols x, y are different (even though they are); this expression is appropriately interpreted to mean that the things referred to by the symbols x, y are different.

1309. Notation.
$(x = y \neq z)$ stands for $(x = y$ and $y \neq z)$;
$(x \neq y = z)$ stands for $(x \neq y$ and $y = z)$;
$(w = x \neq y = z)$ stands for $(w = x$ and $x \neq y$ and $y = z)$;
and so on.

1310. Exercises.

a. For any things x, y, z such that $x = y \neq z$: $x \neq z$.

b. *Disprove.* For any things x, y, z such that $x \neq y \neq z$: $x \neq z$.

1311. In mathematical discourse the word *the* means *the one and only*; before we may properly use the expression *the so-and-so* we must be sure that there is **precisely one** so-and-so.

The is improperly used in *The real number that equals its square* because there is more than one real number that equals its square.

The is improperly used in *The real number whose square is negative* because there is no real number whose square is negative.

The is properly used in *The real number x such that $x + x = x$* because there is precisely one such real number, namely 0.

1312. Exercises. (for those who have studied inequalities)

a. Criticize the following argument.

Let x denote the real number that is greater than 2.
Since $x + 1 \neq x$, $x + 1$ is not greater than 2.
Therefore $x + 1 \leq 2$.
So, $2 < x < x + 1 \leq 2$.
Hence, $2 < 2$.

b. Criticize the following argument.

Let t denote the real number such that $t^2 + 2t + 2 = 0$.
Then, $0 \leq (t + 1)^2 < (t + 1)^2 + 1 = t^2 + 2t + 2 = 0$.
Hence, $0 < 0$.

1313. The student now knows that improper usage of *the* may be disastrous.

Sets

1401. A *set* is a fictitious thing that can be explained but apparently cannot be defined.

A set may be thought of as the result of mentally gathering things into one totality; the things so gathered are called *members of the set*.

For example, the mind can gather the following things into one totality: Mozart's Ninth Piano Concerto, the planet Mars, the American concept of religious freedom, the Empire State Building; the result is a set having four members.

Although we are accepting the ideas of *set* and *membership* as undefined concepts, we shall adopt, in this lesson, two axioms and an expedient assumption to guide us.

NOTE. We do not rule out the possibility that a set be a member of another set.

1402. The words *collection, class, aggregate, family* (but not *group*) are synonyms for *set*.

1403. Definition. For any sets S, T:
S, T *have the same members* provided that
each member of S is a member of T, and
each member of T is a member of S.

1404. Immediate consequence. For any sets A, B:
if $A = B$, then A, B have the same members.

NOTE. The converse of this proposition cannot be proved; hence we adopt it as an axiom.

1405. Axiom. For any sets A, B:
if A, B have the same members, then $A = B$.

NOTE. This axiom provides a useful method of proving that two sets are equal: we prove that they have the same members.

1406. Immediate consequences.

a. For any sets A, B:
$A = B$ if and only if
A, B have the same members.

NOTE. This proposition may also be expressed as follows.

For any sets A, B:
$A = B$ if and only if
for each thing t: t is a member of $A \Leftrightarrow t$ is a member of B.

b. For any sets A, B:
$A \neq B$ if and only if
there is a thing t such that
either t is a member of A but not of B
or t is a member of B but not of A.

NOTE. This proposition provides a useful method of proving that two sets are distinct: we find a thing that is a member of one set but not the other.

1407. It is often said that a set is determined by its members;
however, the expression *is determined by its members* is seldom defined.
Here is one possible definition:

A set S is *determined by its members* provided that
for each set T such that S, T have the same members: $S = T$.

By 1405, it immediately follows that each set is determined by its members.

NOTE. We often say that a set *consists of its members*.

1408. Recall (111) that *at most one* means *not more than one*. One standard method of proving that there is at most one so-and-so is to prove that any two so-and-so's are equal.

1409. Example. We shall use 1405 to prove the following statement.

There is at most one set, say M, such that
for each thing x: x is a member of $M \Leftrightarrow x$ is human.

Proof. Consider any sets A, B such that
for each thing x: x is a member of $A \Leftrightarrow x$ is human,
and
for each thing x: x is a member of $B \Leftrightarrow x$ is human.

Then A, B have the same members,   (?)
and so by 1405, $A = B$.

1410. The reader will recall (902) that a condition is any expression that contains precisely one unquantified letter and becomes a statement when all occurrences of that unquantified letter are replaced by a suitable noun or name.

NOTE. In the condition (r admires r), the letter r is the unquantified letter, and it occurs twice, not three times. The fifth letter in *admires* does not count as an occurrence of the unquantified letter r.

1411. Notation. For any condition C and any symbol λ that either is available or is the unquantified letter in C or is a name or a noun: the expression C_λ stands for the result of substituting the symbol λ for each occurrence of the unquantified letter in C.

1412. Examples.

  a. (x is mortal)$_y$ stands for (y is mortal).
  (x is mortal)$_x$ stands for (x is mortal).
  (x is mortal)$_{\text{Bach}}$ stands for (Bach is mortal).

  b. ($y + 0 = y$)$_x$ stands for ($x + 0 = x$).
  ($y + 0 = y$)$_y$ stands for ($y + 0 = y$).
  ($y + 0 = y$)$_2$ stands for ($2 + 0 = 2$).
  ($y + 0 = y$)$_0$ stands for ($0 + 0 = 0$).

  c. (For each man x: x admires y)$_y$ stands for (For each man x: x admires y).
  (For each man x: x admires y)$_t$ stands for (For each man x: x admires t).
  (For each man x: x admires y)$_{\text{Bach}}$ stands for
  (For each man x: x admires Bach).

  d. (There is a thing x such that v admires x)$_t$ stands for
  (There is a thing x such that t admires x).

1413. Definition. An *extension* of a condition C is any set Y such that for each thing x: x is a member of $Y \Leftrightarrow C_x$.

NOTE. This is an important definition.

1414. Example.
An extension of the condition (t is human) is any set M such that for each thing x: x is a member of $M \Leftrightarrow x$ is human.

NOTE. By 1409, there is at most one extension of (t is human).

1415. Exercise. For each condition there is at most one extension thereof.

1416. The next theorem will shock the student who believes that for each condition there is at least one extension thereof.

1417. Theorem (Bertrand Russell). There is no extension of the condition (t is a set that is not a member of t).

Proof. Suppose not.

Then there is an extension, say *B*, of the condition indicated.

So, for each thing *x*:

x is a member of *B* ⇔ *x* is a set that is not a member of *x*.

Since *B* is a set, *B* is a thing.

So, *B* is a member of *B* ⇔ *B* is a set that is not a member of *B*.

Hence, *B* is a member of *B* ⇔ *B* is not a member of *B*.   (?)

Contradiction. See 606.

1418. In view of 1417, the following statement is false.

For each condition there is at least one extension thereof.

We shall soon return to these matters.

1419. The next axiom serves to rule out certain pathological situations.

1420. Axiom. For any sets *G, H*:
if *G* is a member of *H*, then *H* is not a member of *G*.

1421. Theorem. There is no set *T* such that
T is a member of a set that is a member of *T*.

Proof. Suppose not.

Then there is a set *T* such that *T* is a member of a set, say *G*, that is
a member of *T*.

Since *T* is a member of *G*, *G* is not a member of *T*. (1420)

Contradiction.

NOTE. Thus, a set cannot be a member of one of its members.

1422. Corollary. No set is a member of itself.

Proof. Suppose not.

Then there is a set *T* such that *T* is a member of *T*.

So, *T* is a member of a set that is a member of *T*.

Contradiction.

NOTE. It immediately follows that a set is equal to none of its members.

1423. Axiom 1420 is not strong enough to enable us to prove the following:

There is no set *B* such that *B* is a member of a set that is a member of a
set that is a member of *B*.

This proposition (and others like it) and Axiom 1420 can be deduced
from a stronger axiom, the so-called Regularity Axiom, which is explained in many books on set theory; for example, see *Axiomatic Set
Theory* by Suppes.

However, Axiom 1420 will suffice for our purpose.

1424. Exercises.

    a. There is no extension of the condition (t is a thing).

    b. For each set H: there is a thing that is not a member of H.

    NOTE. Thus, there is no set of which every thing is a member.

1425. Definition. An *unsound condition* is any condition C such that the statement (there is an extension of C) is false.

1426. Example. The following conditions are unsound:

    (t is a thing),   (1424a)
    (t is a set that is not a member of t),   (1417)
    (t is a set).   (?)

1427. Logicians have devised ingenious techniques for avoiding all *known* unsound conditions; one such technique is explained in Suppes' book *Axiomatic Set Theory*. Alas, we cannot afford the time now to discuss these techniques.

1428. The author believes that no condition used henceforth is unsound. It is expedient therefore to adopt the following assumption:

Assumption. For each condition used henceforth, there is at least one extension thereof.

NOTE. In view of 1415, we may now assert that for each condition used henceforth, there is precisely one extension thereof.

1429. Example. For the condition (t is a zebra or t is a real number) there is precisely one extension, say M, thereof. Clearly, each zebra is a member of M, each real number is a member of M, and each member of M is either a zebra or a real number.

1430. Different conditions might have the same extension.

E.g., the conditions (u is human) and (v is human) are different but they have the same extension.

Here is a less trivial example.

The conditions ($x = 0$) and (x is a real number such that $x + x = x$) are different but they have the same extension.

Singletons, the Empty Set, Doubletons

1501. Review. An *extension* of a condition C is any set Y such that for each thing x: x is a member of $Y \Leftrightarrow C_x$.

We know (1415) that for each condition there is at most one extension thereof.

We are assuming (1428) that for each condition used henceforth, there is at least one extension thereof.

Hence, for each condition C (used henceforth): we may speak of *the* extension of C.

1502. Notation. For any condition C and any letter β that is available or is the unquantified letter in C:
the extension of C
is called *the set of all things β such that C_β*
and is denoted by the symbol $\{\beta \mid C_\beta\}$.

NOTE. Naturally, the symbol $\{\beta \mid C_\beta\}$ is read as
the set of all things β such that C_β.

The symbol $\mid$ here stands for *such that* as in Lesson 9.

1503. Examples.

a. The extension of (y is a zebra)
may be called *the set of all things x such that x is a zebra,*
and may be denoted by the symbol $\{x \mid x \text{ is a zebra}\}$.

b. The extension of (y is a zebra)
may be called *the set of all things y such that y is a zebra,*
and may be denoted by the symbol $\{y \mid y \text{ is a zebra}\}$.

1504. Example. $\{x \mid x$ is a zebra$\} = \{y \mid y$ is a zebra$\}$.

Proof I. The set indicated first is *the* extension of the condition (y is a zebra). The set indicated second is also *the* extension of the condition (y is a zebra). Hence these sets are equal.

Proof II. Each member of $\{x \mid x$ is a zebra$\}$ is a zebra and hence is a member of $\{y \mid y$ is a zebra$\}$.
Each member of $\{y \mid y$ is a zebra$\}$ is a zebra and hence is a member of $\{x \mid x$ is a zebra$\}$.
So by 1405, these sets are equal.

NOTE I.   The symbols x, y are dummies here.

NOTE II. $\{x \mid x$ is a zebra$\}$ is often called the set of all zebras.

1505. Definition. A *singleton* is any set that has precisely one member.

1506. Exercises. (NOTE. The obviousness of a proposition does not obviate a proof therefor.)

a. $\{x \mid x = \text{Sun}\}$ is a singleton.

b. For each thing b: there is precisely one singleton, namely $\{x \mid x = b\}$, whose (sole) member is b.

1507. Notation. For each thing b: the symbol $\{b\}$ denotes the singleton whose member is b.

NOTE I.   This convention is justified by 1506b.

NOTE II.   The symbol $\{b\}$ is read *singleton b*.

NOTE III.   We say that $\{b\}$ consists of b.

1508. Immediate consequence. For each thing b: $\{b\} = \{x \mid x = b\}$.

1509. Exercise.
For any things u, v: $\{u\} = \{v\} \Rightarrow u = v$.
NOTE. The converse is obvious.

1510. Consider any thing c.
c is not necessarily a set, but $\{c\}$ is a set.
c is the member of $\{c\}$, but $\{c\}$ is not a member of $\{c\}$.   (1422)

1511. Theorem. For each thing c: $\{c\} \neq c$.
Proof.: c is a member of $\{c\}$; hence $\{c\} \neq c$.   (1422NOTE)

1512. Consider any thing d.

$\{\{d\}\}$ is a singleton. Indeed, $\{\{d\}\} = \{y \mid y = \{d\}\}$.
$\{d\}$ is the member of $\{\{d\}\}$.
Hence $\{\{d\}\}$ is not a member of $\{d\}$. (?)
Furthermore, $\{\{d\}\} \neq \{d\}$. (?)
Although d is not a member of $\{\{d\}\}$, (?)
d is a member of a set that is a member of $\{\{d\}\}$.

1513. Theorem. For each thing c: $\{\{c\}\} \neq c$.

Proof.: c is a member of a set that is a member of $\{\{c\}\}$;
hence $\{\{c\}\} \neq c$. (?)

1514. The following statement is false.

For any thing x and sets S, T:
if x is a member of S, and S is a member of T,
then x is a member of T.

Counterexample. Bach for x, $\{$Bach$\}$ for S, $\{\{$Bach$\}\}$ for T.

1515. The extension of the condition $(x \neq x)$ is a peculiar set: it has no members.

1516. Definition. A set is *empty* provided it has no members;
i.e., a set B is empty provided that
for each thing t: t is not a member of B.

1517. Exercise. $\{x \mid x$ is human and x is not human$\}$ is empty.

1518. Theorem. There is precisely one empty set.

Proof.

AT LEAST ONE. See 1517.

AT MOST ONE. Consider any empty sets B, F.
Then each member of B is a member of F,
and each member of F is a member of B. (?)
Hence $B = F$.

QUERY. Has the student forgotten that the word *each* has no existential import?

1519. Notation. The symbol $\emptyset$ denotes the empty set.

NOTE. The empty set is also called *the null set*.

1520. *Nonempty* means *not empty*.

A nonempty set is, therefore, any set that has at least one member.

1521. Examples.

    a. {Bach} is nonempty.

    b. {0} is nonempty.

    c. {∅} is nonempty because ∅ is a member of {∅}.

    d. {{∅}} is nonempty because {∅} is a member of {{∅}}.

    e. No singleton is empty.

1522. Diversion. Consider the following proposition.

    For any sets A, B:
    if
        for any member x of A and any member y of B:
        x is a member of B and y is a member of A,
    then
        $A = B$.

This proposition seems to be true, but actually it is false.
Let us disprove it by proving its negation:

There are sets A, B such that $A \neq B$, and
for any member x of A and member y of B:
x is a member of B and y is a member of A.

Proof. Take ∅ for A, and take {Sun} for B.
Clearly ∅ ≠ {Sun}.
Now consider any member x of ∅ and any member y of {Sun}.
Since each member of ∅ is a member of {Sun},   (?)
x is a member of {Sun}.
Therefore, $x = $ Sun.   (?)
But $y = $ Sun.   (?)
So, $y = x$.
Hence, y is a member of ∅. Q.e.d.

NOTE. This peculiar situation was discovered by Mr. Joseph C. Haletky,
one of the author's students.

1523. Exercise.

    For any nonempty sets A, B:
    if
        for any member x of A and any member y of B:
        x is a member of B and y is a member of A,
    then
        $A = B$.

HINT. One must exploit the hypothesis that A, B are nonempty.

1524. Definition. A *doubleton* is any set that has precisely two distinct members.

NOTE. *Precisely two distinct* means *at least two distinct and at most two.*

1525. Example. $\{x \mid x = \text{Sun or } x = \{\text{Sun}\}\}$ is a doubleton.

Proof. Let H denote the set indicated.

AT LEAST TWO DISTINCT.
Sun is a member of H, and $\{\text{Sun}\}$ is a member of H.
Furthermore, Sun $\neq \{\text{Sun}\}$.

AT MOST TWO.
No thing distinct from Sun and from $\{\text{Sun}\}$ is in H. (?)

1526. The following proposition is easy to prove.

For any two distinct things b, c:
there is precisely one doubleton, namely $\{x \mid x = b \text{ or } x = c\}$,
whose members are b and c.

1527. Notation. For any two distinct things b, c: the symbol $\{b, c\}$ denotes the doubleton whose members are b and c.

NOTE I. This convention is justified by 1526.

NOTE II. The symbol $\{b, c\}$ is read *doubleton b, c.*

NOTE III. We say that $\{b, c\}$ consists of b and c.

1528. Immediate consequence. For any two distinct things b, c:
$\{b, c\} = \{x \mid x = b \text{ or } x = c\}$.

1529. Examples.

a. $\{\text{Bach, Moon}\} = \{t \mid t = \text{Bach or } t = \text{Moon}\}$.

b. $\{\{\emptyset\}, \emptyset\} = \{y \mid y = \{\emptyset\} \text{ or } y = \emptyset\}$.

1530. Theorem. For any two distinct things u, v: $\{u, v\} = \{v, u\}$.
Proof.: $\{u, v\} = \{x \mid x = u \text{ or } x = v\} =_? \{x \mid x = v \text{ or } x = u\} = \{v, u\}$.

1531. Exercises.

a. For any things u, v: $\{u, \{u\}\} = \{v, \{v\}\} \Rightarrow u = v$.
NOTE. The converse is obvious.

b. For any things u, v: $\{u\} \neq \{v, \{v\}\}$.

c. How many members do the following sets have?
$\emptyset, \{\emptyset\}, \{\{\emptyset\}\}, \{\emptyset, \{\emptyset\}\}, \{\emptyset, \{\emptyset, \{\emptyset\}\}\}, \{\{\emptyset\}, \{\{\emptyset\}\}\}$,
$\{\{\{\emptyset\}\}\}, \{\emptyset, \{\emptyset, \{\emptyset\}\}, \{\emptyset, \{\{\emptyset\}\}\}\}, \{\emptyset, \{\emptyset, \{\emptyset, \{\emptyset\}\}\}\}$.

d. *Disprove.* For any thing x and sets S, T:
if x is a member of S, and S is a member of T,
then x is not a member of T. (Compare 1514.)

1532. The convention in 1527 permits us to use the symbol $\{b, c\}$ when we know that $b \neq c$. Frequently we wish to use the symbol $\{b, c\}$ even though we do not know that $b \neq c$. Accordingly, we broaden 1527 as follows.

1533. Notation. For any things b, c: the symbol $\{b, c\}$ denotes $\{x \mid x = b \text{ or } x = c\}$.

1534. Exercises.

   a. For any things b, c: $b = c \Leftrightarrow \{b, c\} = \{c\}$.
   NOTE. Surely then, for each thing t: $\{t, t\} = \{t\}$.

   b. Find things a, b, c such that $\{a, \{b, c\}\} \neq \{\{a, b\}, c\}$.

1535. Notation. For any things a, b, c: the symbol $\{a, b, c\}$ denotes $\{x \mid x = a \text{ or } x = b \text{ or } x = c\}$.

1536. The following proposition is easily proved.

   For any things a, b, c:
   $\{a, b, c\} = \{a, c, b\} = \{b, a, c\} = \{b, c, a\} = \{c, a, b\} = \{c, b, a\}$.

   CAUTION. Despite notational suggestions to the contrary, the members of a set are not arranged in order.

1537. It is clear how we use symbols such as $\{a, b, c, d, f, g, h, i, j, k\}$. No symbol such as $\{a, b, c, \ldots\}$ will be used in this book.

1538. The following expressions are synonymous:

   x is a member of A,
   x is an element of A,
   x is in A,
   x belongs to A,
   x is contained in A,
   A contains x,
   A has x as a member.

   NOTE I.   The author favors the expression *is in*; it's the shortest.

   NOTE II.   When we refer to a thing in a set A, we are, of course, referring to a member of A.

   NOTE III. We shall use the expression A *lacks* x to mean x *is not in* A.

   NOTE IV. Let us refrain from using *includes* as a synonym for *contains*.

1539. Notations.

    a. The Greek letter ϵ (epsilon) stands for the expression *is in*.

    b. The symbol $\notin$ stands for the expression *is not in*.

1540. Examples.

    a. Ike ϵ {Ike}.

    b. {Ike} $\notin$ {Ike}.

    c. Ike ϵ {Moon, Ike} ; Moon ϵ {Moon, Ike}.

    d. {Ike} ϵ {{Ike}}.

    e. Ike $\notin$ {{Ike}}.

    f. $\varnothing \epsilon \{\varnothing\}$.

    g. $\varnothing \notin \varnothing$.

    h. $\varnothing \epsilon \{\varnothing, \{\{\varnothing\}\}\}$.

    i. $\{\varnothing\} \notin \{\varnothing, \{\{\varnothing\}\}\}$, but $\{\{\varnothing\}\} \epsilon \{\varnothing, \{\{\varnothing\}\}\}$.

1541. Exercises.

    a. Find sets A, B, C such that $A \epsilon B$, $B \epsilon C$, and $A \notin C$.

    b. Find sets A, B, C, such that $A \epsilon B$, $B \epsilon C$, and $A \epsilon C$.

    c. There is no set C such $\{C\} \epsilon C$.

1542. Proposition 1406a may now be expressed as follows.

For any sets G, H:
$G = H$ if and only if
for each thing t: $t \epsilon G \Leftrightarrow t \epsilon H$.

Proposition 1406b may be expressed as follows.

For any sets G, H:
$G \neq H$ if and only if
there is a thing t such that
    either ($t \epsilon G$ and $t \notin H$) or ($t \notin G$ and $t \epsilon H$).

Subsets of a Set

1601. Definition. A set A *is a subset of* a set B provided that each member of A is a member of B.

NOTE FOR THE TEACHER. The author believes that the expression *is included in* should not be used as a synonym for *is a subset of*. Students are too apt to confuse *is included in* with *is in*.

1602. Immediate consequence. A set A is not a subset of a set B iff some member of A is not a member of B.

NOTE. *Iff* means *if and only if*.

1603. Examples.

a. ∅ is a subset of ∅.   (?)

b. ∅ is a subset of {Moon}.   (?)

c. ∅ is a subset of every set.   (?)

d. {Bach} is a subset of {Bach}.

e. Each set is a subset of itself.

f. {Bach} is a subset of {Bach, Moon}.

g. {Bach, Moon} is not a subset of {Bach}.

h. {Bach} is not a subset of {{Bach}}.   (?)

i. {Bach, Moon} is a subset of {Moon, Bach, Earth}.

1604. Exercises.

a. Is {∅} a subset of ∅? of {∅}? of {{∅}}? of {∅, {∅}}?

b. Is {∅, {∅}} a subset of ∅? of {∅}? of {{∅}}? of {{∅}, {{∅}}}? of {∅, {∅, {∅}}}?

c. Find a set A at least one of whose members is a subset of A.

1605. Notation. The symbol $\subseteq$ stands for the expression *is a subset of.*

CAUTION. Do not confuse the symbol $\subseteq$ with the symbol ϵ.

1606. Examples.

a. {Bach} ϵ {{Bach}}, but {Bach} is not a subset of {{Bach}}. (?)

b. {Bach} $\subseteq$ {Bach}, but {Bach} $\notin$ {Bach}. (?)

c. $\emptyset \subseteq \emptyset$, but $\emptyset \notin \emptyset$.

d. {Bach} $\subseteq$ {Bach, Moon}, but {Bach} $\notin$ {Bach, Moon}. (?)

e. {Ike} ϵ {Ike, {Ike}}, and {Ike} $\subseteq$ {Ike, {Ike}}. (?)

1607. The distinction between $\subseteq$ and ϵ is further dramatized by the fact that each set is a subset of itself, but no set is a member of itself.

We also know that $\emptyset$ is a subset of every set, but $\emptyset$ is not a member of every set.

1608. The following proposition is a reformulation of what we already know.
For any sets G, H:
$G \subseteq H \iff \left[\text{for each thing } x\colon\ x \epsilon G \Rightarrow x \epsilon H\right].$

1609. Theorem. For any sets A, B: $A = B \iff \left[A \subseteq B \text{ and } B \subseteq A\right].$
Proof.: $A = B \iff$
$\left[\text{for each thing } x\colon\ x \epsilon A \iff x \epsilon B\right] \iff_?$
$\left[(\text{for each thing } x\colon\ x \epsilon A \Rightarrow x \epsilon B) \text{ and}\right.$
$\left.\quad (\text{for each thing } x\colon\ x \epsilon B \Rightarrow x \epsilon A)\right] \iff$
$A \subseteq B \text{ and } B \subseteq A.$

NOTE. This theorem provides a useful method of proving that two sets are equal: we prove that each is a subset of the other.

1610. Corollary. For each set A: $A = \emptyset \iff A \subseteq \emptyset.$
Proof.: $A = \emptyset \iff (A \subseteq \emptyset \text{ and } \emptyset \subseteq A) \iff_? A \subseteq \emptyset.$

1611. Theorem. For any sets A, B, C such that $A \subseteq B$ and $B \subseteq C$: $A \subseteq C.$
Proof.: each member of A is a member of B and hence of C, and so $A \subseteq C.$

1612. Definition. A set G *is a superset of* a set H provided that H is a subset of G.

NOTATION. $\supseteq$ stands for *is a superset of.*

NOTE. Thus, for any sets G, H: $G \supseteq H \iff H \subseteq G.$

1613. Caution. Many writers use the symbol $\subset$ in place of $\subseteq$ and use the symbol $\supset$ in place of $\supseteq$. Furthermore, many logicians use the symbol $\supset$ in place of $\Rightarrow$.

1614. Definition. A set A *is a proper subset of* a set B provided that $A \subseteq B$ and $A \neq B$.

NOTATION. $\subset$ stands for *is a proper subset of*.

NOTE I. Some writers also require that A be nonempty.

NOTE II. To prove that $A \subset B$ it suffices to prove that each member of A is in B and some member of B is not in A.

NOTE III. No set is a proper subset of itself. (?)

NOTE IV. $\emptyset$ is a proper subset of each nonempty set.

1615. The following proposition is false.

For any sets A, B: $A \subseteq B \Rightarrow A \subset B$.

Counterexample. $\emptyset$ for A, $\emptyset$ for B.
Here is another counterexample. {Bach} for A, {Bach} for B.

1616. Exercise. Disprove each of the following.
  i. For each set A: $\emptyset \subset A$.
  ii. For any sets A, B such that $A \subset B$: $B \subset A$.
  iii. For any sets A, B, C such that $A \subseteq B$ and $B \subseteq C$: $A \subset C$.

1617. Exercises.
  a. *Prove or disprove.* For any sets A, B such that $A \subset B$: $A \subseteq B$.
  b. *Prove or disprove.* For any sets A, B, C such that $A \subset B$ and $B \subseteq C$: $A \subset C$.
  c. Find sets A, B, C such that $A \subseteq B$, $B \in C$, and $A \subset C$.
  d. Find sets A, B, C, D such that $A \subset B$, $B \subseteq C$, $B \neq D$, $C = D$, $B \in C$, and $A \notin D$.

1618. Definition. A set A *is disjoint from* a set B provided that no member of A is a member of B.

1619. Examples.
  a. {Bach, Moon} is disjoint from {Mozart, Earth}.
  b. Each set is disjoint from $\emptyset$.
  c. No nonempty set is disjoint from itself.

1620. Exercises.

  a. For any sets A, B such that A is disjoint from B: B is disjoint from A.

  b. *Prove or disprove.* For any sets A, B, C such that A is disjoint from B and B is disjoint from C: A is disjoint from C.

1621. A *set of boys* is any set each member of which is a boy.
Surely then, $\emptyset$ is a set of boys.
Keep in mind that *each* has no existential import. (See 803 and 804.)

A *set of books* is any set each member of which is a book.
Surely $\emptyset$ is a set of books.

A *set of sets* is any set each member of which is a set.
Surely $\emptyset$ is a set of sets.

1622. Examples.

  a. Each of the following is a set of sets: $\emptyset$, $\{\{\text{Bach}\}\}$, $\{\emptyset, \{\text{Bach}\}, \{\text{Moon}\}, \{\emptyset\}\}$, $\{\{\text{Bach, Moon}\}, \{\text{Bach}\}\}$.

  b. $\{\emptyset, \{\emptyset\}, \text{Bach}\}$ is not a set of sets. (?)

Combining Sets

1701. Definition. The *union* of two sets A, B is $\{x \mid x \in A \text{ or } x \in B\}$.

NOTATION. $[A \cup B]$, read *A union B*.

NOTE I. Clearly, $[A \cup B]$ is the set consisting of all members of A and all members of B.

NOTE II. Outermost brackets $[,]$ will often be omitted; braces $\{,\}$ will never be omitted.

1702. Examples.

a. $\{\text{Ike, Moon}\} \cup \{\text{Ike, Earth, Sun}\} = \{\text{Ike, Moon, Earth, Sun}\}$.

b. $\{\text{Ike}\} \cup \{\text{Moon}\} = \{\text{Ike, Moon}\}$.

c. $\{\text{Ike}, \{\text{Ike}\}\} \cup \{\emptyset, \text{Moon}\} = \{\text{Ike}, \{\text{Ike}\}, \emptyset, \text{Moon}\}$.

d. $\emptyset \cup \{\text{Ike}\} = \{\text{Ike}\}$.

e. $\{\emptyset\} \cup \{\text{Ike}\} = \{\emptyset, \text{Ike}\}$.

1703. Immediate consequences.

a. For any sets G, H: $G \cup H = H \cup G$.

b. For any thing x and sets A, B: $x \in [A \cup B] \Leftrightarrow (x \in A \text{ or } x \in B)$.

c. For any thing x and sets A, B: $x \notin [A \cup B] \Leftrightarrow (x \notin A \text{ and } x \notin B)$.

d. For each set A: $\emptyset \cup A = A$.

e. For each set A: $A \cup A = A$.

f. For any sets A, B: $A \subseteq [A \cup B]$, and $B \subseteq [A \cup B]$.

1704. Theorem. For any sets A, B: $A \subseteq B \Leftrightarrow [A \cup B] = B$.

Proof. Consider any sets A, B.
PART I($\Rightarrow$). If $A \subseteq B$, then $[A \cup B] \subseteq_? B$
and $B \subseteq_? [A \cup B]$ and so $[A \cup B] = B$.
PART II($\Leftarrow$). If $[A \cup B] = B$, then A, being a subset of $[A \cup B]$, is a subset of B.

1705. Exercises.

a. For any sets A, B, C: $(A \subseteq C$ and $B \subseteq C) \Leftrightarrow [A \cup B] \subseteq C$.

b. For any sets A, B: $[A \cup B] = \emptyset \Leftrightarrow A = \emptyset = B$.

1706. The following proposition is obvious.

For any sets A, B, C such that $A = B$: $A \cup C = B \cup C$.

1707. Theorem. For any sets A, B, C: $[A \cup B] \cup C = A \cup [B \cup C]$.

Proof. Consider any sets A, B, C. For each thing x:
$x \in [[A \cup B] \cup C] \Leftrightarrow_1$
$x \in [A \cup B]$ or $x \in C \Leftrightarrow_1$
$(x \in A$ or $x \in B)$ or $x \in C \Leftrightarrow$
$x \in A$ or $(x \in B$ or $x \in C) \Leftrightarrow_1$
$x \in A$ or $x \in [B \cup C] \Leftrightarrow_1$
$x \in [A \cup [B \cup C]]$.
Hence, $[A \cup B] \cup C =_2 A \cup [B \cup C]$.
References. 1.1703b; 2.1542.

1708. Notation. $[A \cup B \cup C]$ stands for $A \cup [B \cup C]$.

NOTE. By 1707 we know that for any sets A, B, C:
$A \cup B \cup C = [A \cup B] \cup C$.

1709. Exercise.

For any sets A, B, C: $A \cup B \cup C = C \cup A \cup B$.

1710. Definition. The *intersection* of two sets A, B is $\{x \mid x \in A$ and $x \in B\}$.

NOTATION. $[A \cap B]$, read A *intersection* B.

NOTE. Clearly, $[A \cap B]$ is the set consisting of all things that are in both A and B.

1711. Examples.

a. {Ike, Moon, Sun} ∩ {Sun, Mozart, Moon} = {Moon, Sun}.

b. {Ike} ∩ {Moon} = ∅.

c. ∅ ∩ {Ike, Moon} = ∅.

d. {∅} ∩ {∅} = {∅}. (?)

e. ∅ ∩ ∅ = ∅.

1712. Immediate consequences.

a. For any sets G, H: $G \cap H = H \cap G$.

b. For any thing x and sets A, B: $x \in [A \cap B] \Leftrightarrow (x \in A$ and $x \in B)$.

c. For any thing x and sets A, B: $x \notin [A \cap B] \Leftrightarrow (x \notin A$ or $x \notin B)$.

d. For each set A: $\emptyset \cap A = \emptyset$.

e. For each set A: $A \cap A = A$.

f. For any sets A, B: $[A \cap B] \subseteq A$, and $[A \cap B] \subseteq B$.

g. For any sets A, B: $A \subseteq B \Leftrightarrow [A \cap B] = A$.

h. For any sets A, B, C: $(C \subseteq A$ and $C \subseteq B) \Leftrightarrow C \subseteq [A \cap B]$.

i. For any sets A, B: $[A \cap B] \subseteq [A \cup B]$.

j. For any sets A, B: $(A$ is disjoint from $B) \Leftrightarrow A \cap B = \emptyset$.

1713. The next proposition readily follows by substitution.

For any sets G, H, T such that $G = H$: $G \cap T = H \cap T$.

On the other hand, the following cannot be proved by substitution.

For any sets G, H, T such that $G \subseteq H$: $[G \cap T] \subseteq [H \cap T]$.

Of course, this proposition can easily be proved.

1714. Theorem. For any sets A, B, C: $[A \cap B] \cap C = A \cap [B \cap C]$.

Proof. Similar to proof of 1707.

1715. Notation. $[A \cap B \cap C]$ stands for $A \cap [B \cap C]$.

NOTE. By 1714 we know that for any sets A, B, C:
$A \cap B \cap C = [A \cap B] \cap C$.

1716. Theorem. For any sets G, H, T: $G \cap [H \cup T] = [G \cap H] \cup [G \cap T]$.

Proof. Consider any sets G, H, T. For each thing x:
$x \in [G \cap [H \cup T]] \Leftrightarrow$
$x \in G$ and $x \in [H \cup T] \Leftrightarrow$
$x \in G$ and ($x \in H$ or $x \in T$) $\Leftrightarrow_?$
($x \in G$ and $x \in H$) or ($x \in G$ and $x \in T$) $\Leftrightarrow$
$x \in [G \cap H]$ or $x \in [G \cap T] \Leftrightarrow$
$x \in [[G \cap H] \cup [G \cap T]]$.

1717. Exercise.

For any sets G, H, T: $G \cup [H \cap T] = [G \cup H] \cap [G \cup T]$.

1718. Definition. *The deletion of a set A by a set B is* $\{x \mid x \in A$ and $x \notin B\}$.

NOTATION. $[A - B]$, read *A deletion B*.

NOTE. Clearly, $[A - B]$ is the set consisting of all members of A that are not in B.

1719. Remark on the previous definition. $[A - B]$ is usually called *the complement of B relative to A*. This language justifiably confuses students.

1720. Example. {Mars, Moon, Earth} $-$ {Mars, Sun} $=$ {Moon, Earth}.

1721. Immediate consequences.

  a. For any thing x and sets A, B: $x \in [A - B] \Leftrightarrow (x \in A$ and $x \notin B)$.

  b. For any thing x and sets A, B: $x \notin [A - B] \Leftrightarrow (x \notin A$ or $x \in B)$.

  c. For each set A: $A - \emptyset = A$, $A - A = \emptyset$, $\emptyset - A = \emptyset$.

  d. For any sets A, B: $[A - B] \subseteq A$.

  e. For any sets A, B: $A \subseteq B \Leftrightarrow A - B = \emptyset$. (?)

  f. For any sets A, B: $[A - B] \subset A \Leftrightarrow A \cap B \neq \emptyset$. (?)

  g. For any sets A, B: $A - B = A \Leftrightarrow A \cap B = \emptyset$. (?)

1722. Theorem. For any sets A, B, C: $A - [B \cup C] = [A - B] \cap [A - C]$.

Proof. Consider any sets A, B, C. For each thing x:

$x \in [A - [B \cup C]] \Leftrightarrow$

$x \in A$ and $x \notin [B \cup C] \Leftrightarrow$

$x \in A$ and $(x \notin B$ and $x \notin C) \Leftrightarrow$

$(x \in A$ and $x \notin B)$ and $(x \in A$ and $x \notin C) \Leftrightarrow$

$x \in [A - B]$ and $x \in [A - C] \Leftrightarrow$

$x \in [[A - B] \cap [A - C]]$.

NOTE. The following proposition may be proved in much the same manner.

For any sets A, B, C: $A - [B \cap C] = [A - B] \cup [A - C]$.

1723. Exercises.

a. For any sets A, B: $A - [A - B] = A \cap B$.

b. For any sets A, B, C: $A \cap [B - C] = [A \cap B] - C$.

c. For any sets A, B: $A \cup B = [A - B] \cup [A \cap B] \cup [B - A]$.

d. For any sets T, A, B: $A \subseteq B \Rightarrow [T - B] \subseteq [T - A]$.

e. Prove or disprove the converse of the previous proposition.

f. Find the following:

  i. $\emptyset \cap \{\emptyset\}$

  ii. $\{\emptyset\} \cap \{\emptyset\}$

  iii. $\{\emptyset, \{\emptyset\}\} - \emptyset$

  iv. $\{\emptyset, \{\emptyset\}\} - \{\emptyset\}$

  v. $\{\emptyset, \{\emptyset\}\} - \{\{\emptyset\}\}$

1724. Definitions.

a. The result of *annexing* a thing x to a set A is the set $A \cup \{x\}$.

b. The result of *deleting* a thing x from a set A is the set $A - \{x\}$.

NOTE I. If x is in A, then clearly $A \cup \{x\} = A$.

NOTE II. If A lacks x, then clearly $A - \{x\} = A$.

1725. Discussion. Let G denote the set of all green things, and let A denote the set of all apples. There are many ways to describe the set of all green apples, e.g.,

  i. $G \cap A$

  ii. $\{x \mid x \in [G \cap A]\}$

  iii. $\{x \mid x \in G$ and $x \in A\}$

  iv. $A \cap G$

  v. $\{x \mid x \in [A \cap G]\}$

  vi. $\{x \mid x \in A$ and $x \in G\}$

    vii.   the set of all green things that are apples
   viii. the set of all things in G that are in A
    ix.   the set of all things x in G such that $x \in A$

    x.   the set of all apples that are green
    xi. the set of all things in A that are in G
   xii. the set of all things x in A such that $x \in G$.

Description ix is symbolized thus: $\{x \text{ in } G \mid x \in A\}$. Traditionally the word *in* after the symbol x is replaced by ϵ. Thus, description ix may be symbolized as $\{x \in G \mid x \in A\}$; here the first ϵ should be rendered as *in* rather than as *is in*.

Similarly, description xii may be symbolized thus: $\{x \in A \mid x \in G\}$.

NOTE. The symbol $\{x \in G \mid x \in A\}$ may be rendered *the set of all x in G such that x is in A.*

1726. The student is advised to study 1725 until he understands it completely.

1727. Example. For any sets A, B:

$$A \cap B = \{x \mid x \in A \text{ and } x \in B\} = \{x \in A \mid x \in B\} = \{x \in B \mid x \in A\},$$
$$A - B = \{x \mid x \in A \text{ and } x \notin B\} = \{x \in A \mid x \notin B\}.$$

1728. Most writers use parentheses, brackets, and braces interchangeably; although the author uses these symbols in a variety of ways, he does not always use them interchangeably.

1729. When we use a symbol such as $\{x \mid \ldots\}$, we shall consider the letter x to be available in the ensuing discussion; of course we must re-quantify (i.e., re-introduce) the letter x when we use it again.

Ordered Pairs

1801. Definition. A thing t is a *first component* of (or for) a set H provided that $\{t\} \in H$.

NOTE. We do not require that t be in H.

1802. Examples.

a. Sun is a first component of each of the following three sets: $\{\{Sun\}\}$, $\{\emptyset, Moon, \{Sun\}\}$, $\{\{Sun\}, \{Bach, \{Bach\}\}\}$.
NOTE. Sun is a member of none of these three sets.

b. Sun is a member of and a first component of $\{Sun, \{Sun\}\}$.

c. Both $\{Sun\}$ and Moon are first components of $\{\{Moon\}, \{\{Sun\}\}\}$.

d. Sun is not a first component of $\{Sun, \{\{Sun\}\}\}$.

e. No thing is a first component of $\{\{Sun, \{Sun\}\}\}$. (?)

1803. Exercises.

a. Find all first components of $\{\{Earth\}, \{\{Sun\},\{Moon\}\}, \{\{\emptyset\}\}, \emptyset\}$.

b. Find a set for which $\{\emptyset, \{\emptyset\}\}$ is a first component.

1804. Definition. A thing t is a *second component* of (or for) a set B provided that $\{t, \{t\}\} \in B$.

NOTE. We do not require that t be in B.

1805. Examples.

a. Sun is a second component of $\{\{Sun, \{Sun\}\}\}$.
NOTE. No thing is a first component of this set.

b. Sun is both a first and second component of $\{\{Sun\}, \{Sun, \{Sun\}\}\}$.

NOTE. Sun is not a member of this set.

1806. Exercises.

a. Find a set C for which there is a first component, say b, such that $\{b\}$ is a second component of C.

b. Find a set for which $\{Sun, \{Sun\}\}$ is a second component.

1807. Definition. An *ordered pair* is any doubleton for which there is at least one first component and at least one second component.

NOTE. There are other acceptable ways of defining an ordered pair; however, the author prefers this definition.

1808. Immediate consequence. For any things x, y (not necessarily distinct): $\{\{x\}, \{y, \{y\}\}\}$ is an ordered pair.

NOTE. We know of course that $\{x\} \neq \{y, \{y\}\}$. (1531b)

1809. Example. Each of the following sets is an ordered pair:
$\{\{Sun\}, \{Earth, \{Earth\}\}\}$,
$\{\{Sun\}, \{Sun, \{Sun\}\}\}$,
$\{\{\emptyset, \{\emptyset\}\}, \{\emptyset\}\}$,
$\{\{\{Sun\}\}, \{\emptyset, \{\emptyset\}\}\}$,
$\{\{\{\emptyset, \{\emptyset\}\}\}, \{\emptyset, \{\emptyset\}\}\}$. (?)

NOTE. $\{\emptyset, \{\emptyset, \{\emptyset\}\}\}$ is not an ordered pair. (?)

1810. Theorem. For any things b, c: there is precisely one ordered pair P such that b is a first component of P, and c is a second component of P.

Proof. Consider any things b, c.

AT LEAST ONE.
$\{\{b\}, \{c, \{c\}\}\}$ is such an ordered pair.

AT MOST ONE.
Consider any ordered pair P such that b is a first component of P and c is a second component of P.
$\{b\} \in P$ and $\{c, \{c\}\} \in P$. (?)
Since P is a doubleton, P has no members other than $\{b\}$ and $\{c, \{c\}\}$. (?)
Hence, $P = \{\{b\}, \{c, \{c\}\}\}$.

QUERY. Does the student agree that we have proved AT MOST ONE?

1811. Immediate consequence. For any things b, c: $\{\{b\}, \{c, \{c\}\}\}$ is *the* ordered pair for which b is a first component and for which c is a second component.

1812. Theorem. For each ordered pair there is precisely one first component thereof and precisely one second component thereof.

PRELIMINARY REMARK. Many students maintain that this theorem is trivial. Since a trivial proposition is presumably easy to prove, one is led to assume that these students can prove this theorem. The author's experience in the classroom indicates that this assumption is untenable.

Proof. Consider any ordered pair P.
P is a doubleton for which there is a first component, say b, and a second component, say c.
Hence, $P = \{\{b\}, \{c, \{c\}\}\}$. (1811)
We must prove that b is *the* first component of P, and that c is *the* second component of P.

Consider any first component, say r, of P.
Then $\{r\} \in P$, and so either $\{r\} = \{b\}$ or $\{r\} = \{c, \{c\}\}$.
But $\{r\} \neq \{c, \{c\}\}$. (?)
So $\{r\} = \{b\}$.
Hence $r = b$.
Therefore, b is *the* first component of P.

Consider any second component, say s, of P.
Then $\{s, \{s\}\} = \{c, \{c\}\}$. (?)
Hence $s = c$. (?)
Therefore, c is *the* second component of P.

1813. Notation. For any things x, y: the symbol (x, y) denotes the ordered pair whose first component is x and whose second component is y.

NOTE. The symbol (x, y) is rendered *ordered pair x, y.*

1814. Examples.

a. (Earth, Sun) $= \{\{Earth\}, \{Sun, \{Sun\}\}\}$.

b. (Sun, Sun) $= \{\{Sun\}, \{Sun, \{Sun\}\}\}$.

c. $(\{Sun\}, \emptyset) = \{\{\{Sun\}\}, \{\emptyset, \{\emptyset\}\}\}$.

d. $(\emptyset, \{\emptyset\}) = \{\{\emptyset\}, \{\{\emptyset\}, \{\{\emptyset\}\}\}\}$.

e. For any things x, y: $(x, y) = \{\{x\}, \{y, \{y\}\}\}$.

1815. Theorem. For any things b, c, d, g:
if $(b, c) = (d, g)$, then $b = d$ and $c = g$.

Proof. Consider any things b, c, d, g such that $(b, c) = (d, g)$.
b is *the* first component of (b, c) and hence of (d, g).
But d is *the* first component of (d, g).

Hence $b = d$.
Similarly, $c = g$.

NOTE. This theorem is of fundamental importance; its converse is trivial.

1816. The contrapositive of Theorem 1815 is worth keeping in mind:

For any things b, c, d, g: if $b \neq d$ or $c \neq g$, then $(b, c) \neq (d, g)$.

1817. Immediate consequence. Two ordered pairs are distinct if and only if either their first components are distinct or their second components are distinct.

1818. Since (Bach, Earth) $\neq_?$ (Earth, Bach), it is clear why we call these sets *ordered* pairs.

1819. Consider any things b, c.
We know that b is the first component of (b, c),
and we know that c is the second component of (b, c).
We also know that (b, c) is a doubleton, even if $b = c$.

We know that $\{b\} \in (b, c)$ and that $\{c, \{c\}\} \in (b, c)$.
Could b be a member of (b, c)?
Could c be a member of (b, c)?

1820. Exercises.

   a. Find things b, c such that $b \notin (b, c)$.

   b. Find things b, c such that $b \in (b, c)$.

   c. Find things b, c such that $c \notin (b, c)$.

   d. Find things b, c such that $c \in (b, c)$.

   e. No ordered pair contains both of its components.

1821. Even though the first component of an ordered pair might not be a member thereof, we often "slip" and refer to the first component as the *first member*.

Similarly, we often refer to the second component of an ordered pair as its *second member*.

1822. The word *has* is not a synonym for *contains*.

E.g., when we say that (x, y) *has* a first component, we do not necessarily mean that (x, y) contains its first component.

Similarly, when we say that (x, y) *has* a second component, we do not necessarily mean that (x, y) contains its second component.

1823. Exercises.

PRELIMINARY REMARK. Let us agree that a convention for the symbol (x, y) is *acceptable* if and only if the proposition in 1815 is provable.

a. Prove that the following convention is not acceptable.
For any things x, y: the symbol (x, y) denotes $\{x, \{y\}\}$.

b. Prove that the following convention is acceptable.
For any things x, y: the symbol (x, y) denotes $\{\{x\}, \{x, y\}\}$.

1824. One or both components of an ordered pair may be ordered pairs; e.g.,

((Ike, Moon), Tufts)

(Ike, (Moon, Tufts))

((Ike, Moon), (Ø, Earth)).

1825. An *ordered pair of mice* is any ordered pair each of whose components is a mouse.
An *ordered pair of books* is any ordered pair each of whose components is a book.
And so on.

1826. A *set of ordered pairs* is any set each member of which is an ordered pair.

Example. Ø is a set of ordered pairs. (?)

1827. We shall also use brace notation to describe a set of ordered pairs.

For example, the notation $\{(x, y) \mid x \text{ is married to } y\}$ is rendered
the set of all (x, y) such that x is married to y.

The notation $\{(x, y) \in A \mid x \text{ is the husband of } y\}$ is rendered
the set of all (x, y) in A such that x is the husband of y.
If, for example, A denotes the set of all ordered pairs of Americans,
then this notation denotes the set of all American, husband-wife pairs.

1828. Definition. The *cartesian product* of a set S by a set T is
the set of all ordered pairs whose first component is in S and whose second component is in T.

NOTATION. $[S \times T]$, read *S cross T.*

NOTE. $[S \times T] = \{(x, y) \mid x \in S \text{ and } y \in T\}$.

1829. Example. Let A denote {Ike, Earth, Bach}, and
let B denote {Handel, Mars}.

Then $A \times B$ consists of the following ordered pairs:

(Ike, Handel)
(Ike, Mars)
(Earth, Handel)
(Earth, Mars)
(Bach, Handel)
(Bach, Mars).

1830. Exercises.

a. Referring to 1829, determine $A \times A$, $B \times B$, $B \times A$.

b. Find nonempty sets S, T such that $S \times T = T \times S$.

c. For any nonempty sets S, T such that $S \times T = T \times S$: $S = T$.

d. Determine $\emptyset \times \emptyset$, $\emptyset \times \{\emptyset\}$, $\{\emptyset\} \times \emptyset$, $\{\emptyset\} \times \{\emptyset\}$.

e. There is no set A such that $\{[A \times A]\} = \{A\} \times \{A\}$.

f. There is no set A such that $A \times A = \{(A, A)\}$.

Functions

1901. For purposes of illustration in this and the next lesson we shall use the following lower-case italic letters to denote the things indicated.

a. Aristotle   *j.* the mother of Charlemagne

b. Boston   *m.* Mars

c. Charlemagne   *p.* printing (craft)

d. Donald Duck   *r.* Rembrandt

g. geology (study of)   *t.* Tufts University

h. Handel   *w.* George Washington

NOTE. The reader need not memorize this list.

1902. Definition. A *function* is any set of ordered pairs each distinct two of which have distinct first components.

NOTE. Each function is a set, each member of a function is an ordered pair, and no two distinct ordered pairs in a function have the same first component.

1903. Examples. Each of the following sets of ordered pairs is a function.

A. $\{(b, h), (c, p)\}$

B. $\{(b, h), (c, h)\}$

C. $\{(b, h), (h, b), (p, p)\}$

D. $\{((h, b), c), (h, b)\}$

E. $\{(c, (h, b)), (h, b)\}$

F. $\{(x, y) \mid x$ is human and y is the mother of $x\}$

102

$G.$ $\{(b, (j, p))\}$

$H.$ $\{((r, w), (t, g))\}$

$J.$ $\{(b, h)\}$

$K.$ $\{((b, h), c),\ ((m, r), r),\ ((r, m), d),\ ((h, h), h)\}$

$L.$ $\{(c, (b, h)),\ (r, (m, r)),\ (d, (r, m)),\ (h, (h, h))\}$

$M.$ $\{(c, w),\ ((r, m), (a, g)),\ (\emptyset, (\emptyset, \emptyset)),\ ((\emptyset, \emptyset), g)\}$

NOTE. In this and the next lesson these functions will be denoted by the italicized capital letters preceding their description above.

1904. Examples.

  a. $\emptyset$ is a function because surely each member of $\emptyset$ is an ordered pair and each distinct two members of $\emptyset$ have distinct first components.

  b. $\{(\emptyset, \emptyset)\}$ is a function and has precisely one member.

  c. $\{(h, t), (h, p), (p, \emptyset)\}$ is not a function because it has two distinct members whose first components are equal.

  d. $\{h, (r, t)\}$ is not a function because it has a member that is not an ordered pair.

1905. The student should verify the following statements.

  a. (b, h) is in the following functions (see 1903): A, B, C, J.

  b. (b, h) is in none of the following functions: D, E, F, K, L.

  c. $((h, b), c)$ is in D but not in E and not in K.

  d. $(c, (h, b))$ is in E but is in neither D nor K nor L.

  e. (c, j) is in F.

  f. (j, c) is not in F.

  g. Neither (r, m) nor (a, g) is in M, but $((r, m), (a, g))$ is in M.

1906. Definition. An *argument* of a function is any thing that is the first component of a member of the function.

1907. Examples.

  a. b is an argument of the following functions: A, B, C, G, J.

  b. h is an argument of C, D, E, F, L.

  c. c is an argument of A, B, E, F, L, M. j is an argument of F.

  d. c is not an argument of D and not an argument of K.

e. (h, b) is an argument of D but not of E.

f. No thing is an argument of $\emptyset$.

g. $\emptyset$ is an argument of $\{(\emptyset, t)\}$.

h. D has precisely two distinct arguments.

i. H has precisely one argument.   (?)

1908. Function D has an unusual feature: (h, b) is both an argument and a member of D.

1909. Definition. The *domain* of a function is the set of all its arguments.

NOTATION. The domain of a function T is denoted by *domain T*.

1910. Examples.

a. Domain $A = \{b, c\}$.

b. Domain $B = \{b, c\}$.

c. Domain $C = \{b, h, p\}$.

d. Domain $D = \{(h, b), h\}$.

e. Domain $E = \{c, h\}$.

f. Domain $F = $ the set of all humans.

g. Domain $G = \{b\}$.

h. Domain $H = \{(r, w)\}$.

i. Domain $J = \{b\}$.

j. Domain $K = \{(b, h), (m, r), (r, m), (h, h)\}$.

k. Domain $L = \{c, r, d, h\}$.

l. Domain $M = \{c, (r, m), \emptyset, (\emptyset, \emptyset)\}$.

m. Domain $\emptyset = \emptyset$.

n. Domain $\{(\emptyset, \emptyset)\} = \{\emptyset\}$.

1911. Definitions.

a. A *value* of a function is any thing that is the second component of a member of the function.

b. The *range* of a function is the set of all its values.

NOTATION. The range of a function T is denoted by *range T*.

1912. Examples.

a. Range $A = \{h, p\}$.

b. Range $B = \{h\}$.

c. Range $C = \{h, b, p\}$.

d. Range $D = \{c, b\}$.

e. Range $E = \{(h, b), b\}$.

f. Range F = the set of all human mothers.

g. Range $G = \{(j, p)\}$.

h. Range $H = \{(t, g)\}$.

i. Range $J = \{h\}$.

j. Range $K = \{c, r, d, h\}$.

k. Range $L = \{(b, h), (m, r), (r, m), (h, h)\}$.

l. Range $M = \{w, (a, g), (\emptyset, \emptyset), g\}$.

m. Range $\emptyset = \emptyset$.

n. Range $\{(\emptyset, \emptyset)\} = \{\emptyset\}$.

1913. Function E has an unusual feature: (h, b) is both a value and a member of E.

1914. Exercises.

a. Find the domain and range of
$\{(A, h), (B, p), (C, a), (J, t), (M, G)\}$.

b. Find the domain and range of
$\{(A, B), (J, D), (B, A), (M, E)\}$.

c. Find a function of which something is an argument, a value, and a member.

d. Find a function whose range is a proper subset of its domain.

e. Find a function whose domain is a proper subset of its range.
NOTE. For this exercise you may use your knowledge of real numbers.

f. Find two distinct functions that have the same domain and the same range.

g. Find a function whose domain and range are functions.

1915. Definitions.

    a. A function T is **on** a set S provided domain $T = S$.

    b. A function T is **over** a set S provided domain $T \supseteq S$.

    c. A function T is **onto** a set S provided range $T = S$.

    d. A function T is **into** a set S provided range $T \subseteq S$.

> NOTE I.
> *On V onto W* stands for *on V and onto W.*
> *On V into W* stands for *on V and into W.*
> *Over V onto W* stands for *over V and onto W.*
> And so on.
>
> NOTE II.   Although 1915b has not been used by other writers, we shall find it useful.

1916. Obviously each function T is on domain T onto range T; furthermore, each function is over every subset of its domain and into every superset of its range.

1917. Since functions are sets (of a certain kind), all set-theoretic definitions, notations, and results automatically apply to functions.   For example, two functions are equal iff each is a subset of the other.

1918. Immediate consequences.

    a. Each subset of a function is a function.

    b. The intersection of any two functions is a function.

    c. For any functions V, W: if $V \subseteq W$,
    then domain $V \subseteq$ domain W and range $V \subseteq$ range W.

    d. For any function T and argument x thereof: T has precisely one member whose first component is x.

> NOTE.   1918a,b would be false if $\emptyset$ were not a function.

1919. Exercises.

    a. Disprove the converse of 1918c.

    b. For any functions V, W: if $V \subseteq W$ and domain $V =$ domain W, then $V = W$.   HINT.   Prove that $W \subseteq V$.

1920. Notation.   For any function W and argument x thereof:
the symbol $W(x)$, read W *of* x, denotes
the second component of the member of W whose first component is x.

NOTE I. $W(x)$ is called the thing (or value) that W assigns to x and is also called the value of W at x.

NOTE II.   The symbol $W(x)$ does not denote a product.

NOTE III.   If u denotes a thing that is not an argument of W, then the symbol $W(u)$ is meaningless.

1921. Examples.   (See 1901 and 1903 for notation.)

a. $A(b) = h$; $A(c) = p$.

b. $B(b) = h$; $B(c) = h$.

c. $C(p) = p$.

d. $D((h, b)) = c$.   NOTE.   In a symbol such as $D((h, b))$, one pair of parentheses will henceforth be omitted.

e. $E(c) = (h, b)$.

f. $F(c) = j$.

g. $H(r, w) = (t, g)$.

h. $J(b) = h$.

i. $K(h, h) = h$.

j. $M(\emptyset) = (\emptyset, \emptyset)$; $M(\emptyset, \emptyset) = g$.

k. $\{(\emptyset, \emptyset)\}(\emptyset) = \emptyset$.

1922. Query.   Is the symbol $\emptyset(\emptyset)$ meaningless?

1923. Example.

Let Y denote $\{(r, p), (g, b), (p, m), (d, r)\}$, and
let X denote $\{(t, p), (b, r), (d, h)\}$.   Then
$Y(X(b)) = Y(r) = p$;
$Y(X(t)) = Y(p) = m$;
$X(Y(g)) = X(b) = r$;
the symbol $Y(X(d))$ is meaningless.   (?)

1924.   For any function W and argument x thereof:
$W(x)$ is also called the W-assignment of x, the W-associate of x,
the W-correspondent of x, the W-transform of x, the W-image of x.

1925. The following propositions are obvious.

  a. For any function T and argument x thereof: $(x, T(x)) \in T$.

  b. For any function T and ordered pair (x, y) in T: $y = T(x)$.

  c. For any function T and any things x, y:
     $(x, y) \in T \Leftrightarrow [x \in \text{domain } T, \text{ and } y = T(x)]$.

  d. For each function T: $T = \{(x, T(x)) \mid x \in \text{domain } T\}$.

  e. For each function T: range $T = \{T(x) \mid x \in \text{domain } T\}$.

1926. Theorem. For any functions V, W: $V \subseteq W \Leftrightarrow$
domain $V \subseteq$ domain W, and for each argument x of V: $V(x) = W(x)$.

Proof. Consider any functions V, W.

PART I($\Rightarrow$). Assume that $V \subseteq W$.
Consider any argument x of V.
Then $(x, V(x)) \in V$ and so $(x, V(x)) \in W$. (?)
Hence $x \in$ domain W, and so domain $V \subseteq$ domain W. (?)
Since $(x, W(x))$ is also in W, we have $V(x) =_? W(x)$.

PART II($\Leftarrow$). Assume that domain $V \subseteq$ domain W and that
for each argument x of V: $V(x) = W(x)$.

Consider any member of V, say $(i, V(i))$.
Then i is an argument of W, and $V(i) = W(i)$. (?)
Hence $(i, V(i))$, being equal to $(i, W(i))$, is in W.
So $V \subseteq_? W$.

NOTE. If in the statement of this theorem one replaces the symbol $\subseteq$ by
$\subset$, then a true statement is obtained.

1927. Each of the following three propositions provides a way to prove that
two functions V, W are equal.

  a. $V = W \Leftrightarrow [V \subseteq W \text{ and } W \subseteq V]$.

  Proof. 1609.

  b. $V = W \Leftrightarrow$
     for each ordered pair (x, y): $(x, y) \in V \Leftrightarrow (x, y) \in W$.

  Proof. Use 1542.

c. $V = W \Leftrightarrow$
domain $V =$ domain W, and for each argument x of V: $V(x) = W(x)$.

Proof. $V = W \Leftrightarrow$
$V \subseteq W$ and $W \subseteq V \Leftrightarrow_1$
[domain $V \subseteq$ domain W, and
    for each argument x of V: $V(x) = W(x)$, and
    domain $W \subseteq$ domain V, and
    for each argument x of W: $W(x) = V(x)$] $\Leftrightarrow_?$
domain $V =$ domain W, and for each argument x of V: $V(x) = W(x)$.

Reference. 1.1926. NOTE. Theorem 1926 justifies both directions, $\Leftarrow$ and $\Rightarrow$. However, we shall occasionally supply a reference for just one direction and leave it for the reader to justify the other direction.

1928. To illustrate the use of 1927c, we shall prove 1919b. This proof should not be submitted by the student as his proof of 1919b.

Proof. Consider any functions V, W such that
$V \subseteq W$ and domain $V =$ domain W.

For each argument x of V: $(x, V(x)) \in V$, and so $(x, V(x)) \in_? W$, and hence $(x, W(x)) \in_? W$, and so $V(x) =_? W(x)$.
Therefore by 1927c, $V = W$.

1929. Definition. A *common argument* of two or more functions is any thing that is an argument of each of them.

NOTE. Obviously, the set of all common arguments of two functions V, W is domain $V \cap$ domain W.

1930. Example. Ike is a common argument of $\{(\text{Moon, Tufts}), (\text{Ike, Handel})\}$ and $\{(\text{Tufts, Handel}), (\text{Ike, Aristotle}), (\text{Rembrandt, Earth})\}$.

1931. The union of two functions is not necessarily a function;
e.g., the union of $\{(a, b)\}$ and $\{(a, c)\}$ is not a function.
However, the following three propositions are easy to prove.

a. The union of any two functions whose domains are disjoint is a function.

b. For any functions V, W: $V \cup W$ is a function $\Leftrightarrow$
for each common argument x of V, W: $V(x) = W(x)$.

c. For any functions V, W whose union is a function:
domain $[V \cup W] =$ domain $V \cup$ domain W.

1932. In view of 1927c, a function may be described by specifying its domain and specifying what it assigns to its arguments.

For example, the function F (see 1903) may be described as the function whose domain is the set of all humans and which assigns to each human his mother.

More simply, F may be described as the function that assigns to each human his mother.

1933. Exercise.

Compose a simple description of the following function:

$\{(x, y) \mid x$ is human and y is the name of $x\}$.

NOTE. We are assuming that each person has precisely one name.

1934. Definition. *An operation for a set S is any function on $S \times S$ into S.*

1935. Example. Let S denote $\{a, b\}$.
Then $S \times S = \{(a, a), (a, b), (b, a), (b, b)\}$.
Each of the following functions is an operation for S.

$\{((a, a), a), \ ((a, b), a), \ ((b, a), a), \ ((b, b), a)\}$

$\{((a, a), a), \ ((a, b), a), \ ((b, a), b), \ ((b, b), b)\}$

$\{((a, a), b), \ ((a, b), a), \ ((b, a), a), \ ((b, b), b)\}$

1936. Exercises.

a. Find two more operations for $\{a, b\}$.

b. Find an operation for $\{a, b, c\}$.

c. Find an operation for the set of all living people.

Functions (continued)

2001. This lesson may be omitted now, but it must be studied before Lesson 55.

2002. Definition. A *constant function* is any function whose range has precisely one member.

2003. Examples.

a. The following functions are constant: *B, G, H, J.* (See 1903.)

b. The following functions are not constant: *A, C, D, E, F, K, L, M,* Ø.

2004. Definition. An *identity function* is any function each member of which has equal first and second components.

2005. Example. Each of the following three sets is an identity function:
{(Moon, Moon)}, Ø, {(Moon, Moon), (Boston, Boston)}.

2006. It is obvious that a function V is an identity function iff
for each argument x of V: $V(x) = x$.

2007. It is clear that each identity function has equal domain and range; however, the converse of this proposition is disproved by the following counterexample: {(Bach, Moon), (Moon, Bach)}.

2008. Definition. A *one-one function* is any function each distinct two members of which have distinct second components.

NOTE. One-one functions are also called *one-to-one functions* and *univalent functions.*

111

2009. Examples. (See 1903 for notation.)

    a. Each of the following is a one-one function: $\emptyset$, A, C, D, E, G, H, J, K, L, M.

    b. Neither of the following functions is one-one: B, F.

2010. Immediate consequences.

    a. For each function T: T is one-one $\Leftrightarrow$
for any distinct arguments u, x of T: $T(u) \neq T(x)$.

    b. Each one-one function assigns distinct values to distinct arguments.

    c. Each subset of a one-one function is a one-one function.

2011. Is every identity function one-one?
Is every one-one function an identity function?

2012. Many students erroneously believe that a function whose domain and range are equal is necessarily one-one. In Lesson 55 the student will disprove this proposition.

2013. The following proposition is easy to prove.

    For any one-one function W and arguments x, u thereof:
if $(x, W(x))$ and $(u, W(u))$ are deleted from W, and
if $(x, W(u))$ is annexed to W,
then the resulting set of ordered pairs is a one-one function.

2014. Definition. The *restriction* of a function W to a set S
is the function that assigns to each member x of $S \cap$ domain W
the value $W(x)$.

    NOTATION. $[W|S]$, read W *restricted to* S.
Here the symbol $|$ does not stand for *such that*.

    NOTE I. $[W|S] = \{(x, W(x)) \mid x \in [S \cap \text{domain } W]\}$. Thus, $[W|S]$ is the set of all of W's ordered pairs whose first components are in S.

    NOTE II. Domain $[W|S] = S \cap$ domain W.

    NOTE III. For each argument u of $[W|S]$: $[W|S](u) = W(u)$.

    NOTE IV. The author does not require S to be a subset of domain W.

    NOTE V. If S is disjoint from domain W, then $[W|S] = \emptyset$.

    NOTE VI. We shall frequently omit outermost brackets.

2015. Examples. (See 1901, 1903 for notation.)

a. $A|\{b\} = \{(b, h)\}$.

b. $C|\{h, p\} = \{(h, b), (p, p)\}$.

c. $C|\{t, g\} = \emptyset$.

d. $C|\{t, h\} = \{(h, b)\}$.

e. $K|\{(b, h), (t, p)\} = \{((b, h), c)\}$.

f. $M|\{c, \emptyset, (\emptyset, \emptyset)\} = \{(c, w), (\emptyset, (\emptyset, \emptyset)), ((\emptyset, \emptyset), g)\}$.

2016. The following propositions are obvious.

a. For any function W and set S: $[W|S] \subseteq W$.

b. For each function W: $[W|\text{domain } W] = W$.

2017. Exercise.

For any function W and sets N, S:
$W|[N \cup S] = [W|N] \cup [W|S]$. HINT. Use 1927c.

2018. Definition. The *composition* of a function V with a function W is the function $\{(x, V(W(x))) \mid x \in \text{domain } W, \text{ and } W(x) \in \text{domain } V\}$.

NOTATION. $[V \circ W]$, read V *comp* W.

NOTE I.
Domain $[V \circ W] = \{x \mid x \in \text{domain } W, \text{ and } W(x) \in \text{domain } V\}$;
range $[V \circ W] = \{V(W(x)) \mid x \in \text{domain } W, \text{ and } W(x) \in \text{domain } V\}$.

NOTE II. For each argument u of $V \circ W$: $[V \circ W](u) = V(W(u))$.

NOTE III. The author does not require range W to be a subset of domain V.

NOTE IV. $V \circ \emptyset = \emptyset = \emptyset \circ V$. (?)

2019. Example. Let V denote $\{(r, t), (g, b), (p, m), (d, r)\}$, and let W denote $\{(t, p), (b, r), (d, h)\}$. Then

$V \circ W = \{(t, m), (b, t)\}$,
$W \circ V = \{(r, p), (g, r)\}$,
$V \circ V = \{(d, t)\}$,
$W \circ W = \emptyset$.

Note that $V \circ W \neq W \circ V$.

2020. Exercise.

Referring to 2019, determine $V \circ [W \circ V]$, $[V \circ W] \circ V$, $[W \circ V] \circ V$, $W \circ [V \circ V]$.

2021. Lemma. For any things x, y and functions V, P:
$(x, y) \in [V \circ P] \Leftrightarrow$
there is a thing u such that $(x, u) \in P$ and $(u, y) \in V$.

Proof.:
$(x, y) \in [V \circ P] \Leftrightarrow$
$x \in$ domain P, and $P(x) \in$ domain V, and $y = V(P(x)) \Leftrightarrow_?$
$x \in$ domain P, and there is a thing u such that $u = P(x)$, and $u \in$ domain V,
    and $y = V(u) \Leftrightarrow$
there is a thing u such that $(x, u) \in P$ and $(u, y) \in V$.

2022. Theorem. For any functions V, W and set S: $[V \circ W] | S = V \circ [W|S]$.

Proof. Consider any functions V, W and set S.
Then for any things x, y:
$(x, y) \in [V \circ W] | S \Leftrightarrow$
$x \in S$ and $(x, y) \in [V \circ W] \Leftrightarrow_1$
$x \in S$ and there is a thing u such that $(x, u) \in W$ and $(u, y) \in V \Leftrightarrow_?$
there is a thing u such that $(x, u) \in [W|S]$ and $(u, y) \in V \Leftrightarrow_1$
$(x, y) \in [V \circ [W|S]]$.

Reference. 1.2021.

2023. Exercises.
  a. For any functions P, T: $P \circ T \neq \emptyset \Leftrightarrow$ [domain $P \cap$ range $T] \neq \emptyset$.
  b. For any functions P, T, Y: $[P \circ T] \circ Y = P \circ [T \circ Y]$.
  NOTE. This proposition is important.

2024. Notation. $P \circ T \circ Y$ stands for $P \circ [T \circ Y]$.

2025. Theorem. For any function V and identity function Y:
$V \circ Y = V \Leftrightarrow$ domain $V \subseteq$ domain Y.

Proof. Consider any function V and identity function Y.

PART I($\Rightarrow$). If $V \circ Y = V$, then domain $V =$ domain $[V \circ Y] =$
$\{x \mid x \in$ domain Y, and $Y(x) \in$ domain $V\} \subseteq$ domain Y.

PART II($\Leftarrow$). If domain $V \subseteq$ domain Y, then
$V \circ Y =$
$\{(x, V(Y(x))) \mid x \in$ domain Y, and $Y(x) \in$ domain $V\} =_?$
$\{(x, V(x)) \mid x \in$ domain Y, and $x \in$ domain $V\} =_?$
$\{(x, V(x)) \mid x \in$ domain $V\} =$
V.

2026. Exercise.

For any function V and identity function Y:
$Y \circ V = V \Leftrightarrow$ range $V \subseteq$ range Y.

2027. Theorem. For any functions V, W such that W is onto domain V:
$V \circ W$ is on domain W onto range V.

Proof. Consider any such hypothesized V, W; i.e., consider any functions V, W such that W is onto domain V.

$V \circ W$ is on domain W because domain $[V \circ W] =$
$\{x \mid x \in$ domain W, and $W(x) \in$ domain $V\} =_? \{x \mid x \in$ domain $W\} =$ domain W.

To prove that $V \circ W$ is onto range V it suffices to prove that
range $[V \circ W] \subseteq$ range V and range $[V \circ W] \supseteq$ range V.

PART I($\subseteq$). Range $[V \circ W] = \{[V \circ W](x) \mid x \in$ domain $[V \circ W]\} =_?$
$\{V(W(x)) \mid x \in$ domain $W\} \subseteq$ range V.

PART II($\supseteq$). Consider any member z of range V.
Then there is an argument y of V such that $z = V(y)$.
Since W is onto domain V, there is an argument x of W such that
$y = W(x)$.
So, $z = V(W(x)) = [V \circ W](x)$ and hence $z \in$ range $[V \circ W]$.

2028. Theorem. For any one-one functions V, W: $V \circ W$ is one-one.

Proof.: all distinct arguments u, x of $V \circ W$ satisfy $W(u) \neq_? W(x)$,
and so satisfy $[V \circ W](u) = V(W(u)) \neq_? V(W(x)) = [V \circ W](x)$;
therefore $V \circ W$ is one-one.

2029. Exercises.

a. *Prove or disprove.* The union of any two one-one functions whose domains are disjoint is one-one.

b. For any identity functions V, W: $V \circ W$ is an identity function.

The Inverse of a One-One Function

2101. This lesson may be omitted now, but it must be studied before Lesson 55.

2102. Definition. The *inverse* of an ordered pair (x, y) is the ordered pair (y, x).

2103. Definition. The *inverse* of a one-one function V is the set consisting of the inverse of each member of V.

NOTATION. $[V^{-1}]$, read V *inverse*.

NOTE I. We shall not define the inverse of a function that is not one-one.

NOTE II. $V^{-1} = \{(V(x), x) \mid x \in \text{domain } V\}$.

2104. Examples.

a. $\{(a, b), (c, g), (h, j)\}^{-1} = \{(b, a), (g, c), (j, h)\}$.

b. $\emptyset^{-1} =_? \emptyset$.

c. For each identity function Y: $Y^{-1} = Y$. (?)

2105. Exercises.

a. The inverse of each one-one function is a one-one function.

b. For each one-one function V: $[V^{-1}]^{-1} = V$.

2106. The following obvious propositions are worth keeping in mind.

a. For each one-one function V: domain V^{-1} = range V, and range V^{-1} = domain V.

b. For any one-one function V and argument u of V^{-1}:
$V^{-1}(u)$ is the thing to which V assigns u; i.e.,
$V^{-1}(u)$ is the argument t of V such that $V(t) = u$.

c. For any one-one function V, argument x of V, and value y of V:
$y = V(x) \Leftrightarrow V^{-1}(y) = x$.

2107. Theorems.

a. For any one-one function V and argument x thereof: $[V^{-1} \circ V](x) = x$.
Proof.: $[V^{-1} \circ V](x) = V^{-1}(V(x)) = x$. (2106b)

b. For any one-one function V and value u thereof: $[V \circ V^{-1}](u) = u$.
Proof.: $[V \circ V^{-1}](u) = V(V^{-1}(u)) = u$. (2106b)

2108. Theorem. For each one-one function V:
$V \circ V^{-1}$ is an identity function on range V, and
$V^{-1} \circ V$ is an identity function on domain V.

Proof. Consider any one-one function V.

For each argument u of $V \circ V^{-1}$: u is a value of V, (?)
and so by 2107b, $[V \circ V^{-1}](u) = u$,
and hence $V \circ V^{-1}$ is an identity function.

Furthermore, $V \circ V^{-1}$ is on range V because domain $[V \circ V^{-1}] =$
$\{x \mid x \in \text{domain } V^{-1}, \text{ and } V^{-1}(x) \in \text{domain } V\} =_? \{x \mid x \in \text{range } V\} =$
range V.

For each argument x of $V^{-1} \circ V$: x is an argument of V,
and so by 2107a, $[V^{-1} \circ V](x) = x$,
and hence $V^{-1} \circ V$ is an identity function.

Furthermore, $V^{-1} \circ V$ is on domain V because domain $[V^{-1} \circ V] =$
$\{x \mid x \in \text{domain } V, \text{ and } V(x) \in \text{domain } V^{-1}\} =_? \{x \mid x \in \text{domain } V\} =$
domain V.

2109. Exercises.

a. Find a one-one function T such that $T \circ T^{-1} \neq T^{-1} \circ T$.

b. For each one-one function V whose domain and range are equal:
$V \circ V^{-1} = V^{-1} \circ V$. NOTE. The hypothesis that the domain and range
are equal is essential in view of 2109a.

2110. Theorem. For any one-one functions N, P: $[N \circ P]^{-1} = P^{-1} \circ N^{-1}$.

Proof. Consider any one-one functions N, P.
For any things x, y:
$(x, y) \in [N \circ P]^{-1} \Leftrightarrow$
$(y, x) \in [N \circ P] \Leftrightarrow$
there is a thing u such that $(y, u) \in P$ and $(u, x) \in N \Leftrightarrow$
there is a thing u such that $(x, u) \in N^{-1}$ and $(u, y) \in P^{-1} \Leftrightarrow$
$(x, y) \in [P^{-1} \circ N^{-1}]$.

2111. Exercise. *Disprove.*

For any functions V, T, W such that T is one-one and $V \circ T = W$:
$V = W \circ T^{-1}$.

2112. Theorem. For any functions V, T, W such that T is one-one,
domain $V \subseteq$ range T, and $V \circ T = W$: $V = W \circ T^{-1}$.

Proof.: $V =_1 V \circ [T \circ T^{-1}] = [V \circ T] \circ T^{-1} = W \circ T^{-1}$.

Reference. 1.2025.

NOTE.

The hypothesis that domain $V \subseteq$ range T is essential in view of 2111.

2113. Exercises.

a. For any function V and one-one function W:
if domain $V =$ range W, and for each argument x of V:
   $V(x) \in$ domain W and $W(V(x)) = x$,
then $V = W^{-1}$.

NOTE. The above proposition provides a sufficient condition for a function V to be the inverse of a one-one function W.

b. For any function V and one-one function W:
$V \circ W = \{(W^{-1}(t), V(t)) \mid t \in (\text{domain } W^{-1} \cap \text{domain } V)\}$.

Introduction to the Real Number System

2201. Using concepts from set theory, it is possible to construct many different real number systems. Furthermore, it can be proved that all real number systems are structurally indistinguishable (in a sense that we shall not bother to explain). Accordingly, we shall adopt the convenient fiction that there is precisely one real number system and we shall refer to it as *the* real number system.

The following definition is conceptually the simplest one that the author could devise.

2202. Definition. The *real number system* is a figment of the imagination consisting of a set, denoted by the symbol R, and three functions, called the addition, multiplication, and max functions, satisfying seventeen axioms, four of which are stated next.

2203. Axioms.

a. The set R has at least two distinct members.

NOTE I. By a *real number* we mean any member of R. Henceforth we shall use the word *number* to abbreviate *real number*. According to the above axiom, there are at least two distinct numbers.

NOTE II. By a *number pair* we mean any ordered pair each of whose components is a number.

b. The addition function assigns to each number pair precisely one number.

c. The multiplication function assigns to each number pair precisely one number.

d. The max function assigns to each number pair precisely one number.

NOTE III. According to Axioms 2203b,c,d the domain of the addition, multiplication, and max functions is the set of all number pairs, and the

119

range of these functions is a subset of R. Therefore, each argument of these functions is a number pair, and each value of these functions is a number.

NOTE IV. We shall refer to the addition, multiplication, and max functions as the *basic functions*; the basic functions are operations for R (see 1934).

NOTE V. The remaining thirteen axioms will be found in 2302, 2402, 2502, 4109.

2204. Notations.

a. For any numbers x, y: the symbols $(x + y)$, $[x + y]$ are read x *plus* y and denote the number that the addition function assigns to (x, y).

b. For any numbers x, y: the symbols (xy), $[xy]$, $(x \cdot y)$, $[x \cdot y]$ are read as xy or as x *times* y and denote the number that the multiplication function assigns to (x, y).

c. For any numbers x, y: the symbols $\max(x, y)$, $\max[x, y]$ are read *max of* x, y and denote the number that the max function assigns to (x, y).

NOTE. To conform with the symbols $(x + y)$ and $(x \cdot y)$, one could use a symbol such as $(x \; \Box \; y)$ instead of the symbol $\max(x, y)$; indeed, we shall see later that such an alternate notation is quite helpful in comparing properties of the basic functions.

2205. All parentheses and brackets that appear in a symbol are significant; however, when there is no danger of ambiguity, outermost parentheses and brackets may be omitted. For example, in symbols such as $(x + y)$, (xy), $[x + (y + z)]$, $[(yz) + x]$, $[(ab) + (cg)]$, all parentheses and brackets are significant; however we shall often abbreviate these symbols as follows: $x + y$, xy, $x + (y + z)$, $(yz) + x$, $(ab) + (cg)$.

Later we shall introduce conventions for omitting inner parentheses such as those in the symbols $a + (bc)$, $a + (b + c)$.

We shall never omit parentheses in the ordered pair notation (x, y) and in symbols such as $\max(a, b)$.

2206. Immediate consequence. *Closure.*
For any numbers x, y: $(x + y)$ is a number, (xy) is a number, and $\max(x, y)$ is a number. (2204).

NOTE. For any numbers x, y:
we call $x + y$ *the sum of* x *and* y or *the result of adding* x *to* y,
we call xy *the product of* x *and* y or *the result of multiplying* x *by* y, and
we call $\max(x, y)$ *the maximum of* x, y.

2207. Theorems.

   a. For any numbers a, b, u, v such that $a = b$ and $u = v$:
$a + u = b + v, \quad au = bv, \quad$ and $\max(a, u) = \max(b, v)$.

   b. For any numbers c, u, v such that $u = v$:
$c + u = c + v, \quad cu = cv, \quad$ and $\max(c, u) = \max(c, v)$.

   c. For any numbers a, b, r such that $a = b$:
$a + r = b + r, \quad ar = br, \quad$ and $\max(a, r) = \max(b, r)$.

Proofs. Substitution (1304d).

2208. We shall use 2206 and 2207 without making explicit reference thereto.

2209. No number is called *infinity*, *minus infinity*, or *plus infinity*.
No number is denoted by the symbols ∞, $-\infty$, or $+\infty$.

2210. The following remarks may clarify the general ideas about systems that were summarized in 1241.

The primary definition of the real number system consists of the statement in 2202 together with seventeen axioms. The primitives are the set R (and its members) and the three basic functions. The primitive terms are *real number* (or simply *number*), *addition function, multiplication function*, and *max function*. By virtue of Axiom 2203a, which is existential, at least two distinct numbers are definitionally existent. There will be many secondary definitions (and notational conventions), none of which will be existential. Our first existence theorem will appear in 2306 and the number whose existence will be proved there is deductively existent.

Most other books on real numbers start with a primary definition of the system of whole numbers (called the Peano System), and then after a long chain of theorems and secondary definitions finally arrive at a secondary definition of real numbers. This method is called the constructive (or genetic) method as distinguished from the method used in this book.

The Addition Function

2301. We know that the addition function assigns to each number pair (x, y) precisely one number, called the sum of x and y and denoted by the symbols $(x + y)$, $[x + y]$. Next we state three more axioms of the real number system.

2302. Axioms.

a. *Commutativity of addition*
For any numbers x, y: $x + y = y + x$,
i.e., the addition function assigns the same number to (x, y) and (y, x).

b. *Associativity of addition*
For any numbers x, y, z: $x + (y + z) = (x + y) + z$,
i.e., the addition function assigns the same number to $(x, y + z)$ and $(x + y, z)$.

c. *Solvability with respect to addition*
For any numbers a, b: there is at least one number x such that $a + x = b$.

2303. Remark. Axioms 2203b, 2302a,b,c characterize the so-called additive group properties of the real number system.

2304. Theorem. For any numbers a, b, c:
$$(a + b) + c =_1 c + (a + b) =_1 c + (b + a) =_1 (b + a) + c =_2$$
$$b + (a + c) =_1 (a + c) + b =_1 (c + a) + b =_1 b + (c + a) =_2$$
$$(b + c) + a =_1 (c + b) + a =_1 a + (c + b) =_1 a + (b + c).$$
Proof. References. 1.2302a; 2.2302b.

NOTE I. Informally this theorem means that the sum of any three (possibly equal) numbers is independent of the order in which they are added and independent of the manner in which they are associated.

NOTE II. Observe that in the proof we did not bother to refer to 2206 and 2207 even though, for example, the second equality requires 2206 and 2207b as well as 2302a.

2305. Exercise.
For any numbers w, x, y, z: $(w + x) + (y + z) = (w + z) + (y + x)$.

2306. Theorem. There is precisely one number q such that $q + q = q$.

Proof.

AT LEAST ONE.
By 2203a, there is a number, say b;
by 2302c, there is a number q such that $b + q = b$;
by 2302c, there is a number t such that $b + t = q$; therefore,
$q + q = (b + t) + q =_? (b + q) + t = b + t = q$.

AT MOST ONE.
Consider any numbers w, z such that $w + w = w$ and $z + z = z$.
We prove that $w = z$.
By 2302c, there is a number r such that $w + r = z$;
By 2302c, there is a number s such that $z + s = w$; therefore,
$w = z + s = (z + z) + s = z + (z + s) = z + w = (w + r) + w =_?$
$(w + w) + r = w + r = z$.

NOTE. This is an existence theorem.

2307. Notation. The symbol 0, read *zero*, denotes the number q such that
$q + q = q$.

NOTE. Numerals are symbols permanently chosen to denote particular numbers; for example, the symbol 0 is a numeral. None of the following symbols is a numeral: $\infty, -\infty, +\infty$.

2308. In introducing the previous notation, we used the phrase *the number q such that* $q + q = q$. To justify such language we first proved Theorem 2306. It is important for the student to understand the methodological principle involved here: one may not employ the expression *the so-and-so* until one has proved that there is precisely one so-and-so.

2309. What is the number called zero?

Is it the symbol 0?
No. A number is not a symbol.

Is it the word *zero*?
No. A number is not a word.

Is it a quantity?
This question is meaningless because we have not defined *quantity*.

The number called *zero* is a certain member of the set R.

2310. Immediate consequence. $0 + 0 = 0$. (2307)

2311. Theorem. For each number y: $0 + y = y + 0 = y$.

> *Proof.* Consider any number y.
> By 2302a, $0 + y = y + 0$;
> by 2302c, there is a number x such that $0 + x = y$; hence
> $y + 0 = (0 + x) + 0 = (0 + 0) + x = 0 + x = y$.

2312. Axiom 2203b stipulates that the range, say B, of the addition function is a subset of R.
Now we can prove that $B = R$.
It suffices, of course, to prove that $R \subseteq B$.

> *Proof.* Consider any member y of R.
> Since $0 + y = y$, the addition function assigns to $(0, y)$ the number y.
> Therefore y is a value of the addition function, and so $y \in B$.
> Hence $R \subseteq B$.

2313. Theorems.

a. For any numbers a, u, v: $a + u = a + v \Rightarrow u = v$.

> *Proof.* Consider any numbers a, u, v such that $a + u = a + v$.
> By 2302c, there is a number x such that $a + x = 0$; therefore
> $u = 0 + u = (a + x) + u = x + (a + u) = x + (a + v) = (a + x) + v = 0 + v = v$.

b. For any numbers a, u, v: $u + a = v + a \Rightarrow u = v$.

> *Proof.* Use 2302a and 2313a.

2314. As an example of the use of 2313b, we shall prove the following proposition.

For any numbers w, a: $w + a = a \Rightarrow w = 0$.

> *Proof.*: $w + a = a \Rightarrow w + a = 0 + a \Rightarrow w = 0$.

2315. Theorem. For any numbers a, b:
there is precisely one number x such that $a + x = b$.

> *Proof.*
>
> AT LEAST ONE. See 2302c.
>
> AT MOST ONE. For any numbers a, b, u, v such that
> $a + u = b$ and $a + v = b$:
> $a + u = a + v$, and so $u = v$.

2316. Notation. For any numbers a, b: the symbols $(b - a)$, $[b - a]$ are read b *minus* a and denote the number x such that $a + x = b$.

NOTE I. See 2205 concerning omission of parentheses and brackets.

NOTE II. For any numbers a, b: $b - a$ is called *the difference between b and a* and *the result of subtracting a from b*.

2317. Immediate consequences.

a. For any numbers a, b: $(b - a) + a = a + (b - a) = b$. (2302a, 2316)

b. For any numbers a, b, x: $a + x = b \Leftrightarrow x = b - a$. (2316)

c. For each number y: $y = y - 0$. (2311, 2317b)

d. $0 = 0 - 0$. (2317c)

e. For each number y: $0 = y - y$. (2311, 2317b)

2318. Theorem. For any numbers a, b, u, v: if $a = b$ and $u = v$, then $a - u = b - v$.

Proof. By substitution.

2319. Exercise. There is precisely one number x such that $x - x = x$.

2320. Theorems.

a. For any numbers x, y, z: $x + (y - z) = (x + y) - z$.

Proof.: $[x + (y - z)] + z = x + [(y - z) + z] = (x + y)$, and so $[x + (y - z)] =_? (x + y) - z$.

b. For any numbers x, y, z: $x - (y - z) = (x - y) + z$.

Proof.:
$[(x - y) + z] + (y - z) = (x - y) + [z + (y - z)] = (x - y) + y = x$,
and so $[(x - y) + z] = x - (y - z)$.

c. For any numbers x, y, z: $x - (y + z) = (x - y) - z$.

Proof.:
$[(x - y) - z] + (y + z) = [((x - y) - z) + z] + y = (x - y) + y = x$,
and so $[(x - y) - z] = x - (y + z)$.

NOTE. Cleanup clauses such as the previous line are often omitted.

2321. The following propositions are easy to prove and are listed for the purpose of future comparison.

a. For any numbers a, b, u, v: $(a - u) + (b - v) = (a + b) - (u + v)$.

b. For any numbers b, g, u: $(b + u) - (g + u) = b - g$.

c. For any numbers a, b, c, g: $(a - b) - (c - g) = (a + g) - (b + c)$.

d. For any numbers a, b, c, g: $a - c = b - g \Leftrightarrow a + g = c + b$.

2322. Definition. The *negative of a number* x is the number $(0 - x)$.

NOTATION. $(-x)$, read as *the negative of* x or as *minus* x.

NOTE I. We shall neither use nor require symbols such as $(+x)$.

NOTE II. Nothing has yet been said to justify our speaking of negative numbers or positive numbers; such distinctions will be discussed in a subsequent lesson.

2323. Theorems.

a. $-0 = 0$.

Proof. $-0 =_? 0 - 0 =_? 0$.

NOTE. Later we shall prove that no other number equals its negative.

b. For each number x: $-(-x) = x$.

Proof.: $-(-x) =_1 0 - (-x) = 0 - (0 - x) =_2 (0 - 0) + x = 0 + x = x$.

References. 1.2322; 2.2320b.

2324. Exercises.

a. For any numbers x, y such that $-x = -y$: $x = y$.

b. For any numbers a, b such that $-a = b$: $a = -b$.

2325. Theorem. For any numbers u, v: $u + (-v) = u - v$.

Proof.: $u + (-v) = u + (0 - v) =_? (u + 0) - v = u - v$.

2326. Exercises.

a. For each number x: $(-x) + x = x + (-x) = 0$.

b. For any numbers a, b: $a - (-b) = a + b$.

2327. Theorem. For any numbers x, v: $-(x + v) = (-x) + (-v)$.

Proof.:
$-(x + v) = 0 - (x + v) = (0 - x) - v = (-x) - v =_? (-x) + (-v)$.

2328. Exercise. For any numbers x, y: $-(x - y) = y - x$.

2329. Notation. $-x + y$ stands for $(-x) + y$.

2330. *Nonzero number* means *number different from* 0.

2331. Immediate consequence. There is at least one nonzero number. (2203a)

2332. Theorem. The negative of each nonzero number is nonzero;
i.e., for each number x: $x \neq 0 \implies -x \neq 0$.

Proof. Suppose not.
Then there is a number x such that $x \neq 0$ and $-x = 0$.
So, $x =_? -0 = 0$. Contradiction.

2333. The contrapositive of Theorem 2332 is the following proposition.
For each number x: $-x = 0 \implies x = 0$.

The student knows (317a) that each conditional is similar to its contrapositive; accordingly, one may prove 2332 by proving its contrapositive.

NOTE. An indirect proof of a conditional may often be recast as a direct proof of its contrapositive.

2334. Exercise. Prove 2332 by proving its contrapositive directly.

2335. Notation.
$z + u + v$ stands for $z + (u + v)$;
$y + z + u + v$ stands for $y + (z + u + v)$;
$x + y + z + u + v$ stands for $x + (y + z + u + v)$.

2336. Immediate consequence. For any numbers a, b, c: $c + a + b = c + b + a = b + a + c = b + c + a = a + c + b = a + b + c$.
(2335, 2304)

2337. Exercise.
For any numbers u, v, x, y: $u + v + x + y = y + u + x + v$.

2338. Notation.
$x + y - z$ stands for $(x + y) - z$,
$x - y + z$ stands for $(x - y) + z$,
$x - y - z$ stands for $(x - y) - z$.

The Multiplication Function

2401. We know that the multiplication function assigns to each number pair (x, y) precisely one number, called the product of x and y and denoted by the symbols (xy), $[xy]$, $(x \cdot y)$, $[x \cdot y]$. Next we state four more axioms of the real number system.

2402. Axioms.

a. *Commutativity of multiplication*
For any numbers x, y: $xy = yx$,
i.e., the multiplication function assigns the same number to (x, y) and (y, x).

b. *Associativity of multiplication*
For any numbers x, y, z: $x(yz) = (xy)z$,
i.e., the multiplication function assigns the same number to (x, yz) and (xy, z).

c. *Solvability with respect to multiplication*
For any nonzero number a and any number b:
there is at least one number x such that $ax = b$.

d. *Distributivity of multiplication with respect to addition*
For any numbers x, y, z: $x(y + z) = (xy) + (xz)$.

NOTE I. The student should compare 2402a,b,c with 2302a,b,c.

NOTE II. 2402d provides a connection between multiplication and addition.

2403. Remark. Axioms 2203c, 2402a,b,c characterize the so-called multiplicative group properties of the real number system. The so-called field properties of the real number system are characterized by Axioms 2203a,b,c, 2302a,b,c, 2402a,b,c,d.

2404. Theorem. For any numbers a, b, c:
$$(ab)c = c(ab) = c(ba) = (ba)c = b(ac) = (ac)b =$$
$$(ca)b = b(ca) = (bc)a = (cb)a = a(cb) = a(bc).$$

Proof. The student may readily supply the necessary references and will find it interesting to compare this theorem with 2304.

2405. Notation.

   zuv stands for $z(uv)$;

   $yzuv$ stands for $y(zuv)$;

   $xyzuv$ stands for $x(yzuv)$.

2406. Immediate consequence. For any numbers a, b, c:
$$cab = cba = bac = bca = acb = abc. \quad (2405, 2404)$$

2407. Parentheses in symbols such as $(xy) + (xz)$, $(xy) - (xz)$, $a + (bc)$ are usually omitted in accordance with the stipulation that multiplication is performed before addition and subtraction.

2408. Exercises.
   a. For any numbers a, b, c, g: $a(b + c + g) = ab + ac + ag$.
   b. For any numbers x, y, z: $(y + z)x = yx + zx$.
   c. For any numbers a, b, c, g: $(a + b)(c + g) = ac + ag + bc + bg$.

2409. Theorems.
   a. For any numbers x, y, z: $x(y - z) = xy - xz$.
      Proof.: $x[y - z] + xz =_1 x[(y - z) + z] = xy$. $\quad (1.2402d)$
   b. For each number x: $0 \cdot x = x \cdot 0 = 0$.
      Proof.: $0 \cdot x = x \cdot 0$,
      and $x \cdot 0 + x \cdot 0 = x \cdot (0 + 0) = x \cdot 0$, and so $x \cdot 0 =_? 0$.
   c. For any numbers x, y: $(-x)y = -(xy) = x(-y)$.
      Proof.: $(-x)y = y(0 - x) = y \cdot 0 - (yx) = 0 - (xy) = -(xy)$,
      and then $-(xy) = -(yx) =_? (-y)x = x(-y)$.
      NOTE. The student who cannot answer the previous question should realize that we had already proved one half of the theorem, namely that for any numbers u, v: $(-u)v = -(uv)$.
   d. For any numbers x, z: $(-x)(-z) = xz$.
      Proof.: $(-x)(-z) =_1 -[x(-z)] = -[-(xz)] =_2 xz$.
      $(1.2409c; 2.2323b)$

2410. Notation. $-xy$ stands for $-(xy)$.

2411. Since $0 \cdot 0 =_? 0$, we know that there is a number p such that $pp = p$; the next theorem provides a more useful fact.

2412. Theorem. There is precisely one nonzero number p such that $pp = p$.

Proof.

AT LEAST ONE.
By 2331, there is a nonzero number, say a;
by 2402c, there is a number p such that $ap = a$, and
p is nonzero because otherwise a would be 0;   (?)
by 2402c, there is a number t such that $at = p$, and hence
$pp = pat =_? at = p$.

AT MOST ONE.
Consider any nonzero numbers w, z such that $ww = w$ and $zz = z$.
By 2402c, there is a number r such that $wr = z$;
by 2402c, there is a number s such that $zs = w$; therefore
$w = zs = zzs = zw = wz = wwr = wr = z$.

2413. Notation. The symbol 1, read *one*, denotes the nonzero number p such that $pp = p$.

NOTE. The symbol 1 is a numeral.

2414. In Theorem 2412, the hypothesis *nonzero* is essential; i.e., if it is omitted, then the proposition is false because there is more than one number p such that $pp = p$, e.g., 0 and 1.

2415. What is the number called one? It is a certain member of the set R.

2416. Immediate consequences.

  a. $1 \neq 0$.   (2413)

  b. $1 + 1 \neq 1$.   (2416a, 2307)

  c. $1 \cdot 1 = 1$.   (2413)

  d. $(-1)(-1) = 1$.   (2409d, 2416c)

  e. $-1 \neq 0$.   (2416a, 2332)

  NOTE. In the next lesson we shall prove that $-1 \neq 1$, from which it will readily follow (?) that $1 + 1 \neq 0$. To prove these two propositions, additional axioms are required.

2417. Theorem. For each number y: $1 \cdot y = y \cdot 1 = y$.

Proof.: $1 \cdot y = y \cdot 1$, and by 2416a, 2402c, there is a number x such that $1 \cdot x = y$, and so $y \cdot 1 = 1 \cdot x \cdot 1 =_? 1 \cdot x = y$.

NOTE. Obviously the range of the multiplication function is R.   (?)

2418. Corollary. For each number w: $-w = (-1)w$.

Proof.: $-w = 1(-w) =_1 (-1)w$. (1.2409c)

2419. Theorem. *Left cancellation.*

For any numbers a, u, v: if $a \neq 0$ and $au = av$, then $u = v$.

Proof. Consider any numbers a, u, v such that $a \neq 0$ and $au = av$. By 2402c, there is a number x such that $ax = 1$, and so
$u = 1 \cdot u = xau = xav = 1 \cdot v = v$.

NOTE. The student may readily state and prove the theorem for right cancellation.

2420. Let us prove that in Theorem 2419 the hypothesis $a \neq 0$ is essential. We must disprove the following proposition.

For any numbers a, u, v: if $au = av$, then $u = v$.

Counterexample. 0 for a, 0 for u, 1 for v.

2421. Theorem. For any numbers x, y: $xy = 0 \Rightarrow (x = 0$ or $y = 0)$.

PREFATORY REMARK. It suffices to prove that
for any numbers x, y such that $xy = 0$ and $x \neq 0$: $y = 0$. (See 315h.)

Proof.: $xy = 0 = x \cdot 0$, and so $y =_? 0$.

NOTE. The contrapositive of this theorem is equally important and may be stated as follows:

The product of any two nonzero numbers is nonzero.

2422. Exercise.

For any nonzero number a and any number b:
there is precisely one number x such that $ax = b$.
HINT. Review the proof of 2315.

2423. If we omit the hypothesis *nonzero* from 2422 we obtain the following.
For any numbers a, b: there is precisely one number x such that $ax = b$.

We shall disprove this proposition.
It suffices to disprove either one of the following propositions. (?)

i. For any numbers a, b: there is at least one number x such that $ax = b$.
ii. For any numbers a, b: there is at most one number x such that $ax = b$.

It so happens that both of these propositions are false.

Proposition i is false because for the numbers 0, 1 there is no number x such that $0 \cdot x = 1$. (?)

Proposition ii is false because for the numbers 0, 0 there is more than one number x such that $0 \cdot x = 0$. (?)

2424. Notation. For any number b and nonzero number a:

the symbols b/a, $\dfrac{b}{a}$ are read b *over* a and denote

the number x such that $ax = b$.

NOTE. b/a is called *the quotient of b by a, the result of dividing b by a,* and *the result of dividing a into b.*

2425. The previous convention does not authorize us to write $1/0$. Nevertheless, let us try to find *the* number that would appropriately be denoted by the symbol $1/0$. To conform with 2424, the symbol $1/0$ should denote *the* number whose product with 0 is 1; however, there is no such number. Accordingly, we consider the symbol $1/0$ to be meaningless.

Let us try to find *the* number that would appropriately be denoted by the symbol $0/0$. To conform with 2424, the symbol $0/0$ should denote *the* number whose product with 0 is 0; however, there is more than one such number. Accordingly, we consider the symbol $0/0$ to be meaningless.

These remarks suggest the next convention.

2426. Convention. For each number x: the symbols $x/0$, $\dfrac{x}{0}$ are meaningless.

NOTE. See 2209.

2427. Immediate consequences.

a. For any nonzero number a and any number b:
$(b/a)a = a(b/a) = b$.   (2402a, 2424)

b. For any nonzero number a and any numbers b, x:
$ax = b \Leftrightarrow x = b/a$. (2424)

c. For each number y: $y = y/1$.   (2417, 2427b)

d. $1 = 1/1$.   (2427c)

e. For each nonzero number y: $1 = y/y$.   (2417, 2427b)

f. For any number u and nonzero number x: $u/x = 0 \Leftrightarrow u = 0$.
(2427b, 2409b)

g. For any nonzero number x: $0/x = 0$.   (2427f)

h. For any nonzero numbers v, x: $v/x \neq 0$.   (2427f)

NOTE. Compare 2427a,b,c,d,e with 2317a,b,c,d,e.

2428. The following proposition follows by substitution.

For any numbers a, b and nonzero numbers u, v:
if $a = b$ and $u = v$, then $a/u = b/v$.

2429. Exercise.

There is precisely one nonzero number x such that $x/x = x$.
HINT. Review your proof of 2319.

2430. Exercises. (Compare with 2320a,b,c.)

a. For any numbers x, y, z such that $z \neq 0$: $x \dfrac{y}{z} = \dfrac{xy}{z}$.

b. For any numbers x, y, z such that $y \neq 0$ and $z \neq 0$: $\dfrac{x}{y/z} = \dfrac{x}{y}z$.

c. For any numbers x, y, z such that $y \neq 0$ and $z \neq 0$: $\dfrac{x}{yz} = \dfrac{x/y}{z}$.

2431. Notation.

xy/z stands for $(xy)/z$;

x/yz stands for $x/(yz)$;

ab/uv stands for $(ab)/(uv)$.

2432. Theorem. For any numbers a, b and nonzero numbers c, g:

$\dfrac{a}{c} = \dfrac{b}{g} \Leftrightarrow ag = cb$. (Compare with 2321d.)

Proof.: $\dfrac{a}{c} = \dfrac{b}{g} \Leftrightarrow \dfrac{a}{c}(cg) = \dfrac{b}{g}(cg) \Leftrightarrow_? ag = bc$.

2433. Theorems.

a. For any number x and nonzero number y: $(-x)/(-y) = x/y$.

Proof. Use 2432 and 2409c.

b. For any number x and nonzero number y:
$-(x/y) = (-x)/y = x/(-y)$.

Proof.: $-(x/y) = (-1)(x/y) = [(-1)x]/y = (-x)/y$,
and $(-x)/y = x/(-y)$ because $(-x)(-y) = yx$.

2434. Exercises. (Compare with 2321a,b,c.)

a. For any numbers a, b and nonzero numbers u, v: $\dfrac{a}{u} \cdot \dfrac{b}{v} = \dfrac{ab}{uv}$.

b. For any number b and nonzero numbers g, u: $\dfrac{bu}{gu} = \dfrac{b}{g}$.

c. For any number a and nonzero numbers b, c, g: $\dfrac{a/b}{c/g} = \dfrac{ag}{bc}$.

2435. Theorems.

a. For any numbers a, b and nonzero number u: $\dfrac{a}{u} + \dfrac{b}{u} = \dfrac{a+b}{u}$.

   Proof.: $u\left(\dfrac{a}{u} + \dfrac{b}{u}\right) = u \cdot \dfrac{a}{u} + u \cdot \dfrac{b}{u} = a + b$.

b. For any numbers a, b and nonzero number u: $\dfrac{a}{u} - \dfrac{b}{u} = \dfrac{a-b}{u}$.

   Proof. Similar to the previous proof. Use 2409a.

c. For any numbers a, b and nonzero numbers u, v: $\dfrac{a}{u} + \dfrac{b}{v} = \dfrac{av + ub}{uv}$.

   Proof.: $\dfrac{a}{u} + \dfrac{b}{v} = \dfrac{av}{uv} + \dfrac{ub}{uv} = \dfrac{av + ub}{uv}$.

d. For any numbers a, b and nonzero numbers u, v: $\dfrac{a}{u} - \dfrac{b}{v} = \dfrac{av - ub}{uv}$.

   Proof. Similar to the previous proof.

2436. Definition. The *reciprocal* of a nonzero number x is the number $1/x$.

   NOTE. We do not define the reciprocal of 0.

2437. The following propositions are immediate consequences of previously proved propositions and are listed for the purpose of comparison.

a. The reciprocal of 1 is 1. (Compare 2323a.)

b. The reciprocal of each nonzero number is nonzero. (Compare 2332.)

c. For each nonzero number x:
the reciprocal of the reciprocal of x is x. (Compare 2323b.)

d. For any number u and nonzero number v: $u(1/v) = u/v$. (Compare 2325.)

e. For each nonzero number x: $(1/x)x = x(1/x) = 1$. (Compare 2326a.)

f. For any number a and nonzero number b: $a/(1/b) = ab$. (Compare 2326b.)

g. For any nonzero numbers x, v: $1/(xv) = (1/x)(1/v)$. (Compare 2327.)

h. For any nonzero numbers x, y: $1/(x/y) = y/x$. (Compare 2328.)

2438. The student has been requested to compare certain propositions in this lesson with propositions in the previous lesson. No doubt he has noted a kind of "duality" principle: if in a true proposition one interchanges multiplication with addition, division with subtraction, 1 with 0, the reciprocal of a number with its negative, and one deletes or inserts non-zero requirements, then the resulting proposition (called the *dual* of the original) might be true.

Note that the dual of 2409b is false.

The dual of a true proposition might be false because the dual of Axiom 2402d (distributivity) is false. The dual of Axiom 2402d is as follows:

For any numbers x, y, z: $x + (yz) = (x + y)(x + z)$.

Counterexample. 1 for x, 1 for y, 0 for z.

The Max Function

2501. We know that the max function assigns to each number pair (x, y) precisely one number, called the maximum of x, y and denoted by the symbols $\max(x, y)$, $\max[x, y]$.

Next we state five more axioms of the real number system, bringing our total to sixteen. The seventeenth (and last) axiom will be stated much later (in 4109).

2502. Axioms.

a. *Commutativity.* For any numbers x, y: $\max(x, y) = \max(y, x)$.

b. *Associativity.* For any numbers x, y, z:
$\max[x, \max(y, z)] = \max[\max(x, y), z]$.

c. *Definiteness.* For any numbers x, y: $\max(x, y) = x$ or $\max(x, y) = y$.

d. *Distributivity of addition with respect to the max function*
For any numbers x, y, z: $x + \max(y, z) = \max(x + y, x + z)$.

e. *Distributivity of multiplication with respect to the max function*
For any numbers x, y, z such that $\max(0, x) = x$:
$x \cdot \max(y, z) = \max(xy, xz)$.

NOTE I. Axiom 2502e does not assert that there is a number x such that $\max(0, x) = x$; this axiom may be recast in the following manner.
For any numbers x, y, z:
if $\max(0, x) = x$, then $x \cdot \max(y, z) = \max(xy, xz)$.
Soon we shall see that if the qualification $\max(0, x) = x$ were omitted from this axiom, then the real number system would be inconsistent.

NOTE II. The student should compare 2502a, 2402a, 2302a, and 2502b, 2402b, 2302b. To see the similarities among 2502d, 2502e, 2402d, the author recommends replacing the symbol max(u, v) by the symbol ($u \; \square \; v$); e.g., Axiom 2502d would then be written as follows:

For any numbers x, y, z: $x + (y \; \square \; z) = (x + y) \; \square \; (x + z)$.

In this form, 2502d looks more like a distributive law.

2503. Remark. The sixteen axioms thus far introduced characterize the so-called ordered field properties of the real number system.

2504. A theorem analogous to 2304 and 2404 may readily be proved.

2505. Theorem. For each number z: max(z, z) = z.
Proof. 2502c.

NOTE. Obviously the max function is onto R. (?)

2506. Exercises.
  a. For any numbers x, y: max[y, max(x, y)] = max(x, y).
  b. For any numbers a, b, x, y:
  max[max(a, b), max(x, y)] = max[max(a, x), max(b, y)].

2507. Theorems.

  a. max(0, 1) = 1.
  Proof. Suppose not.
  Then max(0, 1) = 0.   (2502c)
  So, $-1 = (-1) + 0 = (-1) + $ max(0, 1) $=$
  max[$(-1) + 0$, $(-1) + 1$] = max(-1, 0) = max(0, -1). Hence
  $1 = (-1)(-1) = (-1)$max(0, -1) $=_?$ max[$(-1) \cdot 0$, $(-1)(-1)$] =
  max(0, 1) = 0.
  Contradiction.

  b. max(-1, 0) = 0.
  Proof. max(-1, 0) = $(-1) + $ max(0, 1) = $(-1) + 1 = 0$.

  c. max(-1, 1) = 1.
  Proof. max(-1, 1) = max[-1, max(0, 1)] $=_?$ max[max(-1, 0), 1] = max(0, 1) = 1.

NOTE. We have already used all axioms in 2502.

2508. Exercise. *Disprove.*
For any numbers a, b: there is a number y such that max(a, y) = b.

2509. Theorem. $-1 \neq 1$.

    Proof. Suppose that $-1 = 1$.
    Then $1 = \max(0, 1) = \max(0, -1) = 0$. Contradiction.

    NOTE. We may now assert that $-1, 0, 1$ are distinct.

2510. The three basic functions of the real number system are distinct because
they assign different numbers to $(-1, 1)$:
$$-1 + 1 = 0, \quad (-1)(1) = -1, \quad \max(-1, 1) = 1.$$

2511. Exercise. $1 + 1 \neq -1$.
    NOTE. We now know that $1+1$ is distinct from $-1, 0, 1$.   (2509, 2416b)

2512. Notation. The symbol 2, read *two*, denotes the number $1 + 1$.

    NOTE I. In some treatments of the real number system, the fact that
$2 = 1 + 1$ is of deep significance; here, this fact emerges by convention.

    NOTE II. We know that $-1, 0, 1, 2$ are distinct.   (?)

2513. Example. $2 - 1 = (1 + 1) - 1 = 1 + (1 - 1) = 1 + 0 = 1$.

2514. Immediate consequence. For each number x: $x + x = 2x$.   (2408b)

2515. Exercises.
    a. No nonzero number equals its negative, i.e.,
    for each nonzero number x: $x \neq -x$.
    NOTE. By 2323a, we may now assert that 0 is *the* number that equals its
    negative.

    b. There are precisely two distinct numbers that equal their reciprocals.

    c. -2 is distinct from $-1, 0, 1, 2$.

    d. $\max(0, 2) = 2$.

2516. Theorem. For each number x:
    $\max(-x, 0) = 0 \Leftrightarrow \max(x, 0) = x \Leftrightarrow \max(-x, x) = x$.

    Proof.: $\max(-x, 0) = 0 \Leftrightarrow x + \max(-x, 0) = x + 0 \Leftrightarrow$
    $\max(0, x) = x \Leftrightarrow 2 \cdot \max(0, x) = 2x \Leftrightarrow \max(0, 2x) = 2x \Leftrightarrow$
    $-x + \max(0, 2x) = -x + 2x \Leftrightarrow \max(-x, x) = x$.

    NOTE. This is not a round-robin proof.

2517. Corollary. For each number u:
    $\max(u, 0) = 0 \Leftrightarrow \max(-u, 0) = -u \Leftrightarrow \max(-u, u) = -u$.

    Proof. 2516 with u for $-x$.

2518. Exercises.

   a. $\max(-2, 2) = 2$.

   b. $\max(-1/2, 1/2) = 1/2$.

2519. Let us examine the qualification $\max(0, x) = x$ in 2502e.

Assume that we had omitted this qualification from 2502e.

Then, surely, all the propositions so far proved would still be provable. (?)

Accordingly, we would have

$-1 = (-1) \cdot 1 = (-1) \cdot \max(0, 1) = \max[(-1) \cdot 0, \ (-1) \cdot 1] =$
$\max(0, -1) = 0,$

and this contradicts 2416e, thereby rendering our system inconsistent.

2520. Exercise.

For any numbers x, y:

$\max(0, x) \cdot \max(0, y) = \max[0, \ \max(0, x) \cdot \max(0, y)]$.

HINT. $\max(0, x) \cdot \max(0, y)$ is either zero or nonzero.

2521. It is interesting to know that if 2520 were used as an axiom instead of 2502e, then the "new" system so created would be "equivalent" to the "old" system because every theorem in the "old" system would be a theorem in the "new" system, and conversely.

2522. Exercise.

Replace 2502e by 2520 and prove 2502e in the "new" system.

NOTE. One must avoid using results whose proof required 2502e.

The Minimum of Two Numbers

2601. Having studied our three basic functions in considerable detail, we turn next to the problem of defining the minimum of two numbers.

Consider any numbers x, y.
How shall we define $\min(x, y)$, i.e., the minimum of x, y?
If $x = y$, then surely we want $\min(x, y)$ to equal x (and hence y).
If $x \neq y$, then we desire $\min(x, y)$ to equal x or y whichever does not equal $\max(x, y)$.
It is evident that the number $x + y - \max(x, y)$ behaves as desired, and so may be used to define $\min(x, y)$.

2602. Definition. The *minimum* of two numbers x, y is $x + y - \max(x, y)$.

NOTATIONS. $\min(x, y)$, $\min[x, y]$, read *min of x, y*.

2603. Examples.

a. $\min(0, 1) = 0 + 1 - \max(0, 1) = 0 + 1 - 1 = 0.$

b. $\min(-1, 0) = -1 + 0 - \max(-1, 0) = -1.$

c. $\min(-1, 1) = -1 + 1 - \max(-1, 1) = -1.$

d. $\min(1, 1) = 1 + 1 - \max(1, 1) = 1.$

e. $\min(-2, 2) = -2 + 2 - \max(-2, 2) = -2.$

2604. Theorem. For each number z: $\min(z, z) = z$.

Proof.: $\min(z, z) = z + z - \max(z, z) = z + z - z = z.$

2605. Theorem. For any numbers u, v: $\min(u, v) = -\max(-u, -v)$.

Proof.: $\min(u, v) = (u + v) - \max(u, v) =_?$
$(u + v) - [(u + v) + \max(-v, -u)] = -\max(-u, -v)$.

NOTE. This theorem may be recast as follows.
For any numbers u, v: $-\min(u, v) = \max(-u, -v)$.

2606. Corollary. For any numbers r, s: $\max(r, s) = -\min(-r, -s)$.

NOTE. This corollary may be formulated as follows.
For any numbers r, s: $-\max(r, s) = \min(-r, -s)$.

2607. Exercises.

a. For any numbers u, v: $\min(u, v) = v \iff \max(u, v) = u$.

b. For each number y:
$\min(-y, 0) = 0 \iff \min(y, 0) = y \iff \min(-y, y) = y$.
(Compare 2516.)

2608. Theorems. (Compare with 2502.)

a. *Commutativity.* For any numbers x, y: $\min(x, y) = \min(y, x)$.

Proof.: $\min(x, y) = x + y - \max(x, y) = y + x - \max(y, x) = \min(y, x)$.

Alternate proof.: $\min(x, y) = -\max(-x, -y) = -\max(-y, -x) = \min(y, x)$.

b. *Associativity.* For any numbers x, y, z:
$\min[x, \min(y, z)] = \min[\min(x, y), z]$.

Proof.: $\min[x, \min(y, z)] = -\max[-x, -\min(y, z)] =_?$
$-\max[-x, \max(-y, -z)] = -\max[\max(-x, -y), -z] =$
$-\max[-\min(x, y), -z] = \min[\min(x, y), z]$.

c. *Definiteness.* For any numbers x, y: $\min(x, y) = x$ or $\min(x, y) = y$.

Proof.: $\min(x, y)$ equals $-\max(-x, -y)$ which equals either $-(-x)$ or $-(-y)$.

d. *Distributivity of addition with respect to min*
For any numbers x, y, z: $x + \min(y, z) = \min(x + y, x + z)$.

Proof.: $x + \min(y, z) = x + y + z - \max(y, z) =_?$
$(x + y) + (x + z) - \max(x + y, x + z) = \min(x + y, x + z)$.

2609. It is easy to prove a theorem analogous to 2304 and 2404.

2610. Exercises.

    a. (*Surprise.*) Disprove the analogue of 2502e.

    b. For any numbers x, y, z such that $\min(0, x) = 0$:
$x \cdot \min(y, z) = \min(xy, xz)$.

    c. For any numbers x, y: $\min[x, \min(x, y)] = \min(x, y)$.

    d. *Disprove.* For any numbers x, y:
$\min(0, x) \cdot \min(0, y) = \min[0, \min(0, x) \cdot \min(0, y)]$.

    e. For any numbers x, y:
$\min(0, x) \cdot \min(0, y) = \max[0, \min(0, x) \cdot \min(0, y)]$.

    f. *Prove or disprove.* For any numbers a, b:
$\min[\max(a, b), b] = \max[\min(a, b), b]$.

    g. For any numbers x, y: $\min(x, y) \cdot \max(x, y) = xy$.

    h. For any numbers a, b: if $\min(a, b) = \max(a, b)$, then $a = b$.

    i. For each number a: $\min[\max(0, a), \max(0, -a)] = 0$.

2611. Definition. The *square* of a number x (or the second power of x) is the number xx and is denoted by the symbol x^2.

2612. Example. $(-1)^2 = (-1)(-1) = 1$.

2613. The following proposition is easily proved.

    For any numbers x, y:

$$(x + y)^2 = x^2 + 2xy + y^2,$$
$$(x - y)^2 = x^2 - 2xy + y^2,$$
$$(xy)^2 = x^2 y^2,$$
$$(x + y)(x - y) = x^2 - y^2.$$

2614. The next convention is often abused by students.

2615. Notation. An expression such as $(x = \pm y)$ stands for $(x = y$ or $x = -y)$.

NOTE. This convention does not grant us license to use a symbol such as ± 2 by itself; furthermore, it does not state that a symbol such as ± 2 denotes a number. Indeed, the symbol ± 2 is meaningless when standing alone.

2616. Examples.

    a. $1 = \pm 1$ because surely $1 = 1$ or $1 = -1$.

NOTE. The proposition ($1 = 1$ or $1 = -1$) is true because ($1 = 1$) is true.

b. $-1 = \pm 1$ because surely $-1 = 1$ or $-1 = -1$.

c. For each number u: $\max(-u, u) = \pm u$ because $\max(-u, u) = u$ or $\max(-u, u) = -u$.

d. For each number u: $\min(-u, u) = \pm u$.

2617. Exercise. *Prove or disprove.*

For any numbers a, b, c: if $a = \pm c$ and $b = \pm c$, then $a = b$.

2618. Theorem. For any numbers x, y: $x^2 = y^2 \Leftrightarrow x = \pm y$.

Proof.:
$x^2 = y^2 \Leftrightarrow (x + y)(x - y) = 0 \Leftrightarrow$
$(x - y = 0 \text{ or } x + y = 0) \Leftrightarrow x = \pm y$.

2619. Exercise. *Prove or disprove.*

For any numbers a, b, c such that $a = \pm c$ and $b = \pm c$: $a = \pm b$.

The Signum of a Number

2701. The next definition is vital to our subsequent work.

2702. Definition.

The *signum* of 0 is 0;

the *signum* of a nonzero number x is $\dfrac{\max(-x,\, x)}{x}$.

NOTATION. sgn(y), read as *signum of y* or as *signum y*. We also use the symbol sgn[y].

2703. Examples.

a. sgn(0) = 0.

b. sgn(1) = max(-1, 1)/1 = 1/1 = 1.

c. sgn(2) = max(-2, 2)/2 = 2/2 = 1.

d. sgn(1/2) = max($-1/2$, 1/2)/(1/2) = 1.

e. sgn(-1) = max(1, -1)/(-1) = -1.

f. sgn(-2) = max(2, -2)/(-2) = -1.

g. sgn($-1/2$) = max(1/2, $-1/2$)/($-1/2$) = -1.

2704. Pitfalls.

For each number x: sgn($-x$) = -1.
For each number x: sgn(x) = 1.

Counterexample for both propositions. -1 for x.

2705. Exercise. For each number u: sgn($-u$) = $-$sgn(u).

144

2706. Theorem. For each number x: $\text{sgn}(x) = 0 \Leftrightarrow x = 0$.

Proof.

PART I($\Leftarrow$). Use 2702.

PART II($\Rightarrow$).
Suppose not.
Then there is a number x such that $\text{sgn}(x) = 0$ and $x \neq 0$.
So $\max(-x, x)/x = 0$, and hence $\max(-x, x) = 0$, and therefore $x =_? 0$.
Contradiction.

2707. Corollary. For each number x: $\text{sgn}(x) \neq 0 \Leftrightarrow x \neq 0$.

2708. Theorem. For each nonzero number x: $\text{sgn}(x) = 1/\text{sgn}(x)$.

Proof.: either $\max(-x, x) = -x$ or $\max(-x, x) = x$;
in the first case, $\text{sgn}(x) = -x/x = -1 = 1/(-1) =_? 1/\text{sgn}(x)$;
in the second case, $\text{sgn}(x) = x/x = 1 = 1/1 = 1/\text{sgn}(x)$.

2709. Corollary. For each nonzero number x: $\text{sgn}(x) = \pm 1$.   (2708, 2515b)

2710. Theorem. For each number x: precisely one of the following holds:
$$\text{sgn}(x) = -1, \quad \text{sgn}(x) = 0, \quad \text{sgn}(x) = 1.$$
Proof. Consider any number x.

AT MOST ONE. Obvious.

AT LEAST ONE. Either $x = 0$ or $x \neq 0$.
In case $x = 0$, then $\text{sgn}(x) = 0$.
In case $x \neq 0$, then by 2709, $\text{sgn}(x) = -1$ or $\text{sgn}(x) = 1$.

2711. Theorems.

a. For each number x: $\text{sgn}(x) = 1 \Leftrightarrow [x \neq 0 \text{ and } \max(x, 0) = x]$.
Proof.: $\text{sgn}(x) = 1 \Leftrightarrow [x \neq 0 \text{ and } \max(-x, x)/x = 1] \Leftrightarrow$
$[x \neq 0 \text{ and } \max(-x, x) = x] \Leftrightarrow_1 [x \neq 0 \text{ and } \max(x, 0) = x]$.
(1.2516)

b. For each number x: $\text{sgn}(x) = -1 \Leftrightarrow [x \neq 0 \text{ and } \max(x, 0) = 0]$.
Proof.:
$\text{sgn}(x) = -1 \Leftrightarrow_1 \text{sgn}(-x) = 1 \Leftrightarrow_2$
$[-x \neq 0 \text{ and } \max(-x, 0) = -x] \Leftrightarrow_3$
$[x \neq 0 \text{ and } \max(x, 0) = 0]$.
References. 1.2705; 2.2711a; 3.2517.

2712. Exercise. For each number x: $\text{sgn}[\text{sgn}(x)] = \text{sgn}(x)$.

2713. Theorem. For any numbers x, y: $\operatorname{sgn}(x) \cdot \operatorname{sgn}(y) = \operatorname{sgn}(xy)$.

Proof. Consider any numbers x, y.
Either $xy = 0$ or $xy \neq 0$.

In event $xy = 0$, the desired equation is obvious. (?)
In event $xy \neq 0$, then either $\operatorname{sgn}(x) = 1$ or $\operatorname{sgn}(x) = -1$.

CASE I. $\operatorname{sgn}(x) = 1$.
Then $x \neq 0$ and $\max(x, 0) = x$, and so

$$\operatorname{sgn}(x) \cdot \operatorname{sgn}(y) = \operatorname{sgn}(y) = \frac{x}{x} \cdot \frac{\max(-y, y)}{y} = \frac{\max(-xy, xy)}{xy} = \operatorname{sgn}(xy).$$

CASE II. $\operatorname{sgn}(x) = -1$.
Then $\operatorname{sgn}(-x) = 1$, and so
$$\operatorname{sgn}(x) \cdot \operatorname{sgn}(y) = -\operatorname{sgn}(-x) \cdot \operatorname{sgn}(y) =_? -\operatorname{sgn}(-xy) = \operatorname{sgn}(xy).$$

2714. Exercises.

a. For any number u and nonzero number v: $\operatorname{sgn}(u/v) = \operatorname{sgn}(u)/\operatorname{sgn}(v)$.

b. For any number u and nonzero number v: $\operatorname{sgn}(uv) = \operatorname{sgn}(u/v)$.

2715. Definition. A number x *has the same sign as* a number y provided that $x \neq 0$ and $\operatorname{sgn}(x) = \operatorname{sgn}(y)$.

NOTATION. $x \, \S \, y$, read as x *has the same sign as* y or as x, y *have like sign*.

NOTE. This definition introduces the relationship *has the same sign as*; it does not grant us license to speak of the sign of a number.

2716. Examples.

a. $1/2 \, \S \, 2$ because $1/2 \neq 0$ and $\operatorname{sgn}(1/2) = \operatorname{sgn}(2)$.

b. $-2 \, \S \, -1$ because $-2 \neq 0$ and $\operatorname{sgn}(-2) = \operatorname{sgn}(-1)$.

c. $1, 0$ do not have like sign because $\operatorname{sgn}(1) \neq \operatorname{sgn}(0)$.

d. $0, 0$ do not have like sign. (?)

e. No number has the same sign as 0.

Proof. Suppose there is a number x such that $x \, \S \, 0$.
Then $x \neq 0$ and $\operatorname{sgn}(x) = \operatorname{sgn}(0) = 0$. Contradiction. (2706)

2717. Exercises.

a. For any numbers x, y such that $x \, \S \, y$: $y \neq 0$.

b. *Reflexivity.* For each nonzero number u: $u \, \S \, u$.

c. *Symmetry.* For any numbers u, v such that $u \, \S \, v$: $v \, \S \, u$.

d. *Transitivity.* For any numbers u, v, w such that $u \, \S \, v$ and $v \, \S \, w$: $u \, \S \, w$.

e. For any nonzero numbers x, y: $xy \, \S \, x/y$.

f. For each nonzero number x: $x \, \S \, \operatorname{sgn}(x)$.

2718. Definition. A number x *has the opposite sign of* a number y
(or x, y have unlike sign) provided that $x \neq 0$ and $\operatorname{sgn}(x) = -\operatorname{sgn}(y)$.

NOTE. This does not authorize us to speak of the sign of a number.

2719. Examples.

a. -1, 2 have unlike sign because $-1 \neq 0$ and $\operatorname{sgn}(-1) = -\operatorname{sgn}(2)$.

b. 1, 0 do not have unlike sign.   (?)

2720. Pitfall. For any numbers x, y: either x, y have like sign or
x, y have unlike sign.

Counterexample. 1 for x, 0 for y.

2721. Theorem. For any nonzero numbers x, y:
either x, y have like sign or x, y have unlike sign.

Proof. 2709, 2715, 2718.

2722. Exercises.

a. No number has the opposite sign of 0.

b. For any numbers x, y such that x, y have unlike sign: y, x have unlike
sign.

c. For any numbers x, y, z such that x, y have unlike sign and y, z have
unlike sign: x § z.

2723. Diversion. Consider the following "definition."

For each number x:

(i) the *nib* of x is 0 iff $x = 0$;

(ii) the *nib* of x is $x^2 - x$ iff $x \neq 0$.

This definition is self-contradictory because we can use it to prove that
$0 = 1$.

Proof. By (ii), since $1 \neq 0$, the *nib* of 1 is $1^2 - 1$ which equals 0.
It then follows by (i) that $1 = 0$.   (?)

QUERY. Does the student see what is wrong with this definition?

Positive, Negative

2801. In this lesson we shall distinguish two kinds of nonzero numbers.

2802. Definition.
A *positive number* is any number whose signum is 1;
a *negative number* is any number whose signum is -1.

2803. Examples.

a. 2 is positive because $\text{sgn}(2) = 1$.

b. $1/2$ is positive because $\text{sgn}(1/2) = 1$.

c. -2 is negative because $\text{sgn}(-2) = -1$.

d. -1 is negative.

e. 0 is neither positive nor negative.   (?)

2804. Immediate consequences.

a. *Trichotomy.* For each number x: precisely one of the following holds:
x is negative, $x = 0$, x is positive.   (2710, 2706, 2802)

b. For each number x:
x is positive $\Leftrightarrow$ $[x \neq 0$ and $\max(x, 0) = x]$.   (2802, 2711a)

c. For each number x:
x is negative $\Leftrightarrow$ $[x \neq 0$ and $\max(x, 0) = 0]$.   (2802, 2711b)

2805. Pitfalls.

For each number x: $0 + x$ is positive.

For each number x: $-x$ is negative.

Counterexample for both propositions. -2 for x.

148

2806. 2 is the negative of −2, but 2 is not negative. Thus, the negative of a number is not necessarily negative. One must carefully distinguish between the concepts *negative of a number* and *negative number*. It is truly unfortunate that the word *negative* is used for two different purposes.

2807. Exercises.

a. For each positive number u: −u is negative.
NOTE. This proposition may be stated as follows.
The negative of each positive number is negative.

b. For each negative number v: −v is positive.
NOTE. This proposition may be stated as follows.
The negative of each negative number is positive.

2808. Theorems.

a. Two numbers have like sign iff they are both negative or both positive.

Proof. For any numbers x, y:
x, y have like sign $\Leftrightarrow$
$x \neq 0$ and $\text{sgn}(x) = \text{sgn}(y)$ $\Leftrightarrow$
$[\text{sgn}(x) = \text{sgn}(y) = -1]$ or $[\text{sgn}(x) = \text{sgn}(y) = 1]$ $\Leftrightarrow$
both x, y are negative or both x, y are positive.

b. Two numbers have unlike sign iff one is negative and the other is positive.

Proof. For any numbers x, y:
x, y have unlike sign $\Leftrightarrow$
$[x \neq 0$ and $\text{sgn}(x) = -\text{sgn}(y)]$ $\Leftrightarrow$
$[\text{sgn}(x) = 1$ and $\text{sgn}(y) = -1]$ or $[\text{sgn}(x) = -1$ and $\text{sgn}(y) = 1]$.

2809. Theorems.

a. The sum of any two positive numbers is positive; i.e.,
for any positive numbers x, y: $x + y$ is positive.

Proof. Consider any positive numbers x, y.
By 2804b, it suffices to prove that
$x + y \neq 0$ and $\max(x + y, 0) = x + y$.
$x + y \neq 0$ because otherwise −$x = y$ and so −x would be positive. (?)
Lastly, $x + y = x + \max(y, 0) = x + \max[y, \max(0, -x)] =$
$x + \max[\max(y, 0), -x] = x + \max(y, -x) = \max(x + y, 0)$.

b. The product of any two positive numbers is positive.

Proof. For any positive numbers x, y:
$\text{sgn}(xy) = \text{sgn}(x) \cdot \text{sgn}(y) = 1 \cdot 1 = 1$.

c. The quotient of any two positive numbers is positive.

Proof. For any positive numbers x, y: $\text{sgn}(x/y) = \text{sgn}(xy) = 1$.

2810. Exercises.

a. The product of two numbers is positive iff they have like sign.

b. The quotient of two numbers is positive iff they have like sign.

c. The sum of any two negative numbers is negative.

d. The product of two numbers is negative iff they have unlike sign.

e. The reciprocal of each negative number is negative.

f. The square of each nonzero number is positive.

2811. Theorem. There is no number x such that $x^2 = -1$.

Proof. Suppose there is a number x such that $x^2 = -1$.
Then $x \neq_? 0$, and so x^2 is positive (2810f).
Contradiction. (?)

NOTE. Recall that in this book *number* means *real number*.

2812. *Nonnegative* means *not negative*; *nonpositive* means *not positive*.

NOTE. By trichotomy (2804a), for each number x:
x is nonnegative $\Leftrightarrow$ ($x = 0$ or x is positive),
x is nonpositive $\Leftrightarrow$ ($x = 0$ or x is negative).

2813. Examples.

a. 2 is nonnegative.

b. -1 is nonpositive.

c. 0 is nonnegative.

d. 0 is nonpositive.

2814. Exercises.

a. There is precisely one number that is both nonnegative and nonpositive.

b. For each number x: x is nonnegative $\Leftrightarrow$ $\min(x, 0) = 0$.

c. For each number x: x is nonpositive $\Leftrightarrow$ $\max(-x, x) = -x$.

d. For each number u: u is nonpositive $\Leftrightarrow$ $-u$ is nonnegative.

Less than, Greater than

2901. One way to define the relationship *less than* is as follows.
A number x is less than a number y provided that $y - x$ is positive.

The author believes that the following definition is easier to remember.

2902. Definition.
A number x *is less than* a number y provided that $x - y$ is negative.

NOTATION. We use the symbol $<$ to stand for *is less than*; however, occasionally it is convenient to render the symbol $<$ as *less than*.

2903. Examples.

a. $-2 < -1$ because $-2 - (-1)$ is negative.   (?)

b. $-2 < 0$ because $-2 - 0$ is negative.

c. $-1 < 0$ because $-1 - 0$ is negative.

d. $-1 < 1$ because $-1 - 1$ is negative.

e. $0 < 1$ because $0 - 1$ is negative.

f. $1 < 2$ because $1 - 2$ is negative.

g. $1/2 < 1$ because $(1/2) - 1$ is negative.

h. 1 is not less than 1 because $1 - 1$ is not negative.

NOTE. In general, no number is less than itself.

2904. Exercise.

For any numbers x, y: $x < y \Leftrightarrow y - x$ is positive.

NOTE. The student may not use the definition rejected in 2901.

2905. Immediate consequences.

a. For each number x: $x < 0 \Leftrightarrow x$ is negative. (2902)

b. For each number t: $0 < t \Leftrightarrow t$ is positive. (2904)

2906. Theorem. *Trichotomy.*

For any numbers x, y: precisely one of the following holds:
$x < y$, $x = y$, $y < x$.

Proof. Consider any numbers x, y.
By 2804a, precisely one of the following holds:
$x - y$ is negative, $x - y = 0$, $x - y$ is positive.

Furthermore,

$x - y$ is negative $\Leftrightarrow x < y$, (2902)

$x - y = 0 \Leftrightarrow x = y$,

$x - y$ is positive $\Leftrightarrow y < x$, (2904).

2907. Theorem. *Strict transitivity.*

For any numbers x, y, z such that $x < y$ and $y < z$: $x < z$.

Proof.: $(x - y) + (y - z)$ is negative (?) and so $x - z$ is negative.

2908. Convention. Each expression in the left column stands for the adjacent expression in the right column.

$u = v < w$	$u = v$ and $v < w$
$u < v = w$	$u < v$ and $v = w$
$u < v < w$	$u < v$ and $v < w$
$u < v < w < x$	$u < v$ and $v < w$ and $w < x$
$u < v < w < x < y$	$u < v$ and $v < w$ and $w < x$ and $x < y$
And so on	

NOTE. An expression such as $u < v = w < x < y = z$ stands for the expression ($u < v$ and $v = w$ and $w < x$ and $x < y$ and $y = z$).

2909. Examples.

a. $-2 < -1 < 1$.   (2903a,d)

b. $-1 < 0 < 1 < 2$.   (2903c,e,f)

c. Theorem 2907 may now be stated as follows.
For any numbers x, y, z such that $x < y < z$: $x < z$.

2910. Convention. Each expression in the left column stands for the adjacent expression in the right column.

For any numbers $u < v$	For any numbers u, v such that $u < v$
There are numbers $u < v$	There are numbers u, v such that $u < v$
For any numbers $u < v < x$	For any numbers u, v, x such that $u < v < x$
There are numbers $u < v < x$	There are numbers u, v, x such that $u < v < x$
And so on	

2911. Example. Theorem 2907 may now be stated as follows.
For any numbers $x < y < z$: $x < z$.

2912. Exercise.
For any numbers $u < v < w < x$: $u < x$.

2913. Theorem. *Strict monotonicity of addition.*
For any numbers a, x, y: $x < y \Rightarrow x + a < y + a$.

Proof.: if $x < y$, then $x - y$ is negative and so $(x + a) - (y + a)$ is negative.

2914. Corollaries.

a. For any numbers c, u, v: $u < v \Rightarrow u - c < v - c$.
Proof. Use 2913 with $-c$ for a, u for x, v for y.

NOTE. The converse of 2913 is now obvious.

b. For any numbers r, s: the following are equivalent:

$r < s$,
$r - s < 0$,
$-s < -r$,
$0 < s - r$,
$r \neq s$ and $\min(r, s) = r$,
$r \neq s$ and $\max(r, s) = s$.

Proof (round-robin).:
$r < s \Rightarrow_1$
$r - s < 0 \Rightarrow_1$
$-s < -r \Rightarrow_2$
$0 < s - r \Rightarrow_3$
$s - r$ is positive $\Rightarrow_?$
$r \neq s$ and $\min(s - r, 0) = 0 \Rightarrow_?$
$r \neq s$ and $\min(r, s) = r \Rightarrow$
$r \neq s$ and $\max(r, s) = s \Rightarrow_?$
$r \neq s$ and $\max(r - s, 0) = 0 \Rightarrow$
$r - s$ is negative $\Rightarrow$
$r < s$.

References. 1.2914a; 2.2913; 3.2905b.

c. For any numbers $u < v$ and numbers $x < y$: $u + x < v + y$.

Proof.: $u + x < v + x < v + y$.

2915. Pitfalls.

For any numbers $a < b$ and numbers $x < y$: $a - x < b - y$.
For any numbers $a < b$ and numbers $x < y$: $b - y < a - x$.

Counterexample for both. 0 for a, 1 for b, 1 for x, 2 for y.

2916. Theorem. *Strict monotonicity of multiplication.*
For any numbers b, x, y such that $0 < b$: $x < y \Rightarrow bx < by$.

Proof.: if $x < y$, then b and $(x - y)$ have unlike sign, and so their product, $bx - by$, is negative.

NOTE. The hypothesis $0 < b$ is essential.

2917. Corollaries.

a. For any numbers t, u, v such that $0 < t$: $u < v \Rightarrow u/t < v/t$.

Proof.: $0 <_? 1/t$, and so $u/t = (1/t)u < (1/t)v = v/t$.

NOTE. The converse of 2916 is now obvious.

b. For any numbers a, b, x, y such that $0 < by$: $\dfrac{a}{b} < \dfrac{x}{y} \Leftrightarrow ay < bx$.

Proof.: $\dfrac{a}{b} < \dfrac{x}{y} \Leftrightarrow (by)\dfrac{a}{b} < (by)\dfrac{x}{y} \Leftrightarrow ay < bx$.

2918. Exercises.

a. For any numbers r, x, y such that $r < 0$: $x < y \Rightarrow ry < rx$.

b. For any numbers t, x, y such that $t < 0$: $x < y \Rightarrow y/t < x/t$.
NOTE. The converse of 2918a is now obvious.

c. For any numbers u, w that have like sign and any positive number c: $u < w \Leftrightarrow c/w < c/u$.

d. For each number x such that $0 < x < 1$: $x^2 < x < 1/x$.

e. For each number x such that $1 < x$: $1/x < x < x^2$.

2919. Pitfalls.

a. For any numbers x, y: $x < y \Rightarrow 1/x < 1/y$.
Counterexample. 1 for x, 2 for y.

b. For any numbers x, y: $x < y \Rightarrow 1/y < 1/x$.
Counterexample. -1 for x, 1 for y.

2920. Later we shall obtain a result about "multiplication" of inequalities.

2921. Theorem. For any nonnegative numbers a, x: $a < x \Leftrightarrow a^2 < x^2$.
Proof.: either $a = 0$ or $0 < a$;
in case $a = 0$, the desired result follows readily;   (?)
in case $0 < a$, then
$a < x \Leftrightarrow_? 0 < (x + a)(x - a) \Leftrightarrow a^2 < x^2$.

2922. Corollary. For any nonpositive numbers b, y: $b < y \Leftrightarrow y^2 < b^2$.
Proof.: $b < y \Leftrightarrow -y < -b \Leftrightarrow_? (-y)^2 < (-b)^2 \Leftrightarrow y^2 < b^2$.

2923. Pitfall. For any numbers $x < y$: $x^2 < y^2$.
Counterexample. -1 for x, 0 for y.

2924. Definition. A number x is *strictly between* numbers b, c provided that either $b < x < c$ or $c < x < b$.

2925. Examples.

a. 1 is strictly between $-1, 2$.

b. 1 is strictly between $2, -1$.

c. $1/2$ is strictly between $0, 1$.

2926. Theorem. For any numbers $x < z$:
there is a number y such that $x < y < z$.

Proof.: the number $(x + z)/2$ is strictly between x, z because
$x = (x + x)/2 <_? (x + z)/2 < (z + z)/2 = z$.

NOTE. This theorem may be stated as follows.
Strictly between any two distinct numbers there is a number.

2927. Exercises.

a. For any numbers x, c, d:
x is strictly between c, d $\iff$ $0 < (c - x)(x - d)$.

b. For any numbers x, c, d such that x is strictly between c, d:
$0 < (x - c)/(d - c)$.

c. For any number x and distinct numbers a, b:
x is strictly between a, b $\iff$
there are positive numbers u, v such that $u + v = 1$ and $x = au + bv$.

d. For any numbers z, c: $z^2 < c^2$ $\iff$ z is strictly between $-c$, c.
NOTE. No square roots allowed yet.

2928. Definition. A number y *is greater than* a number x provided that
x is less than y.

NOTATION. We use the symbol $>$ to stand for *is greater than*; however,
occasionally it is convenient to render the symbol $>$ as *greater than*.

2929. Immediate consequence.
For any numbers y, x: $y > x$ $\iff$ $y - x$ is positive.

2930. Conventions analogous to 2908 and 2910 will be used; however, the
student is advised to avoid mixed expressions such as $a < b > c$.

2931. Some statements are more perspicuous when both of the symbols $<$ and $>$
are used; e.g., 2918a may be expressed as follows.
For any numbers r, x, y such that $r < 0$: $x < y$ $\Rightarrow$ $rx > ry$.

2932. Notation.

The symbol	rendered	denotes
3	*three*	$1 + 2$
4	*four*	$1 + 3$
5	*five*	$1 + 4$
6	*six*	$1 + 5$
7	*seven*	$1 + 6$
8	*eight*	$1 + 7$
9	*nine*	$1 + 8$
10	*ten*	$1 + 9$

2933. Examples.

   a. $2 + 3 = 1 + 1 + 3 = 1 + 4 = 5.$

   b. $2 \cdot 2 = (1 + 1)(1 + 1) = 1 \cdot 1 + 1 \cdot 1 + 1 \cdot 1 + 1 \cdot 1 = 1 + 1 + 2 = 1 + 3 = 4.$

   c. $3 \cdot 2 = (1 + 2)2 = 2 + 4 = 1 + 1 + 4 = 1 + 5 = 6.$

2934. Exercises.

   a. $9 + 4 = 7 + 6.$

   b. $3 \cdot 3 = 9.$

2935. Theorem. $-10 < -9 < -8 < -7 < -6 < -5 < -4 < -3 < -2 < -1 < 0 < 1 < 2 < 3 < 4 < 5 < 6 < 7 < 8 < 9 < 10.$

   Proof. $-10 = -(9 + 1) = (-9) + (-1) < (-9) + 0 = -9,$ and then from $-10 < -9$ all the other results follow by repeated use of 2913 with 1 for a.

2936. Exercise.

   For any numbers a, b, c, x such that $b^2 - 4ac < 0$:
$$\mathrm{sgn}(ax^2 + bx + c) = \mathrm{sgn}(a).$$

Precedes (≦), *Exceeds* (≧)

3001. Readers will kindly defer judgment on the wisdom of the author's decision to use the word *precedes* instead of the clumsy but traditional expression *is less than or equal to*. The word *precedes* has many useful grammatical variations.

3002. Definition. A number x *precedes* a number y provided that either $x < y$ or $x = y$.

NOTATION. The symbol ≦ stands for *precedes*; however, occasionally it is convenient to render the symbol ≦ as *preceding*.

NOTE. There is no harm in rendering the symbol ≦ by the awkward expression *is less than or equal to*.

CAUTION. Many writers use the word *precedes* to mean *is less than*.

3003. Examples.

a. $1 \leqq 1$ because $1 = 1$ and so surely $(1 < 1$ or $1 = 1)$.

NOTE. In general, each number precedes itself.

b. $1 \leqq 2$ because $1 < 2$ and so surely $(1 < 2$ or $1 = 2)$.

NOTE. In general, for any numbers x, y: $x < y \Rightarrow x \leqq y$. The converse of this proposition is false of course.

3004. An expression such as $a \leqq b \leqq c$ stands for $(a \leqq b$ and $b \leqq c)$; in general we shall use abbreviations like those in 2908 and 2910.

An expression such as $a \leqq b < c$ stands for $(a \leqq b$ and $b < c)$; etc.

3005. Theorem. For each number x: $0 \leqq x^2$.

Proof.: either $x = 0$ or $x \neq 0$;
in case $x = 0$, then $0 = x^2$ and so $0 \leqq x^2$;
in case $x \neq 0$, then by 2810f, $0 < x^2$ and so $0 \leqq x^2$.

3006. The following theorems are stated without proof; the proofs, mostly of the case type (1227 and 1230), are straightforward but tedious. The student should scrutinize these theorems and satisfy himself that he could prove them if requested.

3007. Theorems.

a. For each number x: $x \leqq 0 \Leftrightarrow x$ is nonpositive.

b. For each number x: $0 \leqq x \Leftrightarrow x$ is nonnegative.

c. For any numbers x, y: $x < y \Leftrightarrow (x \leqq y$ and $x \neq y)$.

d. For any numbers x, y: $x \leqq y$ or $y \leqq x$.

e. For any numbers x, y: $x < y$ or $y \leqq x$, but not both.

f. For any numbers x, y, z:
$x \leqq y \leqq z \Rightarrow x \leqq z,$
$x \leqq y < z \Rightarrow x < z,$
$x < y \leqq z \Rightarrow x < z.$

g. For any numbers a, x, y:
$x \leqq y \Rightarrow x + a \leqq y + a,$
$x \leqq y \Rightarrow x - a \leqq y - a.$

h. For any numbers r, s: the following are equivalent:
$r \leqq s, \quad r - s \leqq 0, \quad -s \leqq -r, \quad 0 \leqq s - r,$
$\min(r, s) = r, \quad \max(r, s) = s.$

NOTE. It is now clear that for any numbers x, y:
$\min(x, y)$ is either x or y, whichever precedes the other.

i. For any numbers u, v, x, y:
$(u \leqq v$ and $x \leqq y) \Rightarrow u + x \leqq v + y,$
$(u < v$ and $x \leqq y) \Rightarrow u + x < v + y.$

j. For any numbers b, x, y:
$(0 < b$ and $x \leqq y) \Rightarrow bx \leqq by,$
$(0 \leqq b$ and $x \leqq y) \Rightarrow bx \leqq by,$
$(0 \leqq b$ and $x < y) \Rightarrow bx \leqq by.$

k. For any numbers r, x, y:
$(r < 0$ and $x \leqq y) \Rightarrow ry \leqq rx,$
$(r \leqq 0$ and $x \leqq y) \Rightarrow ry \leqq rx,$
$(r \leqq 0$ and $x < y) \Rightarrow ry \leqq rx.$

l. For any numbers t, u, v:
$(0 < t \text{ and } u \leqq v) \Rightarrow u/t \leqq v/t$,
$(t < 0 \text{ and } u \leqq v) \Rightarrow v/t \leqq u/t$.

m. For any numbers a, b, x, y such that $0 < by$:
$a/b \leqq x/y \Leftrightarrow ay \leqq bx$.

n. For any numbers u, w that have like sign:
$u \leqq w \Leftrightarrow 1/w \leqq 1/u$.

o. For any numbers u, w that have like sign and any nonnegative number c:
$u \leqq w \Leftrightarrow c/w \leqq c/u$.

3008. Exercise.

For any numbers u, v such that $u \leqq v \leqq u$: $u = v$.

3009. Theorem. For any numbers a, b, x, y such that $0 \leqq a < x$ and $0 \leqq b < y$: $0 \leqq ab < xy$.

Proof.: $0 \leqq ab \leqq xb < xy$. (?)

NOTE. Surely the student can prove the proposition obtained by replacing $<$ by $\leqq$.

3010. Pitfalls.

For any numbers a, b, x, y such that $a < b$ and $x < y$: $ax < by$.
For any numbers a, b, x, y such that $a < b$ and $x < y$: $by < ax$.
Counterexample for both. -1 for a, 1 for b, -1 for x, 1 for y.

3011. Theorem. For any nonnegative numbers a, x: $a \leqq x \Leftrightarrow a^2 \leqq x^2$.

Proof.: $a \leqq x \Rightarrow [a < x \text{ or } a = x] \Rightarrow_1$
$[a^2 < x^2 \text{ or } a^2 = x^2] \Rightarrow a^2 \leqq x^2$;
conversely, if $a^2 \leqq x^2$, then it is impossible$_1$ that $x < a$, and so $a \leqq x$.

Reference. 1.2921.

3012. Corollary. For any nonpositive numbers b, y: $b \leqq y \Leftrightarrow y^2 \leqq b^2$.
Proof.: $b \leqq y \Leftrightarrow -y \leqq -b \Leftrightarrow_? (-y)^2 \leqq (-b)^2$.

3013. Exercises.

a. For each positive number x: $2 \leqq x + 1/x$.

b. For any numbers x, y: $2xy \leqq x^2 + y^2$.

c. For any numbers a, b, c, g such that $a^2 + b^2 = 1 = c^2 + g^2$:
$ac + bg \leqq 1$.

d. For any numbers A, B, C, G such that $A^2 + B^2 = 1 = C^2 + G^2$:
$-1 \leqq AC + BG$.

e. For any numbers x, y such that $x^2 + y^2 = 0$: $x = 0 = y$.

f. For any numbers a, b, c, g such that
$a^2 + b^2 = c^2 + g^2 = ac + bg = 1$: $a = c$ and $b = g$.

NOTE. Propositions 3013c,d,e,f are useful in vector algebra.

3014. Imagine that we wish to prove that a certain number, say u, precedes a certain number, say v. Assume that we could prove that each number less than u precedes every number greater than v. Would this entitle us to conclude that u precedes v?

3015. Theorem. For any numbers u, v:
if each number less than u precedes every number greater than v,
then $u \leqq v$.

Proof. Suppose not. Then there are numbers u, v such that each number less than u precedes every number greater than v, and $v < u$.

By 2926, there is a number c such that $v < c < u$,
and then by 2926, there is a number b such that $v < b < c < u$.
Since c is less than u and since b is greater than v, we have $c \leqq_? b$.
Contradiction.

3016. Corollaries.

a. If a number precedes every positive number, then it is nonpositive.

Proof. Consider any number u that precedes every positive number. Each number less than u precedes every number greater than 0. (?) By 3015 with 0 for v, we have $u \leqq 0$.

b. If a number is less than every positive number, then it is nonpositive.

Proof. The hypothesis here is stronger than that of 3016a.

3017. Exercises.

a. For any numbers u, v such that u precedes every number greater than v: $u \leqq v$.

b. For any numbers u, v such that each number less than u precedes v: $u \leqq v$.

3018. Imagine that we wish to prove that a certain number u precedes a certain number v. Assume that we could find a number b which has the following properties: $b < u$, and every number strictly between b, u precedes v. Would this entitle us to conclude that u precedes v?

3019. Exercises.

   a. Prove that the correct answer to 3018 is *yes*.

   b. *Prove or disprove.* For any numbers u, v:
if for each positive number p: $u < v + p$,
then $u < v$.

   c. *Prove or disprove.* For any numbers u, v:
if for each positive number p: $u \leqq v + p$,
then $u \leqq v$.

3020. Definition. The *cube* of a number x (or the third power of x)
is the number xx^2 and is denoted by the symbol x^3.

3021. Example. $2^3 = 2 \cdot 2^2 = 2 \cdot 4 = 2(3 + 1) = 6 + 2 =$
$6 + 1 + 1 = 7 + 1 = 8$.

3022. The following proposition is easy to prove.

For any numbers x, y:
$$(xy)^3 = x^3 y^3,$$
$$(x + y)^3 = x^3 + 3x^2 y + 3xy^2 + y^3,$$
$$(x - y)^3 = x^3 - 3x^2 y + 3xy^2 - y^3,$$
$$x^3 - y^3 = (x - y)(x^2 + xy + y^2),$$
$$x^3 + y^3 = (x + y)(x^2 - xy + y^2).$$

3023. Exercise.

For any numbers x, y: $0 \leqq x^2 + xy + y^2$,
and if $x \neq y$, then $0 < x^2 + xy + y^2$.

3024. Theorem. For any numbers x, y: $x < y \Leftrightarrow x^3 < y^3$.

Proof.: $x < y \Leftrightarrow x - y < 0 \Leftrightarrow_?$
$(x - y)(x^2 + xy + y^2) < 0 \Leftrightarrow x^3 - y^3 < 0$.

NOTE. Some students have concocted two-page proofs of this.

3025. Corollary. For any numbers x, y: $x = y \Leftrightarrow x^3 = y^3$.   (2906, 3024)

3026. Theorem. For any numbers x, y: $\min(x, y) \leqq x \leqq \max(x, y)$.

Proof.: either $x \leqq y$ or $y \leqq x$;
in case $x \leqq y$, then $\min(x, y) = x \leqq y = \max(x, y)$;
the second case is similar.

QUERY. How about $\min(x, y) \leqq y \leqq \max(x, y)$?

3027. Theorems.

a. For any numbers v, x, b: $\max(v, x) < b \Leftrightarrow (v < b$ and $x < b)$.

Proof.: if $\max(v, x) < b$, then $v \leqq \max(v, x) < b$ and $x \leqq \max(v, x) < b$; the other part is obvious because $\max(v, x) = v$ or $\max(v, x) = x$.

b. For any numbers v, x, b: $b < \max(v, x) \Leftrightarrow (b < v$ or $b < x)$.

Proof.: if $b < v$ or $b < x$, then $b < v \leqq \max(v, x)$ or $b < x \leqq \max(v, x)$, and so $b < \max(v, x)$;
the other part is obvious.   (?)

c. For any numbers v, x, b: $\min(v, x) < b \Leftrightarrow (v < b$ or $x < b)$.

Proof.: $\min(v, x) < b \Leftrightarrow -\max(-v, -x) < b \Leftrightarrow$
$-b < \max(-v, -x) \Leftrightarrow (-b < -v$ or $-b < -x)$.

d. For any numbers v, x, b: $b < \min(v, x) \Leftrightarrow (b < v$ and $b < x)$.

Proof.: $b < \min(v, x) \Leftrightarrow_? \max(-v, -x) < -b \Leftrightarrow$
$(-v < -b$ and $-x < -b)$.

e. For any numbers $v < g$ and numbers $x < h$: $\max(v, x) < \max(g, h)$.

Proof.: $v < g \leqq \max(g, h)$, and $x < h \leqq \max(g, h)$, and so by 3027a with $\max(g, h)$ for b, we have $\max(v, x) < \max(g, h)$.

f. For any numbers $v < g$ and numbers $x < h$: $\min(v, x) < \min(g, h)$.

Proof. Similar to the previous proof.

3028. Corollaries.

a. For any numbers v, x, b: $\max(v, x) \leqq b \Leftrightarrow (v \leqq b$ and $x \leqq b)$.

b. For any numbers v, x, b: $b \leqq \max(v, x) \Leftrightarrow (b \leqq v$ or $b \leqq x)$.

c. For any numbers v, x, b: $\min(v, x) \leqq b \Leftrightarrow (v \leqq b$ or $x \leqq b)$.

d. For any numbers v, x, b: $b \leqq \min(v, x) \Leftrightarrow (b \leqq v$ and $b \leqq x)$.

e. For any numbers $v \leqq g$ and numbers $x \leqq h$: $\max(v, x) \leqq \max(g, h)$.

f. For any numbers $v \leqq g$ and numbers $x \leqq h$: $\min(v, x) \leqq \min(g, h)$.

Proofs. Similar to those in 3027.

3029. Theorem.

For any numbers g, h, s, t: $\max(g + h, s + t) \leqq \max(g, s) + \max(h, t)$.

Proof.: $g + h \leqq \max(g, s) + \max(h, t)$, and
$s + t \leqq \max(g, s) + \max(h, t)$, and so by 3028a
[with $g + h$ for v, $s + t$ for x, $\max(g, s) + \max(h, t)$ for b],
we have $\max(g + h, s + t) \leqq \max(g, s) + \max(h, t)$.

3030. Exercises.

    a. *Prove or disprove.*
For any numbers v, g, x such that $v < g$: $\max(v, x) < \max(g, x)$.

    b. For any numbers v, g, x such that $v \leqq g$: $\max(v, x) \leqq \max(g, x)$.

    c. For any numbers a, b such that $\min(a, b) \neq \max(a, b)$: $a \neq b$.

    d. *Prove or disprove.* For any numbers a, b, u, v:
$\min[\max(a, b), \max(u, v)] \leqq \max[\min(a, b), \min(u, v)]$.

    e. *Prove or disprove.* For any numbers a, b, u, v:
$\max[\min(a, b), \min(u, v)] \leqq \min[\max(a, b), \max(u, v)]$.

    f. For any numbers a, b, u, v: $\min(a, u) + \min(b, v) \leqq \min(a + b, u + v)$.

    g. For any nonnegative numbers g, h, s, t:
$\max(gh, st) \leqq \max(g, s) \cdot \max(h, t)$.

    h. For any nonnegative numbers g, h, s, t:
$\min(g, s) \cdot \min(h, t) \leqq \min(gh, st)$.

3031. Definition. A number x is *between* numbers u, v provided that either $u \leqq x \leqq v$ or $v \leqq x \leqq u$.

CAUTION. Many writers use *between* to mean *strictly between*.

3032. Exercise.

For any numbers x, c, d: x is between $c, d \iff 0 \leqq (c - x)(x - d)$.
HINT. Exploit 2927a.

3033. Definition. A number u *exceeds* a number v provided that v precedes u.

NOTATION. The symbol $\geqq$ stands for *exceeds*.

NOTE. There is no harm in rendering the symbol $\geqq$ by the awkward but traditional expression *is greater than or equal to*.

CAUTION. Many writers use the word *exceeds* to mean *is greater than*.

3034. Immediate consequence. For any numbers x, y: $x \geqq y \iff y \leqq x$.

Absolute Value

3101. Definition. The *absolute value* of a number x is the number $x \cdot \text{sgn}(x)$.

NOTATION. $|x|$, read as *absolute value of x* or as *absolute x*.

3102. Examples.

$|2| = 2 \cdot \text{sgn}(2) = 2.$

$|0| = 0 \cdot \text{sgn}(0) = 0.$

$|-3| = (-3)\text{sgn}(-3) = 3.$

$|1/2| = (1/2)\text{sgn}(1/2) = 1/2.$

3103. Pitfalls.

For each number x: $|x| = x$. *Counterexample.* -3 for x.

For each number x: $|x| = -x$. *Counterexample.* 2 for x.

For each number x: $|-x| = x$. *Counterexample.* -3 for x.

For each number x: $|-x| = -x$. *Counterexample.* 2 for x.

3104. Immediate consequences.

a. For each number x: $|x| = \max(-x, x)$.   (3101, 2702)

b. For each number u: $|-u| = |u|$.   (3104a)

c. For any numbers x, y: $|x - y| = |y - x|$.   (3104b with $y - x$ for u)

d. For each number x: $|x| = -\min(-x, x)$.   (3104a, 2606)

e. For each number x: $|x| = \pm x$.   (3104a, 2616c)

f. For each number x: $|x|^2 = x^2$.   (3104e)

3105. Exercises.

   a. For any numbers x, y: $\max(x, y) = [x + y + |x - y|]/2$.

   b. For any numbers x, y: $\min(x, y) = [x + y - |x - y|]/2$.

   c. For each number x: $|x| = 2 \cdot \max(0, x) - x$.

   d. For each number x: $x = |x|\operatorname{sgn}(x)$.

   e. For each number x: $|\operatorname{sgn}(x)| = \operatorname{sgn}|x|$.

3106. We know that for each number x: $x = 0 \Rightarrow |x| = 0$.   (?)
Is the converse obvious?

3107. Exercise.

   For each number x: $|x| = 0 \Rightarrow x = 0$.

3108. Corollary. For each number x:

$$|x| = 0 \Leftrightarrow x = 0,$$

$$|x| \neq 0 \Leftrightarrow x \neq 0.$$

3109. Theorem. For any numbers x, y: $|xy| = |x| \cdot |y|$.

   Proof.: $|xy| = (xy)\operatorname{sgn}(xy) =_1 [x \cdot \operatorname{sgn}(x)][y \cdot \operatorname{sgn}(y)] = |x| \cdot |y|$.
(1.2713)

3110. Corollary. For any numbers u, v such that $v \neq 0$: $|u/v| = |u|/|v|$.

   Proof.: $|u/v| = |u/v| \cdot |v|/|v| = |(u/v)v|/|v| = |u|/|v|$.

3111. Exercise.

   For any numbers a, b, c: $|abc| = |a| \cdot |b| \cdot |c|$.

   NOTE. This is the extension of 3109 to three numbers.

3112. Pitfall. For any numbers x, y: $|x + y| = |x| + |y|$.

   Counterexample. -1 for x, 1 for y.

3113. Theorem. *Triangle Inequality.* For any numbers x, y: $|x + y| \leq |x| + |y|$.

   Proof.: $|x + y| = \max[-(x + y), (x + y)] =$
$\max[(-x) + (-y), x + y] \leq_1$
$\max(-x, x) + \max(-y, y) = |x| + |y|$.   (1.3029).

   NOTE I. Surely the student can extend this theorem to three numbers.

   NOTE II. In 3122, we shall prove that
for any numbers x, y: $|x + y| = |x| + |y| \Leftrightarrow 0 \leq xy$.

3114. Corollaries.

a. For each number x: $0 \leq |x|$.

   Proof.: $0 = |x + (-x)| \leq |x| + |-x| = 2|x|$.

b. For any numbers a, b, c: $|a - c| \leq |a - b| + |b - c|$.

   Proof.: $|a - c| = |(a - b) + (b - c)| \leq |a - b| + |b - c|$.

c. For any numbers u, v: $|u| - |v| \leq |u - v| \leq |u| + |v|$.

   Proof.: $|u| - |v| = |(u - v) + v| - |v| \leq |(u - v)| + |v| - |v| =$
$|u - v| = |u + (-v)| \leq |u| + |-v| = |u| + |v|$.

d. For any numbers x, y: $||x| - |y|| \leq |x - y|$.

   Proof.: $||x| - |y|| = \max[|y| - |x|, |x| - |y|] \leq_1$
$\max[|y - x|, |x - y|] = |x - y|$.   (1.3028e)

e. For any numbers x, y: $(x + y)\mathrm{sgn}(x + y) \leq x \cdot \mathrm{sgn}(x) + y \cdot \mathrm{sgn}(y)$.
(3113)

3115. Exercises.

a. *Prove or disprove.* For any numbers x, y: $|x - y| \leq |x + y|$.

b. *Prove or disprove.* For any numbers x, y: $|x + y| \leq |x - y|$.

c. *Prove or disprove.* For any numbers x, y: $|x| - |y| \leq |x + y|$.

3116. The next theorem was intentionally postponed until now.

3117. Theorem. For each number x: $|x| = \begin{cases} x & \text{iff } 0 \leq x \\ 0 & \text{iff } x = 0 \\ -x & \text{iff } x \leq 0 \end{cases}$.

   Proof.:

$|x| = x \Leftrightarrow x \cdot \mathrm{sgn}(x) = x \Leftrightarrow_? [x = 0 \text{ or } \mathrm{sgn}(x) = 1] \Leftrightarrow 0 \leq x$;
$|x| = 0 \Leftrightarrow x = 0$; (3108)
$|x| = -x \Leftrightarrow |-x| = -x \Leftrightarrow_? 0 \leq -x \Leftrightarrow x \leq 0$.

3118. Corollary. For each number x:

$|x| = x \Leftrightarrow x$ is nonnegative,

$|x| = -x \Leftrightarrow x$ is nonpositive.

NOTE. This corollary follows immediately by 3117 and provides one answer to the perennial question: what does $|x|$ equal?

3119. Exercises.

a. For each number c: $||c|| = |c|$.

b. For any numbers u, v: $|u| = |v| \Leftrightarrow u = \pm v \Leftrightarrow_1 u^2 = v^2$. (1.2618)

3120. Theorem. For each number x: $|x|$ is the nonnegative number whose square equals x^2.

Proof. Consider any number x.
$|x|$ is such a number because $0 \le |x|$ and $|x|^2 = x^2$.
$|x|$ is the only such number because
for each nonnegative number u such that $u^2 = x^2$: $u = |u| = |x|$.

3121. The following propositions provide five more ways to conceive of the absolute value of a number: 3104a, 3104d, 3105c, 3117, 3120. Most writers choose 3117 to serve as the definition of the absolute value of a number.

3122. Theorem. For any numbers x, y: $|x + y| = |x| + |y| \Leftrightarrow 0 \le xy$.

Proof.: $|x + y| = |x| + |y| \Leftrightarrow_? ||x + y|| = ||x| + |y|| \Leftrightarrow_1$
$|x + y|^2 = (|x| + |y|)^2 \Leftrightarrow_? (x + y)^2 = x^2 + 2|xy| + y^2 \Leftrightarrow$
$xy = |xy| \Leftrightarrow 0 \le xy$.
Reference 1.   3119b with $|x + y|$ for u, $|x| + |y|$ for v.

3123. Exercise.

For any numbers x, c, d:
x is between $c, d \Leftrightarrow |c - x| + |x - d| = |c - d|$.

Absolute Value (continued)

3201. Now we shall treat various inequalities involving absolute value.

3202. Theorem. For each number x: $-|x| \leq x \leq |x|$.

Proof.: $-|x| = \min(-x, x) \leq x \leq \max(-x, x) = |x|$.

3203. Exercises.

  a. For each number x: $-|x| \leq -x \leq |x|$. HINT. Use 3202.

  b. For each number b: there is a number x such that $b < x^2$.
  NOTE. No square roots allowed yet.

  c. For any numbers b, c such that $|b - c|$ precedes every positive number:
  $b = c$.

3204. Theorems.

  a. For any numbers x, r: $|x| < r \Leftrightarrow -r < x < r$.
  Proof.: $|x| < r \Leftrightarrow \max(-x, x) < r \Leftrightarrow_1 [-x < r \text{ and } x < r] \Leftrightarrow$
  $-r < x < r$.   (1.3027a)

  b. For any numbers y, b, r: $|y - b| < r \Leftrightarrow b - r < y < b + r$.
  Proof.: $|y - b| < r \Leftrightarrow -r < y - b < r \Leftrightarrow b - r < y < b + r$.

3205. Corollaries.

  a. For any numbers x, r: $0 < |x| < r \Leftrightarrow [-r < x < 0 \text{ or } 0 < x < r]$.
  Proof.: $0 < |x| < r \Leftrightarrow [0 < x < r \text{ or } 0 < -x < r] \Leftrightarrow$
  $-r < x < 0 \text{ or } 0 < x < r$.

  b. For any numbers y, b, r:
  $0 < |y - b| < r \Leftrightarrow [b - r < y < b \text{ or } b < y < b + r]$.
  Proof.: $0 < |y - b| < r \Leftrightarrow [-r < y - b < 0 \text{ or } 0 < y - b < r] \Leftrightarrow$
  $[b - r < y < b \text{ or } b < y < b + r]$.

3206. The following can be proved in a manner similar to 3204, 3205.

    a. For any numbers x, r: $|x| \leq r \Leftrightarrow -r \leq x \leq r$.

    b. For any numbers y, b, r: $|y - b| \leq r \Leftrightarrow b - r \leq y \leq b + r$.

    c. For any numbers x, r: $0 < |x| \leq r \Leftrightarrow [-r \leq x < 0 \text{ or } 0 < x \leq r]$.

    d. For any numbers y, b, r:
        $0 < |y - b| \leq r \Leftrightarrow [b - r \leq y < b \text{ or } b < y \leq b + r]$.

3207. Caution. Students frequently confuse the next two propositions with 3204a and 3206a.

3208. Theorems.

    a. For any numbers x, r: $r < |x| \Leftrightarrow [r < -x \text{ or } r < x]$.
    Proof.: $r < |x| \Leftrightarrow r < \max(-x, x) \Leftrightarrow_1 [r < -x \text{ or } r < x]$.
    (1.3027b)

    b. For any numbers x, r: $r \leq |x| \Leftrightarrow [r \leq -x \text{ or } r \leq x]$.
    Proof. Similar to previous proof.

3209. Exercises.

    a. *Prove or disprove.* For any numbers y, b, r: $|y - b| < r \Rightarrow |b| - r < y$.

    b. *Prove or disprove.* For any numbers y, b, r:
        $|b| - r < y < |b| + r \Rightarrow |y - b| < r$.

    c. *Prove or disprove.* For any numbers y, b, r: $|y - b| < r \Rightarrow y < |b| + r$.

    d. For any numbers b, x, y, c such that $b < x < c$ and $b < y < c$:
        $|x - y| < c - b$.

3210. Theorem. For any numbers a, y, c such that $a < y < c$:
    $|y| < \max(|a|, |c|)$.

    Proof.: $|y| = \max(-y, y) <_1 \max(-a, c) \leq_2 \max(|-a|, |c|) = \max(|a|, |c|)$.

    References. 1.3027e; 2.3028e.

    NOTE. One can easily prove the proposition obtained by replacing $<$ with $\leq$.

3211. Exercise.

Disprove the converse of 3210; i.e., disprove the following.

For any numbers a, y, c such that $|y| < \max(|a|, |c|)$: $a < y < c$.

3212. Pitfalls.

a. For any numbers x, y: $x < y \Rightarrow |x| < |y|$.
Counterexample. -1 for x, 0 for y.

b. For any numbers x, y: $x < y \Rightarrow |y| < |x|$.
Counterexample. 0 for x, 1 for y.

c. For any numbers x, y: $|x| < |y| \Rightarrow x < y$.
Counterexample. 0 for x, -1 for y.

d. For any numbers x, y: $|x| < |y| \Rightarrow y < x$.
Counterexample. 0 for x, 1 for y.

NOTE. These propositions are false even if $<$ is replaced by $\leq$.

3213. Theorem. For any numbers x, y such that $0 \leq x < y$: $|x| < |y|$.

Proof.: $|x| = x < y = |y|$.

3214. Exercise.

For any numbers u, v: $u^2 < v^2 \Leftrightarrow |u| < |v|$. HINT. 2921.
NOTE. Of course this proposition is true if $<$ is replaced by $\leq$.

3215. For review purposes we prove the following proposition.

For each positive number p: every number x that satisfies $|x - 3| < \min(1, p/7)$ satisfies $|x^2 - 9| < p$.

Proof. Consider any positive number p.
For each number x such that $|x - 3| < \min(1, p/7)$:
$$|x^2 - 9| = |x + 3| \cdot |x - 3| = |(x - 3) + 6| \cdot |x - 3| \leq$$
$$(|x - 3| + 6)|x - 3| <_? (1 + 6)p/7 = p.$$

3216. Exercise.

For any number c and positive number p: every number x that satisfies $|x - c| < \min[1, p/(1 + 2|c|)]$ satisfies $|x^2 - c^2| < p$.

3217. Remark. The following statement follows by 3215. (?)

For each positive number p:
there is a positive number d such that
every number x satisfying $|x - 3| < d$ satisfies $|x^2 - 9| < p$.

Statements of this type occur often in calculus.

Number Sets

3301. The student is advised to review Lessons 14, 15, 16, 17 and to give particular attention to the use of the brace notation and the distinction between the notions *is in* and *is a subset of.*

The reader is reminded that the author uses
the symbol R to denote the set of all (real) numbers,
the symbol ϵ to stand for *is in,*
the symbol $\subseteq$ to stand for *is a subset of,*
and the symbol $\subset$ to stand for *is a proper subset of.*

NOTE. In this book the empty set $\emptyset$ is a proper subset of each nonempty set.

3302. Review. To prove that a set A is a subset of a set B, one may prove that each member of A is a member of B; i.e., that each thing in A is in B.

To prove that a set A is a proper subset of a set B, one may prove that A is a subset of B and that some member of B is not in A.

To prove that two sets G, H are equal,
one may prove that $G \subseteq H$ and $G \supseteq H$ (see 1609)
or one may prove that for each thing x: $x \epsilon G \Leftrightarrow x \epsilon H$.

3303. Example. $\{x \epsilon R \mid 1 < 2x\} \subset \{x \epsilon R \mid x \neq 0 \text{ and } 1/x < 2\}$.

Proof. First we shall prove that the left set is a subset of the right set.
Consider any member t of the left set.
Then $1 < 2t$, and so $1/t < 2$, and hence t is in the right set.   (?)
Now we must produce a member of the right set that is not in the left set.
-1 is such a number.

172

3304. Notation. The author uses the symbol
R_0 to denote the set of all nonnegative numbers, and
R_+ to denote the set of all positive numbers.

NOTE. There are no widely accepted symbols for these sets.

3305. The following obvious propositions will serve to reinforce the student's understanding of some important symbols.

a. $R_0 = \{x \in R \mid 0 \le x\}$.

b. $R_+ = \{x \in R \mid 0 < x\}$.

c. $R - R_0 = \{x \in R \mid x < 0\}$.

d. $R_+ \subset R_0 \subset R$.

e. $R_0 = R_+ \cup \{0\}$.

f. $R_0 \cup R_+ = R_0$.

g. $R_+ = R_0 - \{0\}$.

h. $R_0 - R_+ = \{0\}$.

i. $R_+ - R_0 = \emptyset$.

j. $R_0 \cap R_+ = R_+$.

k. $\{0\} \cap R_+ = \emptyset$.

3306. Definition. A *number set* is any set each member of which is a number.

3307. Examples. Each of the following is a number set.

a. R, R_0, R_+.

b. $\{3/2\}$, i.e., the set whose sole member is the number 3/2.

c. $\{-7, 0\}$, i.e., the set consisting of the numbers $-7, 0$.

d. $\{x \in R \mid x(x + 1) < 0\}$, i.e., the set of all numbers x such that $x(x + 1) < 0$.

e. $\{x(x + 1) \in R \mid x < 0\}$, i.e., the set of all numbers $x(x + 1)$ such that $x < 0$. NOTE. This set may also be described as follows:
$\{y \in R \mid$ there is a negative number x such that $y = x(x + 1)\}$.

f. $\{x \in R_0 \mid x^2 \le 1\}$, i.e., the set of all nonnegative numbers whose squares precede 1.

g. $\{w \in R_+ \mid w \le 7\}$, i.e., the set of all positive numbers that precede 7.

REMARK. Sets 3307d,e are distinct because $-3(-3 + 1)$ is in the latter but not in the former. (?) Some students erroneously believe that such sets are created solely to torment them.

3308. Pitfalls.

    a. Each member of $\{x(x+1)\in R \mid x < 0\}$ is negative.

    Counterexample. The positive number $-2(-2+1)$ is in the set.

    b. Each member of $\{x \in R \mid 0 < x(x+1)\}$ is positive.

    Counterexample. -2 is in the set.

3309. When using the brace notation to describe a number set, we shall hence-forth omit the symbol $\in R$ that may precede the vertical stroke $\mid$.

    E.g., we shall write $\{x \mid x(x+1) < 0\}$ instead of $\{x \in R \mid x(x+1) < 0\}$, and we shall write $\{x(x+1) \mid x < 0\}$ instead of $\{x(x+1) \in R \mid x < 0\}$.

    The symbol $\{x \mid x(x+1) < 0\}$ should be read thus: the set of all numbers x such that $x(x+1) < 0$.

    The symbol $\{x(x+1) \mid x < 0\}$ should be read thus: the set of all numbers $x(x+1)$ such that $x < 0$.

3310. $\emptyset$ is a number set because surely each member of $\emptyset$ is a number.

3311. $\{1, R\}$ is not a number set because R is not a number.
However, $\{1\} \cup R$ is a number set. **(?)**

    $\{R, 1, 2, 3, 4\}$ is not a number set.
However, $R \cup \{1, 2, 3, 4\}$ is a number set.

    But $\{R\} \cup \{1, 2, 3, 4\}$ is not a number set. **(?)**

3312. Problems. Describe the following sets using just one pair of braces.

    a. $\{1, 2, 3\} \cup \{2, 3, 4\}$.
    Answer. $\{1, 2, 3, 4\}$.

    b. $\{1, 2, 3\} \cap \{2, 3, 4\}$.
    Answer. $\{2, 3\}$.

    c. $\{x \mid -3 < x < 2\} \cup \{y \mid 0 < y \leq 5\}$.
    Answer. $\{w \mid -3 < w \leq 5\}$.

    d. $\{x \mid -3 < x < 2\} \cap \{y \mid 0 \leq y \leq 5\}$.
    Answer. $\{x \mid 0 \leq x < 2\}$.

    e. $\{x \mid -3 < x < 2\} - \{y \mid -1 < y \leq 5\}$.
    Answer. $\{x \mid -3 < x \leq -1\}$.

    f. $\{x \in R_0 \mid 3x < 5\} \cap \{x \in R_0 \mid -5 < 3x\}$.
    Answer. $\{x \in R_0 \mid 3x < 5 \text{ and } -5 < 3x\}$.

    NOTE. This answer can be simplified to $\{x \mid 0 \leq x < 5/3\}$. **(?)**

g. $\{x \in R_+ \mid x^2 < 1\} - \{x \in R_+ \mid x < 1/2\}$.
Answer. $\{x \in R_+ \mid x^2 < 1 \text{ and } 1/2 \leq x\}$.

NOTE. This answer can be simplified to $\{x \mid 1/2 \leq x < 1\}$. (?)

h. $\{x \in R_+ \mid x^2 < 1\} \cup \{x \in R_+ \mid x \leq 3\}$.
Answer. $\{x \in R_+ \mid x^2 < 1 \text{ or } x \leq 3\}$.

NOTE. This answer can be simplified to $\{x \mid 0 < x \leq 3\}$. (?)

3313. Example. $\{3x \mid 4 < 2x\} = \{y \mid 6 < y\}$.

Proof.

PART I($\subseteq$).
Consider any member of the first set, say $3x$ where $4 < 2x$.
We shall prove that $3x$ is in the second set.
To prove this we must prove that $6 < 3x$.
$6 = 3(4/2) < 3(2x/2) = 3x$.

Let us now compress the proof of PART I as follows.

Consider any member of the first set, say $3x$ where $4 < 2x$.
Then $6 <_? 3x$, and so $3x$ is in the second set.

PART II($\supseteq$).
Consider any member y of the second set.
We shall prove that y is in the first set.
To prove that y is in the first set, we must produce a number x such that
$y = 3x$ and $4 < 2x$.
Clearly, we must choose $y/3$ for x.

Of course we must be sure that $4 < 2(y/3)$;
this follows from the fact that $6 < y$.

Let us compress the proof of PART II as follows.

Consider any member y of the second set.
Then y is in the first set because $y = 3(y/3)$ and $4 <_? 2(y/3)$.

NOTE. The author is fully aware that understanding compressed proofs
requires the student's best effort.

3314. Exercises.

a. $\{x \mid 1 < x < 3\} \subset \{x \mid 1 < x^2 < 9\}$.

b. $\{3 - 2x \mid 1 \leq x\} = \{y \mid y \leq 1\}$.

c. $\{1/x \mid -2 \leq x < 0\} = \{w \mid w \leq -1/2\}$.

3315. When we are requested to *determine* a certain set, we are expected either
to itemize (if possible) all its members, or to find an extremely simple
description of the set.

3316. Problem. Solve the equation $x^2 - 2x - 8 = 0$;
i.e., determine $\{x \mid x^2 - 2x - 8 = 0\}$.

Solution I. Let S denote this set.
Consider any member t of S. Then
$0 = t^2 - 2t - 8 = (t - 4)(t + 2)$, and so $t = 4$ or $t = -2$.
Hence $S \subseteq_? \{4, -2\}$.
[Thus, if there is a number t in S, then $t = 4$ or $t = -2$.]

Although we now know that S is a subset of $\{4, -2\}$, we cannot claim
to have determined S; for all we know, S might be empty.
However, to determine S it suffices to examine just 4 and -2 for possible
membership in S. (?)

Since $4^2 - 2(4) - 8 = 4^2 - 4(2 + 2) = 4^2 - 4^2 = 0$,   4 is in S.
Since $(-2)^2 - 2(-2) - 8 =_? 0$, -2 is also in S.
So, $\{4, -2\} \subseteq S$, and hence $S = \{4, -2\}$.

Solution II.
$S = \{x \mid (x - 4)(x + 2) = 0\} = \{x \mid x = 4 \text{ or } x = -2\} = \{4, -2\}$.

3317. Problem. Solve the equation $|y| = 2y + 1$;
i.e., determine $\{y \mid |y| = 2y + 1\}$.

Solution I. Let S denote this set.
Consider any member z of S. Then
$|z| = 2z + 1$, and so $z^2 = 4z^2 + 4z + 1$,
and hence $0 = (3z + 1)(z + 1)$,
and therefore $z = -1/3$ or $z = -1$. So, $S \subseteq \{-1/3, -1\}$.

To determine S, it now suffices to examine just $-1/3$ and -1 for possible
membership in S.

Since $|-1/3| = 1/3 = 2(-1/3) + 1$, $-1/3$ is in S.
Since $|-1| \neq 2(-1) + 1$, -1 is not in S.
Hence, $S =_? \{-1/3\}$.

Solution II.
$S = \{y \mid y \leq 0 \text{ and } -y = 2y + 1\} \cup \{y \mid 0 \leq y \text{ and } y = 2y + 1\} =_?$
$\{y \mid y = -1/3\} \cup \emptyset = \{-1/3\}$.

3318. Problem. Solve the equation $|w| + w + 1 = 0$;
i.e., determine $\{w \mid |w| + w + 1 = 0\}$.

Solution I. Let S denote this set.
Consider any member y of S. Then
$|y| = -(y + 1)$, and so $y^2 = y^2 + 2y + 1$, and hence $y = -1/2$.
Therefore $S \subseteq \{-1/2\}$.

To determine S, it now suffices to examine just $-1/2$ for membership.
Since $|-1/2| + (-1/2) + 1 = 1 \neq 0$, $-1/2$ is not in S
and so S is empty.
Therefore there is no number w such that $|w| + w + 1 = 0$.

Solution II.
$S = \{w \mid w \leq 0 \text{ and } -w + w + 1 = 0\} \cup$
$\qquad \{w \mid 0 \leq w \text{ and } w + w + 1 = 0\} =$
$\emptyset \cup \emptyset = \emptyset$.

NOTE. Perhaps the student now has a better understanding of "extraneous roots."

3319. Exercises.

   a. Solve the equation $|x| + |x - 1| = 2$.
   b. Solve the equation $[\text{sgn}(x)]^2 = 1$.

3320. Problem. Solve the simultaneous equations $x + y = 5$, $x - y = 1$;
   i.e., determine the set of all number pairs (x, y) such that
   $x + y = 5$ and $x - y = 1$.

   Solution. Let S denote this set.
   Consider any member (x, y) of S.
   Then $x = 5 - y = 5 - (x - 1)$, and so $x = 3$, and hence $y = 2$.
   Therefore $S \subseteq \{(3, 2)\}$.
   Since, furthermore, $\{(3, 2)\} \subseteq_? S$, we have $S = \{(3, 2)\}$.

   NOTE. The set S may also be described in brace notation as follows:
   $\{(x, y) \mid x + y = 5 \text{ and } x - y = 1\}$.

3321. Exercise.
   Solve the simultaneous equations $y - 3x = 0$, $x^2 + y^2 = 10$.

3322. Problem. Solve the inequality $(x - 4)(x + 2) < 0$;
   i.e., determine $\{x \mid (x - 4)(x + 2) < 0\}$.

   Solution. $\{x \mid (x - 4)(x + 2) < 0\} =$
   $\{x \mid x - 4 < 0 \text{ and } x + 2 > 0\} \cup \{x \mid x - 4 > 0 \text{ and } x + 2 < 0\} =_?$
   $\{x \mid -2 < x < 4\}$.

3323. Exercises.

   a. Find what is wrong with the following argument.
   $\{x \mid |x + 1| < x\} = \{x \mid (x + 1)^2 < x^2\} = \{x \mid 2x + 1 < 0\} =$
   $\{x \mid x < -1/2\}$. Since -1 is in the last set, -1 is in the first set.
   Therefore $|-1 + 1| < -1$, and so $0 < -1$.

Solve the following inequalities.

b. $|x + 1| < |x - 3|$.

c. $|3x - 1| < 2x + 5$.

d. $1 < |x| \leq 2$.

e. $0 < (x + 4)(x - 2)$.

f. $1/(x - 1) < 1/(x + 1)$. NOTE. There are solutions.

g. $|x - 2| + |x + 3| < 6$.

3324. Definition. A number set S is *dense* provided that
for any numbers a, c in S such that $a < c$:
there is a number b in S such that $a < b < c$.

NOTE. Some writers use *dense-in-itself* instead of *dense*.

3325. Examples.

a. R, R_0, R_+, $R - R_0$ are dense.

b. $\{3\}$ is dense. (?)

c. $\emptyset$ is dense. (?)

d. $\{x \mid -3 \leq x < 2\}$ is dense.

Proof. Consider any members a, c thereof such that $a < c$.
Then $-3 \leq a < (a + c)/2 < c < 2$, and $(a + c)/2$ is in the set.

e. $\{x \mid -3 \leq x \leq 0$ or $1 \leq x < 2\}$ is not dense.

Proof. 0, 1 are in the set, but no number strictly between 0, 1 is in the set.

3326. Exercises.

a. $\{x \mid |x - 3| < 1\}$ is dense.

b. $\{x \mid x \neq 0\}$ is dense.

c. $\{x \mid x < 1$ or $3 < x\}$ is dense.

d. $\{x \mid x \leq 1$ or $3 \leq x\}$ is not dense.

3327. Definition. The *negative* of a number set B is the set consisting of the
negative of every number in B.

NOTATION. $[\doteq B]$, read as *the negative of B* or as *minus B*.

NOTE. It is obvious that for any number x and number set A:
$x \in A \Leftrightarrow (-x) \in [\doteq A]$.

3328. Examples.

a. $\doteq \emptyset = \emptyset$.

b. $\doteq R = R$.

c. $\doteq R_+ = R - R_0$.

d. For each number set C: $\doteq [\doteq C] = C$.

Lower Bounds of a Number Set

3401. Definition. A number *r precedes* a number set *C* provided that *r* precedes every member of *C*.

NOTE FOR THE TEACHER. There is a great temptation to use the notation $r \leqq C$ to stand for *r precedes C*; however, the author finds that students make too many mistakes with this notation.

3402. Immediate consequence. If a number *r* precedes a number set *C*, then each number less than *r* precedes *C*.

3403. Examples.

a. 1 precedes $\{x \mid 2 < x\}$.

b. 1 precedes $\{x \mid 1 < x\}$. NOTE. 1 *is not in* the set.

c. 1 precedes $\{x \mid 1 \leqq x\}$. NOTE. 1 *is in* the set.

d. Every number precedes $\emptyset$. (?)

e. Every nonpositive number precedes R_0.

f. -1 precedes $\{x \mid x(x + 1) < 0\}$.

Proof. Consider any member x of the set.
We must prove that $-1 \leqq x$.
Since $x(x + 1) < 0$, we have $0 <_? x + 1$, and so $-1 < x$.

Let us compress this proof as follows.

For each member x of the set:
$x(x + 1) < 0$, and so $0 <_? x + 1$, and hence $-1 < x$.

179

g. $-1/4$ precedes $\{x(x + 1) \mid x < 0\}$.

Proof. Consider any member of the set, say $x(x + 1)$ where $x < 0$.
We must prove that $-1/4 \leq x(x + 1)$. Since
$-1/4 \leq x(x + 1) \Leftarrow 0 \leq x^2 + x + 1/4 \Leftarrow 0 \leq (x + 1/2)^2$,
we are done. (?)

NOTE I. The symbol $\Leftarrow$ stands for *if* or for *is implied by*.

NOTE II. In this proof we did not use the fact that $x < 0$; accordingly,
we actually proved that $-1/4$ precedes $\{x(x + 1) \mid x \in R\}$.

3404. Exercises.

a. -1 precedes $\{x \mid |x| \leq 2 + x\}$.

b. 5 precedes $\{3x \mid 4 < 2x\}$.

c. $-1/2$ precedes $\{-x/(2x + 1) \mid 0 \leq x\}$.

d. For any number u and number set C such that every number less than u
precedes C: u precedes C.

3405. Immediate consequence. A number r does not precede a number set C iff
some member of C is less than r.   (3401)

3406. Examples.

a. 2 does not precede R_+ because 1 is in R_+ and is less than 2.

b. $-1/4$ does not precede $\{x \mid x(x + 1) < 0\}$ because $-1/2$ is in the set (?)
and is less than $-1/4$.

NOTE. Again the student has learned that the sets described in 3403g and
3406b are distinct. See 3307REMARK.

3407. Exercises.

a. 0 does not precede $\{x \mid x^2 < 4\}$.

b. 1 does not precede $\{x(x - 1) \mid 0 < x\}$.

c. -3 does not precede $\{x \mid |x + 1| < |x - 3|\}$.

3408. Definitions.

a. A *lower bound* of a number set is any number that precedes the set.

NOTE I. We do not require that lower bounds of a number set be in the set.

NOTE II. If there is a lower bound b of a number set C, then b is said to
be one of C's lower bounds, and C is said to have b as a lower bound.

b. A number set is *bounded below* provided that some number precedes it.

NOTE III. A number set is said to be bounded below by each of its lower bounds.

NOTE IV. $\emptyset$ is bounded below because, for example, 1 precedes $\emptyset$.

3409. Examples.

a. $\{x \mid x(x + 1) < 0\}$ is bounded below, e.g., by -1. (3403f)

b. $\{x(x + 1) \mid x < 0\}$ is bounded below, e.g., by $-1/4$. (3403g)

c. 1 is a lower bound of $\{x \mid 1 < x\}$.

3410. The following propositions follow by 3408 and the indicated propositions.

a. Each number less than a lower bound of a number set is a lower bound thereof. (3402)

b. $\emptyset$ is bounded below by every number. (3403d)

c. If every number less than a number u is a lower bound of a number set C, then u is a lower bound of C. (3404d)

d. A number r is not a lower bound of a number set C iff some member of C is less than r. (3405)

e. $-1/4$ is not a lower bound of $\{x \mid x(x + 1) < 0\}$. (3406b)

3411. Exercise.

Each subset of a bounded below number set is bounded below.

NOTE. This proposition would be false if $\emptyset$ were not bounded below.

3412. *Unbounded below* means *not bounded below*.

3413. Example. R is unbounded below.

Proof. Suppose not.
Then there is a number b that precedes R.
Hence $b \leq_? b - 1$.
Contradiction. (?)

3414. The next theorem provides a direct method for proving that a number set is unbounded below.

3415. Theorem. A number set C is unbounded below iff
each negative number is preceded by some member of C;

i.e., for each number set C:
C is unbounded below $\Leftrightarrow$
for each negative number y: there is a number x in C such that $x \leq y$.

PRELIMINARY REMARK. The contrapositive of this theorem is as follows.

For each number set C:
C is bounded below $\Leftrightarrow$
there is a negative number y such that for each number x in C: $y < x$.

Proof of the contrapositive. Easy.

3416. We submit several illustrations of the use of 3415.

a. R is unbounded below.

Proof (compare with the proof in 3413).
Each negative number y is preceded by y which is in R.

b. $\{x \mid x < -3\}$ is unbounded below.

Proof. Consider any negative number y.
It suffices to find a number that is in the set and precedes y;
i.e., it suffices to find a number x such that $x < -3$ and $x \leq y$.

Clearly, we may choose $\min(-4, y)$ for x.   (?)

c. $\{2 - x \mid 0 < x\}$ is unbounded below.

Proof. Each negative number y is preceded by $2 - (2 - y)$ which is in the set.   (?)

d. $\{1/x \mid -2 \leq x < 0\}$ is unbounded below.

Proof. Consider any negative number y.
It suffices to find a number that is in the set and precedes y;
hence it suffices to find a number x such that $-2 \leq x < 0$ and $1/x \leq y$.

Noting that $[-2 \leq x < 0$ and $1/x \leq y] \Leftarrow_? x = \max(-2, 1/y)$,
we may choose $\max(-2, 1/y)$ for x.

3417. Exercises.

a. $\{x \mid x < 2\}$ is unbounded below.

b. $\{2x \mid x < -1\}$ is unbounded below.

c. $\{3 - 2x \mid 1 \leq x\}$ is unbounded below.

d. $\{1/(1 - x) \mid 1 < x\}$ is unbounded below.

e. $\{x \mid 1 \leq x^2\}$ is unbounded below.

f. For each number u: $\{x \mid x < u\}$ is unbounded below.

g. For each number u: $\{x \mid x \leq u\}$ is unbounded below.

Upper Bounds of a Number Set

3501. Definition. A number *r* *exceeds* a number set *C* provided that *r* exceeds every member of *C*.

3502. Exercises.

a. $1/2$ exceeds $\{x/(2x + 1) \mid 0 < x\}$.

b. 0 neither precedes nor exceeds $\{x \mid |x + 1| < |x - 3|\}$.

c. Prove the following proposition (suitably modified if necessary). For any numbers *u*, *v* and number set *H* such that *u* precedes *H* and *v* exceeds *H*: $u \leq v$.

d. For any number *u* and number set *H*:
u precedes $H \Leftrightarrow -u$ exceeds $[\dot- H]$.

e. For any number *v* and number set *G*:
v exceeds $G \Leftrightarrow -v$ precedes $[\dot- G]$.

3503. Definitions.

a. An *upper bound* of a number set is any number that exceeds the set.

NOTE I. We do not require that upper bounds of a number set be in the set.

NOTE II. If there is an upper bound *b* of a number set *C*, then *b* is said to be one of *C*'s upper bounds, and *C* is said to have *b* as an upper bound.

b. A number set is *bounded above* provided that some number exceeds it.

NOTE III. A number set is said to be bounded above by each of its upper bounds.

3504. The following propositions follow by 3503 and the indicated propositions.

a. $\{x/(2x + 1) \mid 0 < x\}$ is bounded above.   (3502a)

b. $\emptyset$ is bounded above by every number.

c. Every number greater than an upper bound of a number set is an upper bound thereof.

d. If every number greater than a number v is an upper bound of a number set C, then v is an upper bound of C.   (3017a)

3505. Exercise.

For each number set K:
K is bounded above $\Leftrightarrow \div K$ is bounded below.

3506. *Unbounded above* means *not bounded above*.

3507. Theorem. A number set C is unbounded above iff each positive number precedes some member of C.

Proof. The contrapositive is obvious.

3508. Example. $\{3/x \mid 0 < x \leq 2\}$ is unbounded above.

Proof. Consider any positive number p.
It suffices to find a number that is in the set and exceeds p;
hence it suffices to find a number x such that $0 < x \leq 2$ and $p \leq 3/x$.
Noting that $[0 < x \leq 2 \text{ and } p \leq 3/x] \Leftarrow_? x = \min(2, 3/p)$,
we may choose $\min(2, 3/p)$ for x.

3509. Exercise.

$\{2x^2/(x + 1) \mid 1 \leq x\}$ is unbounded above.

HINT. For each number x such that $1 \leq x$:
$x = 2x^2/(x + x) \leq 2x^2/(x + 1)$.

3510. Definition. A number set is *bounded* provided it is bounded below and bounded above.

3511. Immediate consequences.

a. Each subset of a bounded number set is bounded.

b. A number set B is bounded iff $\div B$ is bounded.

3512. Theorem. For each number set C:
C is bounded $\Leftrightarrow$
there is a number q such that each number x in C satisfies $|x| \leq q$.

Proof. Consider any number set C.

PART I($\Rightarrow$).
If C is bounded, then there are numbers a, b such that for each number x in C: $a \leq x \leq b$ (?) and so (3210NOTE), $|x| \leq \max(|a|, |b|)$.

PART II($\Leftarrow$).
If there is a number q such that each number x in C satisfies $|x| \leq q$, then each number in C is between $-q$, q and so C is bounded.

3513. Example. $\{x^2 \mid -1 < x \leq 2\}$ is bounded.

Proof (exploiting 3512). For each member of the set, say x^2 where $-1 < x \leq 2$: $|x| \leq \max(|-1|, |2|) = 2$, and so $|x^2| = |x|^2 \leq 4$.

3514. Exercise.

For each number set C:
C is bounded $\Leftrightarrow$
there is a number t such that each number x in C satisfies $|x| < t$.

HINT. Exploit 3512.

NOTE. Some students erroneously believe that 3512 and 3514 cannot both be true.

3515. *Unbounded* means *not bounded*.

3516. Immediate consequence. A number set is unbounded iff it is unbounded below or unbounded above.

3517. Exercises.

a. Each number set that has an unbounded subset is unbounded.

b. A number set C is unbounded iff
for each number t: there is a number x in C such that $|x| \geq t$.

The Maximum of a Number Set

3601. Theorems.

a. There is a nonempty, bounded-above number set that is exceeded by no member thereof.

Proof. Let B denote $\{x \mid x < 3\}$.
Clearly, B is nonempty and bounded above.
Consider any member v of B.
Since v is less than $(v + 3)/2$ which is in B, v does not exceed B.
Thus, no member of B exceeds B.

b. For each number set H: there is at most one number that is in H and exceeds H.

Proof. For any number set H and numbers b, c that are in H and exceed H:
$b \leqq_? c$ and $c \leqq_? b$ and so $b = c$.

3602. Definition. The *maximum* (if there is one) of a number set H is the number that is in H and exceeds H.

NOTATION. max H, read as *the maximum of H* or simply as *max H*.

NOTE. The maximum of a number set is also called the greatest number in the set.

3603. The following expressions are synonymous:

some number is the maximum of H,
H has a maximum,
max H exists.

NOTE. The expression (max $H = b$) means H *has a maximum, namely b.*

3604. Examples.

a. $\max\{2\} = 2$.

b. $\max\{-1/3, 0, 2\} = 2$.

c. 2 is not the maximum of $\{-1/3, 0\}$.

d. 2 is not the maximum of $\{1, 2, 3\}$.

e. $\max\{x \mid x \leq 2\}$ exists. (?)

NOTE. It is obvious that each number set which has a maximum is bounded above; however, the converse is disproved by the next example.

f. $\{x \mid x < 3\}$ has no maximum.

NOTE. We know now that a nonempty, bounded-above number set does not necessarily have a maximum.

g. $\max\{x/(x^2 + 1) \mid -3 < x\} = 1/2$.

Proof. $1/2$ equals $1/(1^2 + 1)$ which is in the set, and $1/2$ exceeds the set. (?)

h. For any numbers x, y: $\max\{x, y\} = \max(x, y)$.

i. $\emptyset$ has no maximum.

3605. Immediate consequence. For each number set H that has a maximum:

max H is a number,

max H is in H,

max H is an upper bound of H,

max H precedes every upper bound of H. (?)

3606. Exercises.

a. $\{|y| \mid -1 \leq y \leq 3\}$ has a maximum.

b. $\{|1 - x| \mid x^2 \leq 4\}$ has a maximum.

c. $\max\{x \mid 0 < 1 + 2 \cdot \text{sgn}(1 - x)\}$ exists.

d. $\max\{(x + 1)/(x + 2) \mid -2 < x \leq 3\}$ exists.

e. *Prove or disprove.* Each nonempty subset of a number set having a maximum has a maximum.

f. *Prove or disprove.* For any number sets A, B such that max A exists, max B exists, and $A \subseteq B$: max $A \leq$ max B.

g. *Prove or disprove.* For any number sets A, B such that max A exists, max B exists, and $A \subset B$: max $A <$ max B.

h. *Prove or disprove.* For any number sets A, B such that max A exists, max B exists, and each number in A precedes some number in B: max $A \leq$ max B.

i. *Prove or disprove.* For any number sets A, B that have a maximum: $\max[A \cup B] = \max(\max A, \max B)$.

3607. Theorem. A number set C has no maximum iff each member of C is less than some member of C;

i.e., for each number set C:
C has no maximum $\Leftrightarrow$
for each number u in C: there is a number v in C such that $u < v$.

PRELIMINARY REMARK. The contrapositive is as follows:

For each number set C:
C has a maximum $\Leftrightarrow$
there is a number u in C such that for each number v in C: $v \leqq u$.
Proof of the contrapositive. Obvious.

3608. Examples.

a. R has no maximum; i.e., there is no greatest number.
Proof. Each member x of R is less than $x + 1$ which is in R.
NOTE. No unbounded above number set has a maximum.

b. $R - R_0$ has no maximum; i.e., there is no greatest negative number.
Proof. Each negative number y is less than $y/2$ which is negative.
NOTE. Again we see that a nonempty, bounded-above number set does not necessarily have a maximum.

c. $\{x/(x + 1) \mid -1 < x\}$ has no maximum.
Proof. Consider any member thereof, say $x/(x + 1)$ where $-1 < x$. It suffices to find a number that is in the set and is greater than $x/(x + 1)$;
hence, it suffices to find a number t such that $-1 < t$ and $x/(x + 1) < t/(t + 1)$.
Noting that $[x/(x + 1) < t/(t + 1)] \Leftarrow_? x < t$,
we may choose for t any number greater than x, e.g., $x + 3$.

3609. Exercises.

a. $\{x(2 - x) \mid x \neq 1\}$ has no maximum.

b. $\{x - \operatorname{sgn}(x) \mid -1 \leqq x \leqq 1\}$ has no maximum.
NOTE. The previous two number sets are bounded above.

c. *Prove or disprove.* For any number sets A, B that are not disjoint and have a maximum: $A \cap B$ has a maximum.

3610. Example. $\{x \in R_+ \mid x^2 < 2\}$ has no maximum.
Proof. Each member x thereof is less than $(3x + 4)/(2x + 3)$ which is in the set. (?)

NOTE. The set is bounded above, e.g., by 3. (?)

3611. Exercise.

$\{x \in R_+ \mid x^2 < 1\}$ has no maximum.

3612. Theorem. For each positive number p:

$\{x \in R_+ \mid x^2 < p\}$ has no maximum.

Proof. Consider any positive number p.

In view of 3611, it suffices to consider the case that $p \neq 1$.

Each member x of the set is less than $[(p + 1)x + 2p]/[2x + (p + 1)]$ which is in the set.   (?)

NOTE I.   Answering the above question requires a bit of work.

NOTE II.   Example 3610 is, of course, a special instance of 3612.

NOTE III.   Theorem 3612 will be useful in developing the idea of square root.

The Minimum of a Number Set

3701. Theorems.

a. There is a nonempty, bounded-below number set that is preceded by no member thereof.

Proof. $\{x \mid 3 < x\}$ is such a set. (?)

b. For each number set H: there is at most one number that is in H and precedes H.

Proof. Similar to proof of 3601b.

3702. Definition. The *minimum* (if there is one) of a number set H is the number that is in H and precedes H.

NOTATION. min H, read as *the minimum of H* or simply as *min H*.

NOTE. The minimum of a number set is also called the least (or smallest) number in the set.

3703. The following expressions are synonymous:

some number is the minimum of H,
H has a minimum,
min H exists.

NOTE. The expression (min $H = b$) means *H has a minimum, namely b*.

3704. Examples.

a. min $\{2\} = 2$.

b. min $\{-1/3, 0, 2\} = -1/3$.

c. -1 is not the minimum of $\{-1/3, 0\}$.

d. 2 is not the minimum of $\{1, 2, 3\}$.

e. $\min\{x \mid 2 \leq x\}$ exists.

NOTE. It is obvious that each number set which has a minimum is bounded below; however, the converse is disproved by the next example.

f. $\{x \mid 3 < x\}$ has no minimum.

NOTE. A nonempty, bounded-below number set does not necessarily have a minimum.

g. For any numbers x, y: $\min\{x, y\} = \min(x, y)$.

h. $\emptyset$ has no minimum.

3705. Immediate consequence. For each number set H that has a minimum:

min H is a number,
min H is in H,
min H is a lower bound of H,
min H exceeds every lower bound of H.   (?)

3706. Exercises.

a. $\{\operatorname{sgn}(1 - x) \mid x < 0\}$ has a minimum.

b. $\{|x| - 3 \mid -1 \leq x\}$ has a minimum.

3707. The following proposition is obvious.   (?)

For any number b and number set H:
if max $H = b$,
then b is the least number that exceeds H.

3708. Exercise.

Disprove the converse of 3707.

3709. The following proposition is obvious.   (?)

For any number b and number set H:
if min $H = b$,
then b is the greatest number that precedes H.

3710. Exercise.

Prove or disprove the converse of 3709.

3711. Theorem. A number set C has no minimum iff each member of C is greater than some member of C.

Proof. The contrapositive is obvious.

3712. Examples.

   a. There is no least number; i.e., R has no minimum. (?)

   NOTE. No unbounded below number set has a minimum.

   b. There is no least positive number; i.e., R_+ has no minimum. (?)

   NOTE. Again we see that a nonempty, bounded-below number set does not necessarily have a minimum.

   c. $\{x/(x^2 + 1) \mid 1 < x\}$ has no minimum.

   Proof. Consider any member thereof, say $x/(x^2 + 1)$ where $1 < x$.
It suffices to find a number that is in the set and is less than $x/(x^2 + 1)$;
hence, it suffices to find a number t such that $1 < t$ and
$t/(t^2 + 1) < x/(x^2 + 1)$.
Noting that $[t/(t^2 + 1) < x/(x^2 + 1)] \Leftarrow_? x < t$,
we may choose for t any number greater than x, e.g., $x + 1$.

3713. Diversion. We shall "prove" the following proposition.
If there is a least positive number, then it exceeds 1.

   "Proof." If there is a least positive number, say u, then, since $0 < u^2$,
we have $u \leqq_? u^2$, and so (dividing by u), $1 \leqq u$.

   QUERY. Is this proof valid?

3714. Exercise.
   $\{x \in R_+ \mid 1 < x^2\}$ has no minimum.

3715. Theorem. For each positive number p:
   $\{x \in R_+ \mid p < x^2\}$ has no minimum.

   Proof. Consider any positive number p.
In view of 3714, it suffices to consider the case that $p \neq 1$.
Each member x of the set is greater than
$[(1 + p)x + 2p]/[2x + (p + 1)]$ which is in the set. (?)

   NOTE. This theorem will be useful in developing the idea of square root.

3716. Theorems.

   a. For any number set H that has a maximum: $\min[\dot- H] = -\max H$.
   Proof.: $-\max H$ is in $\dot- H$ and precedes $\dot- H$. (?)

   NOTE. The theorem's conclusion may be stated as
$-\min[\dot- H] = \max H$.

   b. For any number set C that has a minimum: $\max[\dot- C] = -\min C$.
   Proof. Similar to the previous proof.

3717. Exercises.

   a. For any number sets A, B such that min A exists, min B exists, and $A \subseteq B$: min $A \geq$ min B.

   b. For each number set H that has a minimum and a maximum: min $H \leq$ max H.

   c. For each number set H such that min $H =$ max H: H has precisely one member.

   d. *Prove or disprove.* For any number sets A, B such that max A exists, min B exists, and each member of A precedes some member of B: max $A \leq$ min B.

Integers

3801. Definition.

The *successor* of a number x is $x + 1$;
the *predecessor* of a number x is $x - 1$.

NOTE. It is not customary to define the successor and predecessor of every number; however, the author considers it useful to do so.

3802. Definition. A *hereditary set* is any set that contains the successor of each number therein.

NOTE. This definition does not require that each member of a hereditary set be a number.

3803. Examples. Each of the following sets is hereditary.

a. R.

b. R_+.

c. R_0.

d. $\{x \mid 1 \leq x\}$.

e. $\{0, 1, 2, 3, 4, 5, 6, 7, 8, 9, 10\} \cup \{x \mid 10 < x\}$.

f. $\{-1, 0\} \cup R_+$.

g. $\emptyset$.

h. $\{y \mid -1/2 \leq y\}$.

i. The set of all apples.

j. [The set of all apples] $\cup R$.

3804. Exercises.

   a. $\{x \in R_+ \mid x \leq x^2\}$ is hereditary.

   b. $\{x \mid x \leq x^2\}$ is not hereditary.

3805. Definition. A 0-*hereditary set* (or *set hereditary from* 0) is any set that contains 0 and is hereditary.

   NOTE. The expression 0-*hereditary* has not been used by other writers.

3806. Examples.

   Sets 3803a,c,e,f,h,j are 0-hereditary.

   Sets 3803b,d,g,i are not 0-hereditary.

3807. Since 0 is in every 0-hereditary set, 1 is in every 0-hereditary set.   (?)
So 2 is in every 0-hereditary set.   (?)
Therefore 3 is in every 0-hereditary set.   (?)

   Is 9 in every 0-hereditary set?   (Why?)

   1/2 is not in every 0-hereditary set because 1/2 is not in the 0-hereditary set described in 3803e.

3808. Definition. An *integer* is any number x such that
either x is in every 0-hereditary set
or $-x$ is in every 0-hereditary set.

   NOTE. A number is said to be *integral* provided it is an integer.

3809. Examples.

   a. 0, 1, 2, 3 are integers because they are in every 0-hereditary set.

   b. $-3, -2, -1$ are integers because their negatives are in every 0-hereditary set.

   c. 1/2 is not an integer.   (?)

   d. $-1/2$ is not an integer.   (?)

3810. Theorem. There is no integer strictly between 0, 1.

   Proof. Consider any number r strictly between 0, 1.
Since neither r nor $-r$ is in the 0-hereditary set described in 3803e,
r is not an integer.

   NOTE. Now we know that the set of all integers is not dense.   (See 3324.)

3811. Exercises.

   a. For each number x: x is an integer $\Leftrightarrow$ $-x$ is an integer.

   b. There is no integer strictly between -1, 0.

3812. A *positive integer* is any integer that is positive, e.g., 1, 2, 3.
A *nonnegative integer* is any integer that is nonnegative, e.g., 0, 1, 2, 3.
A *negative integer* is any integer that is negative, e.g., -3, -2, -1.

3813. Notation. The author uses the symbol
Z to denote the set of all integers,
Z_0 to denote the set of all nonnegative integers,
Z_+ to denote the set of all positive integers.

NOTE. There are no widely accepted symbols for these sets.

3814. Immediate consequence. $Z_+ \subset Z_0 \subset Z$.

3815. Theorem. For each number x:
$x \,\epsilon\, Z_0 \iff x$ is in every 0-hereditary set.
Proof. Consider any number x.
PART I($\Leftarrow$). If x is in every 0-hereditary set, then
x is an integer and x is in R_0,   (?)
and so $x \,\epsilon\, Z_0$.
PART II($\Rightarrow$). It suffices to consider the case that $x \neq 0$.   (?)
If $x \,\epsilon\, Z_0$ and $x \neq 0$, then $-x$ is not in the 0-hereditary set R_0
and so x is in every 0-hereditary set.   (?)

3816. Exercises.
a. The successor of each nonnegative integer is a positive integer.
b. Z_0 is 0-hereditary.

3817. Theorem. If a set is 0-hereditary, then it contains every nonnegative integer.

PRELIMINARY REMARK. This theorem may be stated in the following ways.
Each 0-hereditary set contains every nonnegative integer.
Z_0 is a subset of every 0-hereditary set.

Proof. 3815.

NOTE. Counterexample for the converse of this theorem. $\{-1/2\} \cup Z_0$.

3818. Example. Let β denote the following proposition.
The double of each nonnegative integer is a nonnegative integer,
i.e., for each nonnegative integer x: $2x$ is a nonnegative integer.

Let T denote the set of all numbers whose doubles are nonnegative integers; thus $T = \{x \mid 2x \,\epsilon\, Z_0\}$.

To prove β, does it suffice to prove that T is 0-hereditary?
Yes. For assume that we have proved that T is 0-hereditary.
Then by 3817, each nonnegative integer is in T; i.e.,
each nonnegative integer is a number whose double is in Z_0.

3819. Exercises.

a. $\{x \mid 2x \, \epsilon \, Z_0\}$ is 0-hereditary.
NOTE. We must now accept β (see 3818) as proved.

b. To prove β, why does it suffice to prove that $\{x \, \epsilon \, Z_0 \mid 2x \, \epsilon \, Z_0\}$
is 0-hereditary?

3820. Lemma. The predecessor of each nonnegative integer is an integer.

Proof. It suffices to prove that $\{x \, \epsilon \, Z_0 \mid (x-1) \, \epsilon \, Z\}$ is 0-hereditary. (?)
The set contains 0,   (?)
and contains the successor of each number x therein because
$(x+1) \, \epsilon_? \, Z_0$ and $[(x+1)-1] \, \epsilon_? \, Z$.

3821. Exercise.

To prove 3820, why does it suffice to prove that $\{x \, \epsilon \, R_0 \mid (x-1) \, \epsilon \, Z\}$
is 0-hereditary?

3822. Theorems.

a. The successor of each integer is an integer.

Proof. In view of 3816a, it suffices to prove that the successor of each
negative integer is an integer.
For each negative integer i: $-i \, \epsilon_? \, Z_+$, and $(-i-1) \, \epsilon_? \, Z$, and so $i+1$,
being equal to $-(-i-1)$, is in Z.   (?)

b. The predecessor of each integer is an integer.

Proof. In view of 3820, it suffices to prove that the predecessor of each
negative integer is an integer.
For each negative integer i: $-i \, \epsilon \, Z_+$, and $(-i+1) \, \epsilon_? \, Z$, and so $i-1$,
being equal to $-(-i+1)$, is in Z.

3823. Exercise.

What is wrong with the following "proof" that for each nonnegative
integer n: $3n$ is a nonnegative integer?

"Proof." Consider any nonnegative integer n.
Since $2n$ is a nonnegative integer (3819aNOTE), $3n$, being equal to $2n+n$,
is a nonnegative integer.

3824. Theorem. The sum of any two integers is an integer.

PART I. We shall first prove that for any nonnegative integer x and any integer y: $x + y$ is an integer. It suffices (?) to prove that the following set is 0-hereditary:
$\{x \in Z_0 \mid \text{for each integer } y: (x + y) \in Z\}$.

Proof. The set contains 0, (?)
and contains the successor of each number x therein because $(x + 1) \in Z_0$, and for each integer y: $(x + y) \in_? Z$, and so $(x + 1) + y$, being equal to $(x + y) + 1$, is in Z. (?)

PART II. We shall now prove that for any negative integer w and any integer y: $w + y$ is an integer.

Proof.: $[(-w) + (-y)] \in Z$ (by PART I),
and so $w + y$, being equal to $-[(-w) + (-y)]$, is in Z.

3825. Corollary. The difference between any two integers is an integer.

Proof. For any integers x, y: $(-y)$ is an integer and so $x - y$, being equal to $x + (-y)$, is an integer.

3826. Corollary. No integer is strictly between an integer and its successor; i.e., there are no integers x, y such that $x < y < x + 1$.

Proof. Suppose there are integers x, y such that $x < y < x + 1$. Then $0 < y - x < 1$. Contradiction. (?)

3827. Corollary. For any integers x, y such that $x < y$: $x + 1 \leqq y$.

Proof.: y cannot be less than $x + 1$ because if $y < x + 1$, then we would have $x < y < x + 1$ which contradicts 3826.

3828. Exercises.

a. The product of any two integers is an integer.
HINT. First prove that for any nonnegative integer x and any integer y: xy is an integer.

b. For each integer x: $(x^3 + 2x)/3$ is an integer.

c. For each number t: there is at most one integer strictly between t, $t + 1$.

3829. Since $1/2$ is not an integer, we know that the quotient of an integer by a nonzero integer is not necessarily an integer.

Sets of Integers

3901. In this lesson we shall investigate important properties of sets of integers.

3902. Exercises.

  a. There is no greatest integer; i.e., Z has no maximum.

  b. There is no least integer; i.e., Z has no minimum.

3903. We know that Z has neither maximum nor minimum.
May we conclude therefrom that Z is unbounded below and above?
No. A number set may have neither maximum nor minimum and yet be bounded below and above, e.g., $\{x \mid 0 < x < 1\}$.

After we have stated our last axiom (4109), we shall be able to prove that Z is unbounded below and above.

3904. Theorem. Each nonempty set of integers that is bounded below by an integer has a minimum.

Proof. Consider any nonempty set B of integers that is bounded below by an integer, say i.
Let C denote $\{x - i \mid x \in B\}$.
Of course C is a nonempty set of nonnegative integers.
First we shall prove that C has a minimum and then we shall prove that $i + \min C$ is the minimum of B.

PART I. Suppose that C has no minimum.
Let T denote the set of all nonnegative integers that precede C.
T and C are disjoint; i.e., $T \cap C = \emptyset$. (?)
T contains 0. (?)
T is hereditary because for each number n in T:
$n + 1$ is a nonnegative integer that precedes C (?) and so $n + 1$ is in T.
Therefore T contains every nonnegative integer, and hence C is empty. (?)
Contradiction.

PART II. Since min C is in C, there is a number y in B such that min $C = y - i$. Hence $i + $ min C is in B.   (?)
Furthermore, $i + $ min C precedes B because for each member x of B: $x - i$ is in C and so min $C \le x - i$ and hence $i + $ min $C \le x$. Therefore $i + $ min C is the minimum of B.

3905. Corollaries.

   a. Each nonempty set of nonnegative integers has a minimum.   (3904)

   b. Each nonempty set of positive integers has a minimum.   (3904)

3906. Exercise.

Each nonempty set of integers that is bounded above by an integer has a maximum. HINT. Consider the negative of the set.

3907. Definition. A number set is *well-ordered* provided that every nonempty subset thereof has a minimum.

3908. Examples.

   a. R is not well-ordered because R, which is a nonempty subset of R, has no minimum.

   b. R_0 is not well-ordered because R_+, which is a nonempty subset of R_0, has no minimum.

   c. Z is not well-ordered because Z, which is a nonempty subset of Z, has no minimum.

   d. $\emptyset$ is well-ordered.   (?)

   e. Z_0 is well-ordered.   (3905a)

   f. Z_+ is well-ordered.   (3905b)

   g. $\{x \mid 0 \le x \le 1\}$ is not well-ordered.   (?)

3909. Immediate consequence. Each subset of a well-ordered number set is well-ordered.   (3907)

3910. The *well-ordering principle for Z_0* is simply the true proposition that in each nonempty set of nonnegative integers there is a least member. (3905a)

The *well-ordering principle for Z_+* is simply the true proposition that in each nonempty set of positive integers there is a least member.   (3905b)

3911. Diversion. We shall "prove" that every positive integer is "interesting."

"Proof." Suppose not.

Then the set of all "uninteresting" positive integers is nonempty and hence has a minimum, say c.

Since c is the smallest "uninteresting" positive integer, c is surely a museum piece and hence "interesting." Contradiction.

3912. As an illustration of the potency of the well-ordering principle for Z_+, we shall prove a famous theorem whose discovery by the school of Pythagoras was one of the most exciting mathematical events in history.

3913. Theorem. There are no integers j, n such that $(j/n)^2 = 2$.

Proof. Suppose not.

Then there are *positive* integers j, n such that $(j/n)^2 = 2$.   (?)

Since there is a positive integer whose product with j/n is integral (e.g., n is such a positive integer), there is a least such positive integer, say p.

We shall prove that $p(j/n) - p$ is a positive integer that is less than p and whose product with j/n is integral, and this result will contradict the fact that p is the least positive integer whose product with j/n is integral.

The number $p(j/n) - p$

is an integer,   (?)

is positive because $j/n - 1$ is positive,   (?)

is less than p because $j/n - 1 < 1$,   (?)

and its product with j/n equals $2p - p(j/n)$ which is integral.

3914. Exercises.

a. There are no integers j, n such that $(j/n)^2 = 3$.
HINT. Use essentially the same proof as for 3913.

b. There are no integers j, n such that $(j/n)^2 = 5$.
HINT. The proof of 3913 must be slightly modified.

3915. Definition. A number set S is Archimedean provided that each number in S is strictly between two integers; i.e., for each number x in S: there are integers m, n such that $m < x < n$.

NOTE. It is not customary to define *Archimedean number set*, but the author considers it helpful to do so. Some writers refer to the following statement (or one equivalent thereto) as *the Archimedean property* of the real number system:

For each positive number a: there is a positive integer j such that $1/j < a$.

We shall prove this statement in 4511b.

3916. Immediate consequence (of 3915).

Each subset of an Archimedean number set is Archimedean.

3917. Theorem. Z is Archimedean.

Proof. Each number x in Z is strictly between the integers $x - 1, x + 1$.

3918. Exercise.

$\{1/2, 1\}$ is Archimedean.

3919. After we have stated our last axiom of the real number system in 4109, we shall be able to prove that R is Archimedean, whence it will follow by 3916 that every number set is Archimedean.

3920. Notations.

  a. For each integer i: the author uses the symbol Z_i to denote the set of all integers exceeding i.

  b. For any integers i, j such that $i \leq j$: the author uses the symbol $Z_{i,j}$ to denote the set of all integers between i, j.

3921. Examples.

  a. $Z_{-1,2} = \{-1, 0, 1, 2\}$.

  b. $Z_{1,1} = \{1\}$.

  c. $Z_1 = Z_+$. (?)

3922. The expression *for any integers $i < j$* stands for the expression *for any integers i, j such that $i < j$.*

And so on. See 2910.

Inductive Proofs

4001. A mathematician wishes to prove a proposition α.
He produces a set S and proves that

i. if S is 0-hereditary, then α;
ii. S is 0-hereditary.

Surely he may then claim that α has been proved.

4002. A proof of a proposition α by *induction from* 0 consists in producing a set S and proving that

i. if S is 0-hereditary, then α;
ii. S is 0-hereditary.

4003. To prove a proposition α by induction from 0, we must find a set S that meets requirements 4002i,ii.   The task of finding such a set may require the exercise of considerable ingenuity. If we cannot find such a set, then we cannot prove α by induction from 0.

We shall see that Theorem 3817 is useful for proving that requirement 4002i is met.

4004. We shall prove the following proposition, call it β, by induction from 0.

For each nonnegative integer n: $n < n^2 + 1/10$.

Proof. Let S denote $\{n \,\epsilon\, R_0 \,|\, n < n^2 + 1/10\}$.
Then S meets requirement 4002i because if S were 0-hereditary, then by 3817, S would contain every nonnegative integer, and so β would follow.

Furthermore, S meets requirement 4002ii because 0 is in S (?)
and S contains the successor of each number n therein since
$(n + 1) \,\epsilon_?\, R_0$, and $n + 1 <_? (n^2 + 1/10) + 1 = (n^2 + 1) + 1/10 \leqq_?$
$(n + 1)^2 + 1/10$.

NOTE. Since S is 0-hereditary, it contains every nonnegative integer. The fact that S also contains nonnegative numbers (e.g., 3/2) that are not nonnegative integers should not bother us.

4005. Exercises.

  a. Prove β (see 4004) by using $\{n \in Z_0 \mid n < n^2 + 1/10\}$ for S.

  b. Can β be proved by using $\{n \in R \mid n < n^2 + 1/10\}$ for S?   (Why?)

4006. In proofs by induction from 0 we shall henceforth leave it for the student to verify that requirement 4002i is met. E.g., here is a compressed proof of 4004.

  Proof. $\{n \in R_0 \mid n < n^2 + 1/10\}$ contains 0
  and contains the successor of each number n therein because
  $(n + 1) \in R_0$, and $n + 1 < (n^2 + 1/10) + 1 = (n^2 + 1) + 1/10 \leqq (n + 1)^2 + 1/10$.

  NOTE. In this compressed proof we submitted a set S and proved it to be 0-hereditary. The student is expected to verify that the proposition (β) follows by the assumption that S is 0-hereditary.

4007. Exercises.

  a. Determine which proofs in Lesson 38 are really proofs by induction from 0.

  b. For each nonnegative integer n: $n \leqq n^3$.
  Please prove by induction from 0.

  c. What is wrong with the following "proof" that Z_0 has a maximum?
  "*Proof.*" $\{i \in Z_0 \mid Z_{0,i}$ has a maximum$\}$ contains 0 and
  contains the successor of each number n therein because
  $(n + 1) \in Z_0$ and $Z_{1,n + 1}$ has a maximum.

4008. Definition. A set S is *hereditary from an integer j* provided that S contains j and S is hereditary.

  NOTE. We may also use the expression *j-hereditary* to mean *hereditary from j*.

4009. Examples.

  a. $\{y \mid 3 \leqq y\}$ is hereditary from 3.

  b. Z_{-3} is hereditary from -3 and from each integer greater than -3.

4010. Theorem. If a set is hereditary from an integer j, then it contains every integer exceeding j.

  Proof. Suppose not.
  Then there is a set G and an integer j such that
  G is hereditary from j and G lacks some integer exceeding j.
  So there is a least integer, say m, that exceeds j and is lacked by G.
  $j <_? m$, and so $j \leqq m - 1 < m$, and hence $(m - 1) \in_? G$,
  and so $[(m - 1) + 1] \in_? G$. Contradiction.   (?)

4011. A proof of a proposition α by *induction from an integer j* consists in producing a set S and proving that

   i. if S is hereditary from j, then α;
   ii. S is hereditary from j.

4012. We shall see that Theorem 4010 is useful for proving that requirement 4011i is met.

4013. Example. We shall prove the following by induction from 3.

For each number n in Z_3: $n^2 > n + 5$.

Proof. Let S denote $\{n \in Z_3 \mid n^2 > n + 5\}$.
Then S meets requirement 4011i. (?)
Furthermore, S is hereditary from 3 because
S contains 3, and
S contains the successor of each number n therein since
$(n + 1) \in_? Z_3$, and $(n + 1)^2 = n^2 + 2n + 1 >_? (n + 5) + 2n + 1 = 3n + 6 > (n + 1) + 5$.

NOTE. In such proofs we shall henceforth leave it for the student to verify that requirement 4011i is met.

4014. Exercise.

For each number n in Z_5: $n^2 > 3n + 7$.
Please prove by induction from 5.

4015. Definition.

A set S is *hereditary from an integer j to an integer v* provided that
$j < v$,
S contains j, and
S contains the successor of each number in S that is between j, $v - 1$.

4016. Exercise.

If a set is hereditary from an integer j to an integer v,
then it contains every integer between j, v.

4017. A proof of a proposition α by *induction from an integer j to an integer v* consists in producing a set S and proving that

   i. if S is hereditary from j to v, then α;
   ii. S is hereditary from j to v.

NOTE. This type of proof is often called a *proof by restricted induction*; we shall use such a proof in a subsequent lesson. In this type of proof, Proposition 4016 is useful for proving that requirement 4017i is met.

4018. The remainder of this lesson is devoted to two other types of inductive proofs; although these two types are useful in mathematics, we shall not illustrate their use.

4019. Definition.

A set S is *strongly hereditary from an integer j* provided that

S contains j, and

S contains the successor of each integer n such that

$[j \leq n$ and every integer between j, n is in $S]$.

4020. Exercise.

If a set is strongly hereditary from an integer j,

then it contains every integer exceeding j.

4021. A proof of a proposition α by *strong induction from an integer j* consists in producing a set S and proving that

i. if S is strongly hereditary from j, then α;
ii. S is strongly hereditary from j.

NOTE. In this type of proof, Proposition 4020 is useful for proving that requirement 4021i is met.

4022. Definition.

A set T is *recessive from an integer w to an integer k* provided that

$k < w$,

T contains w, and

T contains the predecessor of each number in T that is between $k + 1$, w.

4023. Exercise. If a set is recessive from an integer w to an integer k,

then it contains every integer between k, w.

HINT. Consider the negative of the set.

4024. Theorem. For any integer i and set T such that

T contains the predecessor of each number in T that is greater than i,

and each integer is less than some integer in T:

T contains every integer exceeding i.

Proof.: if T lacked an integer, say j, exceeding i, then

there would be an integer n in T such that $j < n$,   (?)

and T would be recessive from n to j,   (?)

and so T would contain j, which is impossible.

4025. Proofs that exploit 4024 are usually called *proofs by backward induction*.

The Dedekind Axiom

4101. In this lesson we shall introduce our last axiom of the real number system.

4102. Definition. A number set A *precedes* a number set C provided that each member of A precedes C, i.e.,
for any number x in A and any number y in C: $x \leqq y$.

4103. Examples.

a. $\{x \mid 0 < x < 1\}$ precedes $\{5, 8\}$.

b. $\{x \mid 0 < x < 1\}$ precedes $\{y \mid 5 < y\}$.

c. $\{x \mid x < 5\}$ precedes $\{y \mid 5 < y\}$.

d. $\{x \mid x < 5\}$ precedes $\{y \mid 5 \leqq y < 7\}$.

e. $\{x \mid x \leqq 5\}$ precedes $\{y \mid 5 \leqq y < 7\}$.

f. $\{x \in R_+ \mid x^3 < 3x + 8\}$ precedes $\{y \in R_+ \mid 3y + 8 < y^3\}$.

Proof. Suppose not. Then there is a number x in the first set and a number y in the second set such that $y < x$.
Since $2^3 = 8 < 3y + 8 < y^3$, we have $2 < y$ and hence $3 < y^2$.
Then $0 <_? (x - y)(x^2 + xy + y^2 - 3) = (x^3 - 3x) - (y^3 - 3y)$, and so $8 < y^3 - 3y < x^3 - 3x < 8$. Contradiction.

4104. Exercise. $\{x \in R_+ \mid x^2 < 7\}$ precedes $\{y \in R_+ \mid 7 < y^2\}$.

NOTE. These sets are nonempty. (?)

4105. Definition. A number u is *between* number sets G, H provided that
either u exceeds G and precedes H
or u exceeds H and precedes G.

4106. Examples.

a. 1, 2, 5 are between the sets described in 4103a.

b. 1, 2, 5 are between the sets described in 4103b.

c. 5 is between the sets described in 4103c.

d. 5 is between the sets described in 4103d.

e. 5 is between the sets described in 4103e.

4107. Let A denote $\{x \epsilon R_+ \mid x^3 < 3x + 8\}$, and
let C denote $\{y \epsilon R_+ \mid 3y + 8 < y^3\}$.

By 4103f, we know that A precedes C.
Furthermore, A is nonempty because it contains 2,
and C is nonempty because it contains 3.

Intuitively we expect that there exists a number between A, C;
however, on the basis of the sixteen axioms introduced thus far, it
is impossible to prove that there is a number between A, C.

4108. Consider the following proposition.

For any nonempty number sets G, H such that G precedes H:
there is at least one number between G, H.

This proposition appears to be true; however, it can be proved that
this proposition cannot be proved on the basis of the sixteen axioms
introduced thus far. Accordingly, we adopt this proposition as our last
axiom of the real number system.

4109. Axiom. For any nonempty number sets G, H such that G precedes H:
there is at least one number between G, H.

NOTE. We shall refer to this axiom as *the Dedekind axiom*. Richard
Dedekind (1831–1916) did outstanding work on the real number system.

4110. Example. There is a positive number whose square is 7.

Proof. By 4104 and 4109, there is a number, say b, between
$\{x \epsilon R_+ \mid x^2 < 7\}$, $\{y \epsilon R_+ \mid 7 < y^2\}$.

b is positive. (?)

Since the first set has no maximum (3612), b is not in it (?) and so
$7 \leq b^2$.

Since the second set has no minimum (3715), b is not in it (?) and so
$b^2 \leq 7$.

Hence $b^2 = 7$.

4111. Exercises.

a. There is precisely one positive number whose square is 7.

b. There is precisely one number between the sets described in 4103c.

4112. Theorem. For any number sets A, C such that A precedes C:

there is precisely one number between A, C $\Leftrightarrow$

for each positive number p: there are members x, y of A, C respectively such that $y - x < p$.

Proof. Consider any number sets A, C such that A precedes C.

PART I($\Rightarrow$). Assume that there is precisely one number, say b, between A, C. Consider any positive number p.
Since $b - p/2$ does not exceed A
(otherwise $b - p/2$ would also be between A, C),
there is a member x of A such that $b - p/2 < x \le b$.
Since $b + p/2$ does not precede C,   (?)
there is a member y of C such that $b \le y < b + p/2$.
Therefore $y - x < p$.   (?)

PART II($\Leftarrow$). Assume that for each positive number p: there are members x, y of A, C respectively such that $y - x < p$.

Then A is nonempty and C is nonempty.   (?)
So by 4109, there is at least one number between A, C.
Furthermore, there is at most one number between A, C.
For consider any two numbers between A, C, say u, v where $u \le v$.
Then for each positive number p: there are numbers x, y in A, C
respectively such that $y - x < p$, and so $x \le u \le v \le y$, and hence
$v - u \le y - x < p$;
so by 3016b, $v - u \le 0$, and hence $v \le u$.
Therefore $u = v$.

4113. Exercise. (*Dedekind*)

For any nonempty number sets A, C such that $A \cup C = R$ and
A precedes C: either max A exists or min C exists.

4114. A *complete ordered field* is any system that satisfies our seventeen axioms of the real number system (2202, 2203, 2302, 2402, 2502, 4109). It can be proved that all complete ordered fields are "structurally indistinguishable"; see *Introduction to Set Theory and Logic* by Stoll.

Square Root

4201. In this lesson we shall define, for each nonnegative number b, *the principal square root of b*. At the end of this lesson we shall discuss the common confusion about square roots.

4202. Theorem. For each positive number c: there is precisely one positive number whose square is c.

Proof. Consider any positive number c.

AT MOST ONE. For any positive numbers u, v whose square is c: $u^2 = v^2$ and so $u = v$. (?)

AT LEAST ONE. Let A denote $\{x \in R_+ \mid x^2 < c\}$ and let E denote $\{y \in R_+ \mid c < y^2\}$.

A is nonempty because it contains $(1/2)\min(1, c)$. (?)
E is nonempty because it contains $c + 1$. (?)
A precedes E. (?)
So, there is a number u between A, E.
u is positive. (?)
Since A has no maximum (3612), u is not in A and so $c \leqq u^2$.
Since E has no minimum (3715), u is not in E and so $u^2 \leqq c$.
Hence $u^2 = c$.

4203. Exercise.

There is precisely one number, namely 0, whose square is 0.

4204. Corollary. For each nonnegative number b: there is precisely one nonnegative number whose square is b. (4202, 4203)

4205. Definition. The *principal square root* of a nonnegative number b is the nonnegative number whose square is b.

NOTATION. $\sqrt{b}$, read as *principal square root of b* or as *root b*.

NOTE. We do not define the principal square root of negative numbers.

4206. Theorems.

a. For each nonnegative number b: $(\sqrt{b})^2 = b$. (4205)

b. For each positive number c: $0 < \sqrt{c}$.
Proof.: $0 \leq \sqrt{c}$ (4205), and if $\sqrt{c}$ were equal to 0, then we would have $c = (\sqrt{c})^2 = 0^2 = 0$, which is impossible.

c. For any nonnegative number b and any number y:
$\sqrt{b} = y \Leftrightarrow [0 \leq y \text{ and } y^2 = b]$. (4205)

4207. Examples.

a. $\sqrt{9} = 3$ because $0 \leq 3$ and $3^2 = 9$. (4206c)

b. $\sqrt{9} \neq -3$ because $-3 < 0$. (4206c)
NOTE. Since the statement ($\sqrt{9} = 3$ or $\sqrt{9} = -3$) is true, the statement ($\sqrt{9} = \pm 3$) is true (see 2615). However, the true statement ($\sqrt{9} = \pm 3$) is not worth using because we have the stronger truth ($\sqrt{9} = 3$).

c. $\sqrt{1} = 1$ because $0 \leq 1$ and $1^2 = 1$.

d. $\sqrt{0} = 0$ because $0 \leq 0$ and $0^2 = 0$.

4208. Exercises.

a. *Disprove.* For each number x: $\sqrt{x^2} = x$.

b. For each number x: $\sqrt{x^2} = |x|$.

c. For any nonnegative numbers u, v:
$u < v \Leftrightarrow \sqrt{u} < \sqrt{v}$, and $u = v \Leftrightarrow \sqrt{u} = \sqrt{v}$.

d. For any nonnegative numbers x, y: $\sqrt{xy} = \sqrt{x}\sqrt{y}$.

e. For any number x and nonnegative number p:
$x^2 \leq p \Leftrightarrow |x| \leq \sqrt{p}$.

f. For any nonnegative number u and positive number v:
$\sqrt{u/v} = \sqrt{u}/\sqrt{v}$.

g. For any number x and nonnegative number c:
$x^2 = c \Leftrightarrow x = \pm\sqrt{c}$.

4209. Theorem.

For any numbers a, b, c such that $a \neq 0$ and $0 \leq b^2 - 4ac$:

$$\{x \mid ax^2 + bx + c = 0\} =$$

$$\left\{ \frac{-b + \sqrt{b^2 - 4ac}}{2a}, \ \frac{-b - \sqrt{b^2 - 4ac}}{2a} \right\}.$$

Proof. Consider any such hypothesized a, b, c.
Then for each number x:

x is in the first set $\Leftrightarrow$

$ax^2 + bx + c = 0$ $\Leftrightarrow$

$x^2 + \dfrac{b}{a}x + \dfrac{c}{a} = 0$ $\Leftrightarrow$

$x^2 + \dfrac{b}{a}x + \left(\dfrac{b}{2a}\right)^2 = \left(\dfrac{b}{2a}\right)^2 - \dfrac{c}{a}$ $\quad \Leftrightarrow$

$\left(x + \dfrac{b}{2a}\right)^2 = \dfrac{b^2 - 4ac}{4a^2}$ $\quad \Leftrightarrow_?$

$\left|x + \dfrac{b}{2a}\right| = \dfrac{\sqrt{b^2 - 4ac}}{2|a|}$ $\quad \Leftrightarrow_?$

$x + \dfrac{b}{2a} = \dfrac{\sqrt{b^2 - 4ac}}{2a}$ or $-\left(x + \dfrac{b}{2a}\right) = \dfrac{\sqrt{b^2 - 4ac}}{2a}$ $\quad \Leftrightarrow$

$x = \dfrac{-b + \sqrt{b^2 - 4ac}}{2a}$ or $x = \dfrac{-b - \sqrt{b^2 - 4ac}}{2a}$ $\quad \Leftrightarrow$

x is in the second set.

NOTE. If $b^2 - 4ac = 0$, then $\{x \mid ax^2 + bx + c = 0\} = \{-b/2a\}$.

4210. Exercise.

For any numbers a, b, c, x such that $b^2 - 4ac < 0$:
$ax^2 + bx + c \neq 0$.

4211. Theorem. *Cauchy-Schwarz Inequality (special case).*

For any numbers a, b, u, v: $(au + bv)^2 \leq (a^2 + b^2)(u^2 + v^2)$.

Proof.: $(au + bv)^2 =_? (a^2 + b^2)(u^2 + v^2) - (bu - av)^2 \leq$
$(a^2 + b^2)(u^2 + v^2)$.

4212. Theorem. *Minkowski Inequality* (*special case*).

For any numbers a, b, u, v:
$$\sqrt{(a + u)^2 + (b + v)^2} \leq \sqrt{a^2 + b^2} + \sqrt{u^2 + v^2}.$$

Proof.:

$$\sqrt{(a + u)^2 + (b + v)^2} \leq_?$$

$$\sqrt{a^2 + b^2 + 2|au + bv| + u^2 + v^2} \leq_?$$

$$\sqrt{a^2 + b^2 + 2\sqrt{(a^2 + b^2)(u^2 + v^2)} + u^2 + v^2} =$$

$$\sqrt{(\sqrt{a^2 + b^2} + \sqrt{u^2 + v^2})^2} =$$

$$\sqrt{a^2 + b^2} + \sqrt{u^2 + v^2}.$$

4213. Exercises.

a. For any nonnegative numbers u, v: $\sqrt{uv} \leq (u + v)/2$.

b. For any numbers p, t such that $1 < p$ and $0 < t$:
$\sqrt{p}$ is between t and $(t + p)/(t + 1)$.
HINT. $1 < \sqrt{p} = (p - \sqrt{p})/(\sqrt{p} - 1)$.

4214. Consider any positive number c.
Then there are two distinct numbers whose square is c; one of them is
the positive number $\sqrt{c}$ and the other is the negative number $-\sqrt{c}$.
Most mathematicians call both $\sqrt{c}$ and $-\sqrt{c}$ *square roots of c* and distinguish them by referring to $\sqrt{c}$ as *the principal square root of c*; unfortunately they usually drop the adjective *principal* and refer to $\sqrt{c}$ as
the square root of c. This "abuse of language" justifiably confuses students.

The Supremum of a Number Set

4301. We know by 3707, that the maximum (if there is one) of a number set is, among other things, the least number that exceeds the set.

E.g., 3 is the maximum of $\{x \mid x \leq 3\}$, and 3 is the least number that exceeds the set.

If a number set has no maximum, there nevertheless might be a least number that exceeds the set.

E.g., $\{x \mid x < 3\}$ has no maximum (3604f); nevertheless, 3 is the least number that exceeds the set.

Proof. Let B denote the set.
Clearly, 3 exceeds B.
Consider any upper bound v of B.
It suffices to prove that $3 \leq v$.
Each number less than 3 is in B and so precedes v,
and hence by 3017b, $3 \leq v$. Q.e.d.

If a number set is unbounded above, then surely there is no least number that exceeds it.

Of course, for each number set A: there is at most one least number that exceeds A. (?)

4302. Definition. The *supremum* (if there is one) of a number set A is the least number that exceeds A.

NOTATION. sup A, read *soup A*.

NOTE I. The supremum (if there is one) of a number set is not necessarily in the set. (?)

214

NOTE II. The supremum (if there is one) of a number set A, being the least of all upper bounds of A, is frequently called *the least upper bound* of A and denoted by the symbol lub A.

NOTE III. Each number less than the supremum of a number set A is less than some number in A.   (?)

4303. The following expressions are synonymous:

there is a least number that exceeds A,
A has a supremum,
sup A exists.

NOTE. The expression (sup $A = b$) means *A has a supremum, namely b.*

4304. We know that the maximum (if there is one) of a number set is also the supremum of the set.

However, a set may have a supremum without having a maximum.
E.g., in 4301, we proved that 3 is the supremum of $\{x \mid x < 3\}$ which has no maximum. Let us prove in another way that $\sup\{x \mid x < 3\} = 3$.

Proof. Let A denote the set.
Clearly, 3 exceeds A.
Suppose that 3 is not the least number that exceeds A.
Then there is a number c that is less than 3 and exceeds A.
Since $c < (c + 3)/2$, we know that $(c + 3)/2$ is not in A.
Since $(c + 3)/2 < 3$, we know that $(c + 3)/2$ is in A.
Contradiction.

NOTE. Soon we shall offer an extremely simple proof that $\sup\{x \mid x < 3\} = 3$.

4305. Examples.

a. R has no supremum because no number exceeds R.
NOTE. No number set that is unbounded above has a supremum.

b. $\emptyset$ has no supremum because every number exceeds $\emptyset$ and hence there is no least number that exceeds $\emptyset$.

c. 2 is not the supremum of $\{x \mid x < 4\}$ because 2 does not exceed the set.

d. 6 is not the supremum of $\{x \mid x < 4\}$ because 5, which is less than 6, exceeds the set.

4306. Theorem. For any number b and number set A:

$\sup A = b \Leftrightarrow$

b exceeds A, and
each number less than b precedes some number in A.

Proof. Consider any number b and number set A.

PART I($\Rightarrow$). Obvious. (?)

PART II($\Leftarrow$). Assume that b exceeds A and that each number less than b precedes some number in A.
Then b is the least number that exceeds A (and hence $\sup A = b$) because otherwise some number r less than b would exceed A and then $(r + b)/2$, which is strictly between r, b, would be greater than every number in A, and this is impossible because $(r + b)/2$ precedes some number in A. (?)

4307. To illustrate the use of 4306, we again prove that $\sup\{x \mid x < 3\} = 3$.

Proof. 3 exceeds the set, and
each number r less than 3 precedes r which is in the set.

NOTE. The author claims that this is the simplest possible proof of the proposition.

4308. Example. $\sup\{x \mid -1 < x < 3\} = 3$.

Let A denote the set.

Proof I. Clearly, 3 exceeds A.
Each number r less than 3 precedes $\max(r, 2)$ which is in A. (?)

Proof II. Clearly, 3 exceeds A.
Suppose that 3 is not the least number that exceeds A.
Then there is a number c that is less than 3 and exceeds A.
Since $c < (c + 3)/2$, we know that $(c + 3)/2$ is not in A.
Since $-1 < c < (c + 3)/2 < 3$, we know that $(c + 3)/2$ is in A.
Contradiction.

Proof III. Clearly, 3 exceeds A.
Consider any upper bound v of A.
It suffices to prove that $3 \leq v$.
Each number strictly between $-1, 3$ precedes v,
and so by 3019a (with -1 for b and 3 for u), $3 \leq v$.

4309. Exercise.

For any positive number b and number set A:

$\sup A = b \Leftrightarrow$

b exceeds A, and
each positive number less than b precedes some number in A.

4310. To illustrate the use of 4309, we again prove that
$\sup\{x \mid -1 < x < 3\} = 3$.

Proof. 3 exceeds the set, and
each positive number r less than 3 precedes r which is in the set.

NOTE. 4309 is applicable here because 3 is positive.

4311. Exercise.
$\sup\{x \mid 1 < x < 3\} = 3$.

4312. Example. $\sup\{x/(x + 1) \mid 0 < x\} = 1$.

Proof (using 4309). Let A denote the set.
1 exceeds A. (?)
Consider any positive number r less than 1.
It suffices to find a number that is in A and exceeds r;
hence it suffices to find a number x such that $0 < x$ and $r \leq x/(x + 1)$.
Noting that $[0 < x$ and $r \leq x/(x + 1)] \Leftarrow_? r/(1 - r) = x$,
we may choose x to be $r/(1 - r)$.

4313. Example. $\sup\{x \in R_+ \mid x^2 < 3\} = \sqrt{3}$.

Proof. $\sqrt{3}$ exceeds the set, and each positive number r less than $\sqrt{3}$ precedes r which is in the set. (?)

4314. Example. $\sup\{2x/(4 - 3x) \mid 0 < x < 1\} = 2$.

Proof. 2 exceeds the set. (?)
Consider any positive number r less than 2.
It suffices to find a number that is in the set and exceeds r;
hence it suffices to find a number x such that $0 < x < 1$ and
$r \leq 2x/(4 - 3x)$.
Noting that $[0 < x < 1$ and $r \leq 2x/(4 - 3x)] \Leftarrow_? 4r/(2 + 3r) = x$,
we may choose x to be $4r/(2 + 3r)$.

4315. Example. $\sup\{x - \sqrt{x^2 + 1} \mid 0 \leq x\} = 0$.

Proof (using 4306). Let A denote the set.
0 exceeds A. (?)
Consider any number r less than 0.
It suffices to find a number that is in A and exceeds r;
hence it suffices to find a number x such that $0 \leq x$ and
$r \leq x - \sqrt{x^2 + 1}$.
Noting that $[0 \leq x$ and $r \leq x - \sqrt{x^2 + 1}] \Leftarrow_?$
$[0 \leq x$ and $(r^2 - 1)/2r \leq x]$,
we may choose $\max\{0, (r^2 - 1)/2r\}$ for x.

4316. Exercises.

   a. For each number t: $\sup\{x \mid x < t\} = t$.

   b. $\sup\{2x + 5 \mid x < -1\} = 3$.

   c. $\sup\{x^2 \mid 0 < x < 3\} = 9$.

   d. $\sup\{3x/(2x + 1) \mid 0 \le x\} = 3/2$.

   e. $\sup\{1 + \sqrt{x} \mid 0 \le x < 1\} = 2$.

   f. $\sup\{\sqrt{x^2 - 1} - x \mid 1 \le x\} = 0$.

   g. *Prove or disprove.* For any number b and number set A:
     if $\sup A = b$, then $\max[A \cup \{b\}] = b$.

   h. Prove or disprove the converse of the previous proposition.

   i. For any number sets G, H such that $\sup G$ exists, $\sup H$ exists, and each
     number in G precedes some number in H: $\sup G \le \sup H$.

   j. *Prove or disprove.* If a number set B has a maximum, say u, and
     $B - \{u\}$ is nonempty, then $\sup[B - \{u\}] = u$.

4317. The next theorem reflects the so-called local nature of the relationship
between a number set and its supremum.

4318. Theorem. For any number t and number set B such that $\sup B$ exists and
$t < \sup B$: $\sup\{x \in B \mid t \le x\} = \sup B$.

   Proof.
   Consider any such hypothesized t, B and let A denote $\{x \in B \mid t \le x\}$.
   There is a number v in B such that $t \le v$, and so v is in A. (?)

   Now we shall use 4306 to prove that $\sup A = \sup B$.
   Surely, $\sup B$ exceeds A. (?)
   Each number less than $\sup B$ precedes some number u in B
   and so precedes $\max(u, v)$ which is in A. (?)

4319. Note for the teacher.
The author is intentionally postponing Theorem 4502.

LESSON **44**

The Infimum of a Number Set

4401. We know by 3709 that the minimum (if there is one) of a number set is, among other things, the greatest number that precedes the set.

E.g., 3 is the minimum of $\{x \mid 3 \leq x\}$, and 3 is the greatest number that precedes the set.

If a number set has no minimum, there nevertheless might be a greatest number that precedes the set.

E.g., $\{x \mid 3 < x\}$ has no minimum (3704f); nevertheless, 3 is the greatest number that precedes the set.

Proof. Clearly, 3 precedes the set.
Consider any lower bound u of the set.
It suffices to prove that $u \leq 3$.   (?)
Each number greater than 3 is in the set and so exceeds u,
and hence by 3017a, $u \leq 3$.   Q.e.d.

If a number set is unbounded below, then surely there is no greatest number that precedes it.

Of course, for each number set C: there is at most one greatest number that precedes C.

4402. Definition. The *infimum* (if there is one) of a number set C is the greatest number that precedes C.

NOTATION. inf C.

NOTE I. The infimum (if there is one) of a number set is not necessarily in the set.

NOTE II. The infimum (if there is one) of a number set C, being the greatest of all lower bounds of C, is frequently called *the greatest lower bound* of C and denoted by the symbol glb C.

NOTE III. Each number greater than the infimum of a number set C is greater than some number in C.   (?)

4403. The following expressions are synonymous:

there is a greatest number that precedes C,
C has an infimum,
inf C exists.

NOTE. The expression (inf $C = b$) means C *has an infimum, namely b.*

4404. We know that the minimum (if there is one) of a number set is also the infimum of the set.

However, a set may have an infimum without having a minimum.
E.g., in 4401, we proved that 3 is the infimum of $\{x \mid 3 < x\}$ which has no minimum. Soon we shall offer an extremely simple proof that inf$\{x \mid 3 < x\} = 3$.

4405. Examples.

a. R has no infimum because no number precedes R.

NOTE. No number set that is unbounded below has an infimum.

b. $\emptyset$ has no infimum.

4406. Theorem. For any number b and number set C:

inf $C = b \Leftrightarrow$

b precedes C, and
each number greater than b exceeds some number in C.

Proof. Similar to proof of 4306.

4407. To illustrate the use of 4406, we again prove that inf$\{x \mid 3 < x\} = 3$.

Proof. 3 precedes the set, and
each number r greater than 3 exceeds r which is in the set.

4408. Example. inf$\{x \mid -1 < x < 3\} = -1$.

Proof. Clearly, -1 precedes the set.
Suppose that -1 is not the greatest number that precedes the set.
Then there is a number c that is greater than -1 and precedes the set.
Since $(-1 + c)/2 < c$, we know that $(-1 + c)/2$ is not in the set.
Since $-1 < (-1 + c)/2 < c < 3$, we know that $(-1 + c)/2$ is in the set.
Contradiction.

4409. Theorem. For any negative number b and number set C:

inf $C = b \Leftrightarrow$

b precedes C, and
each negative number greater than b exceeds some number in C.

Proof. Similar to proof of 4309.

4410. To illustrate the use of 4409, we again prove that
inf$\{x \mid -1 < x < 3\} = -1$.

Proof. -1 precedes the set, and
each negative number r greater than -1 exceeds r which is in the set.

4411. Exercises.

a. inf$\{x \mid -1 < x \leq -1/2\} = -1$.

b. inf$\{x/(x + 1) \mid 0 < x\} = 0$.

c. inf$\{x \in R_+ \mid 3 < x^2\} = \sqrt{3}$.

d. inf$\{3x/(2x + 5) \mid 1 < x\} = 3/7$.

e. For each number set A that has an infimum and a supremum:
inf $A \leq$ sup A.

f. For each number set A such that inf $A =$ sup A:
A has precisely one member.

g. For any number set H that has a supremum: inf$[\div H] = -$sup H.

h. For any number set C that has an infimum: sup$[\div C] = -$inf C.

i. For any number w and number set C such that inf C exists and
inf $C < w$: inf$\{x \in C \mid x \leq w\} = $ inf C. (Compare with 4318.)

Completeness

4501. We know that if a number set has a supremum, then it is nonempty and bounded above. The converse of this proposition is very important; we prove it next.

4502. Theorem. Each nonempty, bounded-above number set has a supremum.

Proof. Consider any nonempty, bounded-above number set G, and let H denote the set of all upper bounds of G.

Since G, H are nonempty and G precedes H, there is (by the Dedekind axiom) a number u between G, H, and so u is the supremum of G. (?)

4503. We know that if a number set has an infimum, then it is nonempty and bounded below. The converse of this proposition is very important; see 4504.

4504. Exercise.

Each nonempty, bounded-below number set has an infimum.
HINT. Consider the negative of the set.

4505. Theorem. For any nonempty subset A of a bounded number set B:
$$\inf B \leq \inf A \leq \sup A \leq \sup B.$$

PRELIMINARY REMARK. Implicit in the conclusion is the existence of the infima and suprema.

Proof.: A, B are nonempty, bounded number sets
and so their infima and suprema exist; (?)
since $\inf B$ precedes A, $\inf B \leq \inf A$; (?)
since A is exceeded by $\sup B$, $\sup A \leq \sup B$; (?)
lastly, $\inf A \leq \sup A$. (4411e)

4506. Exercises.

   a. If possible, find nonempty number sets A, C such that each number in A is less than each number in C and sup $A = $ inf C.

   b. For any nonempty number sets A, C such that A precedes C: sup $A \leqq$ inf C.

4507. Theorem. For any number b and number sets A, C such that A precedes C: b is *the* number between A, C $\Leftrightarrow$
sup $A = b = $ inf C.

   Proof. Consider any such hypothesized b, A, C.

   PART I($\Rightarrow$). Assume that b is the number between A, C.
   Then A is bounded above.
   A is nonempty because otherwise $b - 1$ would also be between A, C.
   Hence sup A exists.
   Since C is bounded below and nonempty, inf C exists. (?)
   Since A is exceeded by sup A, and sup A precedes inf C, and inf C precedes C,
   both sup A and inf C are between A, C.
   Hence sup $A = b = $ inf C. (?)

   PART II($\Leftarrow$). Assume that sup $A = b = $ inf C.
   Then b is between A, C. (?)
   Furthermore, for each number u between A, C:
   sup $A \leqq u \leqq$ inf $C = $ sup A, and so $u = $ sup $A = b$.
   Hence b is the number between A, C.

4508. Theorem. Z_+ is unbounded above.

   Proof. Suppose Z_+ is bounded above.
   Then Z_+ has a supremum, say b.
   Then, for each number n in Z_+: $n + 1$ is in Z_+ and so $n + 1 \leqq b$, and hence $n = (n + 1) - 1 \leqq b - 1$.
   Therefore Z_+ is exceeded by $b - 1$. Contradiction. (?)

4509. Corollaries.

   a. Z_0 is unbounded above.

   Proof. If Z_0 were bounded above, then Z_+, being a subset of Z_0, would also be bounded above.

   b. Z is unbounded above.

   Proof. Similar to previous proof.

   c. Z is unbounded below.

   Proof. Z equals $\doteq Z$ which is unbounded below. (?)

4510. Theorems.

a. Each number is less than some integer.

Proof. Suppose not. Then some number exceeds every integer. Contradiction. (?)

b. Each number is greater than some integer.

Proof. Suppose not. Then some number precedes every integer. Contradiction. (?)

NOTE. The next proposition is an extension of Theorem 3904.

c. Each nonempty set of integers that is bounded below has a minimum.

Proof. Each nonempty set of integers that is bounded below is bounded below by an integer (?) and hence has a minimum.   (3904)

NOTE. The next proposition is an extension of Theorem 3906.

d. Each nonempty set of integers that is bounded above has a maximum.

Proof. 4510a and 3906.

4511. Theorems.

a. R is Archimedean.   (See 3915.)

Proof. 4510a, 4510b.

NOTE. In view of 4511a and 3916, every number set is Archimedean.

b. For each positive number a: there is a positive integer j such that $1/j < a$.

Proof.: $1/a$ is less than some integer j (4510a), and so $0 < j$ and hence $1/j < a$.

4512. Example. $\sup\{n/(n + 1) \mid n \in Z_+\} = 1$.

Proof (using 4309). 1 exceeds the set.   (?)

Consider any positive number r less than 1.

It suffices to find a number that is in the set and exceeds r;

hence it suffices to find a positive integer n such that $r \leqq n/(n + 1)$.

Noting that $[n \in Z_+ \text{ and } r \leqq n/(n + 1)] \Leftarrow_? [n \in Z \text{ and } r/(1 - r) \leqq n]$,

and knowing that there is an integer exceeding $r/(1 - r)$,   (?)

we may choose for n any integer exceeding $r/(1 - r)$.

4513. Exercise.

$\inf\{n/(n^2 + 1) \mid n \in Z_+\} = 0$.

4514. Definition. A number set S is *complete* provided that
for each nonempty, bounded subset A of S: $\inf A$ and $\sup A$ are in S.

4515. Immediate consequences.

    a. R is complete.

    b. Z is complete.   (4510c,d)

4516. Soon we shall learn that some number sets are not complete.

4517. Exercises.

    a. *Prove or disprove.* $\{1, 2\}$ is complete.

    b. *Prove or disprove.* R_0 is complete.

    c. *Prove or disprove.* $\emptyset$ is complete.

    d. *Prove or disprove.* R_+ is complete.

$$[x]$$

4601. Theorem. For each number x: there is a greatest integer that precedes x; i.e., the set of all integers preceding x has a maximum.

Proof.: the set of all integers preceding x is nonempty   (4510b) and bounded above (e.g., by x) and so has a maximum.   (4510d)

4602. Notation. For each number x: the symbol $[x]$, read *bracket x*, denotes the greatest integer preceding x.

NOTE. Many writers call $[x]$ the greatest integer in x; soon we shall see that it would be more appropriate to call $[x]$ the integral part of x.

4603. Examples.

a. $[9/2] = 4$ because $4 < 9/2 < 5$ and so 4 is the greatest integer preceding 9/2.

b. $[-9/2] = -5$ because $-5 < -9/2 < -4$.

c. $[\sqrt{2}] = 1$ because $1 < \sqrt{2} < 2$.

d. $[8] = 8$ because $8 \leqq 8 < 9$.

NOTE. For each integer n: $[n] = n$.

4604. It is important to keep in mind that for each number x: $[x]$ is an integer, $[x] \leqq x$, and no integer greater than $[x]$ precedes x.

4605. Exercises.

a. For each number y: $[[y]] = [y]$.

b. For each number x: $x - 1 < [x] \leqq x < [x] + 1$.

c. For each number x: $[x] + 1$ is the least integer greater than x.

226

d. For each number t: $-[-t]$ is the least integer exceeding t.

e. For any numbers x, y: $[x] + [y] \leq [x + y] \leq [x] + [y] + 1$.

f. For any number y and integer n: $[y + n] = [y] + n$.

g. For each number x: $[x] + [-x] = -1$ or $[x] + [-x] = 0$.

4606. Theorem. For each number x: there is precisely one integer n such that $n \leq x < n + 1$.

Proof. Consider any number x.

AT LEAST ONE. $[x]$ is such an integer. (4605b)

AT MOST ONE. For any integers m, p such that $m \leq x < m + 1$ and $p \leq x < p + 1$:
$m < p + 1$ and so $m \leq p$;
$p < m + 1$ and so $p \leq m$;
hence, $m = p$.

4607. Now we know that for each number x:
$[x]$ is *the* integer n such that $n \leq x < n + 1$.

4608. Definition. The *fractional part* of a number x is $x - [x]$.

4609. Theorem.
The fractional part of each number is nonnegative and less than 1.

Proof. For each number x: $[x] \leq x < [x] + 1$, and so $0 \leq x - [x] < 1$.

CAUTION. The fractional part of a number may be 0 or, as will be obvious later, may be irrational.

4610. Theorem.
Each number equals the sum of its fractional part and an integer.

Proof. For each number x: $x = (x - [x]) + [x]$.

NOTE. One could appropriately call $[x]$ the *integral part* of x.

4611. Exercise. For any number y and integer n:
y and $y + n$ have the same fractional part.

4612. One process of dividing a nonzero number b into a number a is as follows.

$$
\begin{array}{r}
[a/b] \\
\hline
b \overline{\smash{)}a} \\
b[a/b] \\
\hline
a - b[a/b]
\end{array}
$$

$a - b[a/b]$ is called the remainder.

4613. Theorem. For any number a and positive number b:
$a = b[a/b] + (a - b[a/b])$ and $0 \leqq a - b[a/b] < b$.

Proof.: The equality is obvious and the inequality follows from the fact that $a/b - 1 < [a/b] \leqq a/b$.

4614. Corollary. For each integer i: $i - 2[i/2]$ equals 0 or 1.

Proof.: $0 \leqq i - 2[i/2] < 2$ and $i - 2[i/2]$ is an integer.

4615. Theorem. *Euclid.*
For any number a and positive number b:
there is precisely one number pair (q, r) such that
q is an integer, $a = bq + r$, and $0 \leqq r < b$,
and in fact, $q = [a/b]$ and $r = a - b[a/b]$.

Proof. Consider any number a and positive number b.

AT LEAST ONE. See 4613.

AT MOST ONE. Consider any integers q, p and numbers r, s such that
$a = bq + r$, $0 \leqq r < b$, $a = bp + s$, $0 \leqq s < b$.
Then $0 \leqq b|q - p| = |bq - bp| = |r - s| <_? b$, and so
$0 \leqq |q - p| < 1$, and hence $q =_? p$.
Lastly, $r = a - bq = a - bp = s$.

NOTE. If both a and b are integers, then clearly r is also an integer.

4616. Definition.
An integer i is *divisible by* an integer n (and n is said to *divide i*)
provided that $n \neq 0$ and there is an integer p such that $i = np$.

4617. Exercises.

a. For any integers i, j that are divisible by an integer n:
$i + j$ and ij are divisible by n.

b. For any integer i and nonzero integer n:
i is divisible by n $\Leftrightarrow$ there is an integer t such that $i = |n| \cdot t$.

4618. Theorem. For any integer i and nonzero integer n:
i is divisible by n $\Leftrightarrow$ $i - n[i/n] = 0$.

Proof.: if i is divisible by n, then there is an integer p such that
$i = np$, and so $i - n[i/n] = np - n[p] = np - np = 0$;
if $i - n[i/n] = 0$, then $i = n[i/n]$ and so i is divisible by n.

Odd, Even

4701. Definition. An *even integer* is any integer that is divisible by 2.

4702. Theorems.

    a. For each integer i:

    i is even $\Leftrightarrow$

    there is an integer p such that $i = 2p$ $\Leftrightarrow$

    $i - 2[i/2] = 0$.

    Proof. 4701, 4616, 4618.

    b. For each even integer i: $-i$ is even.

    Proof.: there is an integer p such that $i = 2p$, and so $-i = 2(-p)$.

    c. For any even integers x, y: $x + y$ and xy are even.

    Proof. 4617a.

4703. Examples.

    a. -6 is even because $-6 = 2(-3)$.

    b. 0 is even because $0 = 2 \cdot 0$.

    c. 4 is even because $4 = 2(2)$.

    d. 3 is not even because $3 - 2[3/2] = 1 \neq 0$. (4702a)

4704. Definition. An *odd integer* is any integer whose successor is even.

4705. Example. -1 is odd because $-1 + 1$ is even.

4706. Theorem. For each integer i: i is odd $\Leftrightarrow$ $i - 1$ is even.

Proof.: i is odd $\Leftrightarrow$ $i + 1$ is even $\Leftrightarrow_1$ $(i + 1) + (-2)$ is even. (1.4702c)

4707. Corollary. The successor of each even integer is odd.

Proof. For each even integer j: $(j + 1) - 1$ is even and so $j + 1$ is odd.

NOTE. By Definition 4704, the successor of each odd integer is even.

4708. Theorems.

a. Each integer is odd or even.

Proof. Consider any integer i.
Either i is even or i is not even.
In case i is even, we are done
In case i is not even, then
$i - 2[i/2] \neq 0$, and hence (4614), $i - 2[i/2] = 1$, and therefore
$i + 1$, which equals $2([i/2] + 1)$, is even, and so i is odd.

b. No integer is both odd and even.

Proof. Suppose there is an integer i that is both odd and even.
Then there are integers p, q such that $i = 2p$ and $i + 1 = 2q$, and so
$1/2$, which equals$_2$ $q - p$, is an integer. Contradiction.

4709. Theorem. For each integer i:
i is odd $\Leftrightarrow$
there is an integer p such that $i = 2p + 1$ $\Leftrightarrow$
$i - 2[i/2] = 1$.

Proof.: i is odd $\Rightarrow$
$i - 1$ is even $\Rightarrow$
there is an integer p such that $i - 1 = 2p$ $\Rightarrow$

there is an integer p such that $i - 2[i/2] = 2p + 1 - 2[(2p + 1)/2] = 2p + 1 - 2[p + (1/2)] =_2 2p + 1 - 2p - 2[1/2] = 1$ $\Rightarrow_?$

$i - 2[i/2] = 1$ $\Rightarrow$
i is not even $\Rightarrow$
i is odd.

NOTE. This is a round-robin proof.

4710. Exercises.

a. For each odd integer j: $-j$ is odd.

b. For any odd integers i, j: $i + j$ is even and ij is odd.

c. For any even integer i and odd integer j: $i + j$ is odd and ij is even.

4711. Definition.

The *parity* of an even integer is 1;
the *parity* of an odd integer is -1.

NOTATION. The parity of an integer n is denoted by the symbol parity(n).

4712. Examples. parity(0) $= 1$, parity(-2) $= 1$, parity(3) $= -1$.

4713. Theorem. For any integers i, j: parity($i + j$) $=$ parity(i) · parity(j).

Proof.: if i, j are even, then parity($i + j$) $= 1 = 1 \cdot 1 =$ parity(i) · parity(j);

if i, j are odd, then parity($i + j$) $= 1 = (-1)(-1) =$ parity(i) · parity(j);

if i is even and j is odd, or if i is odd and j is even, then parity($i + j$) $= -1 =$ parity(i) · parity(j).

NOTE. As a special case of this theorem, we see that for each integer j: parity($1 + j$) $= -$parity(j).

4714. Exercises.

a. For each integer i: parity($-i$) $=$ parity(i).

b. For each integer i: parity(i) $= 1/$parity(i).

c. For each integer i: parity(i) $= 1 - 2i + 4[i/2]$.

4715. Diversion. We shall "prove" that each positive integer is even.

"*Proof.*" Suppose not.
Then there is a least positive integer p such that p is not even.
So, $p - 2$, being less than p, is even.
Hence $(p - 2) + 2$ is even. Contradiction. (?)
Where is the flaw?

Rationals, Irrationals

4801. Definition. A *rational* (or a *rational number*) is any number that equals the quotient of an integer by a nonzero integer.

NOTE. The reader will observe that this definition permits us to use the word *rational* as a noun and as an adjective.

4802. Each integer n is rational because $n = n/1$.
Not every rational is an integer; e.g., $1/2$ is rational but not integral.
Not every number is rational; e.g., $\sqrt{2}$ is not rational.   (3913)

4803. Theorem. For each rational r: there is a least positive integer whose product with r is integral.

Proof.: there are integers i, j such that $r = i/j$, and so
$|j| \cdot r$, being equal to $i \cdot \mathrm{sgn}(j)$, is integral;
since there is a positive integer (e.g., $|j|$) whose product with r is integral, there is, by the well-ordering principle for Z_+, a least such positive integer.

NOTE. This theorem will be useful in our work on rational powers.

4804. Exercises.

a. The product, sum, and difference of any two rationals are rational.
NOTE I. We know now that the negative of each rational is rational.

b. For any rationals r, s such that $s \neq 0$: r/s is rational.
NOTE II. It is now obvious that for any rationals $a < b$: there is a rational r such that $a < r < b$; e.g., take $(a + b)/2$ for r. Thus, the set of all rationals is dense (3324). The next theorem provides a deeper fact.

4805. Theorem. *Eudoxus.*

For any numbers $a < b$: there is a rational r such that $a < r < b$.

Proof.: there is a positive integer n such that $1/n < b - a$, (?), and there is an integer m such that $m < nb \leq m + 1$, (?), and so

$$a < b - \frac{1}{n} \leq \frac{m+1}{n} - \frac{1}{n} = \frac{m}{n} < b,$$

and hence the rational m/n is strictly between a, b.

4806. Corollary. For any number b and positive number p:
there are rationals r, s such that $b - p < r < b < s < b + p$.

Proof. Use 4805 twice.

NOTE. Thus, each number can be approximated by a rational (on either side) with any required degree of accuracy.

4807. Notation. The author uses the symbol
Q to denote the set of all rationals,
Q_0 to denote the set of all nonnegative rationals,
Q_+ to denote the set of all positive rationals.

4808. In view of our discussion in 4802, we have $Z \subset Q \subset R$.

4809. Theorem. For any numbers $b < c$: $\sup\{x \in Q \mid b < x < c\} = c$.

Proof.: c exceeds the set, and
for each number u less than c: $\max(u, b) < c$, and so
there is a rational r such that $\max(u, b) < r < c$,
and hence u precedes r which is in the set. (?)

NOTE. This theorem was easy to prove because we had proved 4805.

4810. Exercises.

a. For any numbers $b < c$: $\inf\{x \in Q \mid b < x < c\} = b$.

b. Q is not complete. (See 4514.)
NOTE. We know that Q is dense. [3324, 4804(NOTE II)]

4811. Definition. An *irrational* (or an *irrational number*) is any real number that is not rational.

4812. Examples.

a. $\sqrt{3}$ is irrational. (3914a)

b. $1/(1 + \sqrt{2})$ is irrational.

Proof. Suppose not. Then there are positive integers m, n such that $1/(1 + \sqrt{2}) = m/n$, and so $\sqrt{2}$ equals $(n - m)/m$ which is rational. Contradiction.

4813. Exercises.

a. The product of any nonzero rational and any irrational is irrational.
NOTE. Hence, the negative of each irrational is irrational.

b. The product of two irrationals is not necessarily irrational.

c. The reciprocal of each irrational is irrational.

d. The sum of any rational and irrational is irrational.

e. The sum of two irrationals is not necessarily irrational.

4814. Theorem. For any numbers $a < b$:
there is an irrational t such that $a < t < b$.

Proof.: there is a rational r such that $a < r < b$, and
there is a positive integer n such that $\sqrt{2}/(b - r) < n$;
then $r + \sqrt{2}/n$ is irrational, and $a < r + \sqrt{2}/n < b$. (?)

4815. Exercises.

a. For any numbers $b < c$: b and c are respectively the infimum and supremum of $\{y \mid y$ is irrational and $b < y < c\}$.

b. The set of all irrationals is dense but not complete.

4816. The following chart summarizes some interesting facts.

	Dense	Complete
Integers (Z)	No	Yes
Rationals (Q)	Yes	No
Irrationals	Yes	No
Reals (R)	Yes	Yes

4817. Theorem. For any nonempty sets A, C of rationals such that $A \cup C = Q$ and A precedes C: there is precisely one number between A, C.

Proof. Consider any such hypothesized sets A, C.

AT LEAST ONE. Use 4109.

AT MOST ONE. Suppose there are two distinct numbers u, v between A, C.
By 4805, there is a rational r strictly between u, v.
So, r is not in A and not in C. (?)
Contradiction. (?)

Positive Integral Powers

4901. Notation (*in force only through* 4914).

The symbol a denotes any given number;

the symbol p denotes any given positive integer.

4902. In this lesson we shall define the pth power of a

and we shall denote it by the symbol a^p, read *a to the p.*

Informally, a^p is the number obtained by multiplying a by itself p times; however, such a vague description can hardly be honored as a definition. The student should not be surprised to learn that we need to do some preliminary spade work before we can rigorously define a^p.

4903. Definition (*for this lesson only*).

A *productor* for a is any function F such that

domain $F = Z_+$,

each value of F is a number,

$F(1) = a$,

for each positive integer n: $F(1 + n) = a \cdot F(n)$.

4904. We shall prove the following two propositions.

a. There is at most one productor for a.

b. There is at least one productor for a.

Most mathematicians agree that 4904a requires proof; however, some mathematicians maintain that 4904b is so obvious that it requires no proof.

For the sake of discussion, let us assume that we have already proved 4904a,b and let us denote the productor for a by the symbol F.
Then, for example,

$F(1) = a,$

$F(2) = F(1 + 1) = a \cdot F(1) = aa,$

$F(3) = F(1 + 2) = a \cdot F(2) = a(aa),$

$F(4) = F(1 + 3) = a \cdot F(3) = a[a(aa)].$

These results suggest that a^p be defined as $F(p)$; indeed, after we have proved 4904a,b, we shall define a^p to be $F(p)$.

4905. Lemma. There is at most one productor for a.

Proof. Consider any productors F, G for a. We prove that $F = G$.

Since F and G are functions that have the same domain, namely Z_+, it suffices to prove that they make the same assignments.
Hence, it suffices to prove that the following set is hereditary from 1:
$\{n \in Z_+ \mid F(n) = G(n)\}$.

The set contains 1,   (?)
and contains the successor of each number n therein because
$1 + n$ is in Z_+ and $F(1 + n) = a \cdot F(n) =_? a \cdot G(n) = G(1 + n)$.

4906. We shall prove that there is at least one productor for a by finding one; to expedite our search we adopt the following temporary definition.

4907. Definition (*for this lesson only*).

An a-iterative set is any set S such that
$(1, a)$ is in S, and
for each number pair (u, v) in S: $(1 + u, av)$ is in S.

NOTE. We did not stipulate that an a-iterative set must be a function.

4908. Examples. Each of the following sets is a-iterative.

a. The set of all number pairs.

b. $\{(1, a)\} \cup \{(n, x) \mid n \in Z_2 \text{ and } x \in R\}$.

c. $\{(1, a), (2, aa)\} \cup \{(n, x) \mid n \in Z_3 \text{ and } x \in R\}$.

d. $\{(1, a), (2, aa), (3, aaa)\} \cup \{(n, x) \mid n \in Z_4 \text{ and } x \in R\}$.

NOTE. None of the above sets is a productor for a.   (?)

4909. Notation (*for this lesson only*).
The symbol φ denotes the set consisting of each number pair that is in every a-iterative set.

NOTE. We shall soon prove that φ is a productor for a.

4910. Exercise. If φ is a-iterative and φ is a function and domain $\varphi = Z_+$, then φ is a productor for a.

4911. Exercises.
  a. φ is a-iterative.
  b. The first component of each number pair in φ is a positive integer.
  c. There is precisely one number pair in φ whose first component is 1, and in fact, this number pair is $(1, a)$.

  NOTE. These propositions will be needed in our proof of the next lemma.

4912. Lemma. φ is a function.

  Proof. In view of 4911b, it suffices (?) to prove that for each positive integer n: there is precisely one number y such that $(n, y) \in \varphi$.

Accordingly, it suffices to prove that the following set, call it B, is hereditary from 1:
$\{n \in Z_+ \mid$ there is precisely one number y such that $(n, y) \in \varphi\}$.

By 4911c, 1 is in B.

To prove that B is hereditary, consider any number n in B.
Then there is precisely one number y such that $(n, y) \in \varphi$.
So $(1 + n, ay) \in \varphi$. (?)

We wish to prove that $1 + n$ is in B.
Clearly, $1 + n$ is in Z_+, and in fact, $2 \leq 1 + n$.
Since $(1 + n, ay) \in \varphi$, we know that there is *at least one* number pair in φ whose first component is $1 + n$.
It now suffices to prove *at most one*.

Consider any number t distinct from ay, and
let S denote $\varphi - \{(1 + n, t)\}$.

We shall prove that S is a-iterative; it will then follow that $(1 + n, t)$ is not in φ, and our proof will be complete. (?)

Since $(1, a) \in \varphi$, and $(1, a) \neq_? (1 + n, t)$, we have $(1, a) \in S$.
Consider any number pair (u, v) in S; we shall prove that $(1 + u, av) \in S$.
Either $u = n$ or $u \neq n$.

CASE I. $u = n$.
Since (n, y) is the only number pair in φ whose first component is n, and since $(n, v) \in_? S$, we have $y = v$.
Therefore $(1 + u, av) = (1 + n, ay)$.
But $(1 + n, ay) \in S$ because $(1 + n, ay) \in \varphi$ and $(1 + n, ay) \neq (1 + n, t)$.
So $(1 + u, av)$ is in S. (?)

CASE II. $u \neq n$.
Then $(1 + u, av) \neq (1 + n, t)$.
Furthermore, $(1 + u, av) \in \varphi$ because $(u, v) \in_? \varphi$.
So $(1 + u, av) \in S$.

4913. Exercise. Domain $\varphi = Z_+$.

4914. We know by 4910, 4911a, 4912, 4913 that φ is a producer for a; therefore, in view of 4905, φ is the one and only producer for a.

For convenience we next summarize our most important results in a manner that may be understood without recalling the temporary definitions and notations set forth in this lesson.

4915. Theorem. For each number a:
there is precisely one function φ (called the producer for a) such that
domain $\varphi = Z_+$,
each value of φ is a number,
$\varphi(1) = a$,
for each positive integer n: $\varphi(1 + n) = a \cdot \varphi(n)$.

NOTE. This theorem has already been proved.   (See 4914.)

4916. Definition. For any number a and positive integer p:
the pth *power* of a is
the number that the producer for a assigns to p.

NOTATION. a^p, read *a to the p*.

4917. Consider any number a, and let φ denote the producer for a.
By 4916, $a^2 = \varphi(2)$, and by 4915, $\varphi(2) = \varphi(1 + 1) = a \cdot \varphi(1) = aa$.
Hence, Definition 4916 is consistent with Definition 2611.
By 4916, $a^3 = \varphi(3)$, and by 4915, $\varphi(3) = \varphi(1 + 2) = a \cdot \varphi(2) = aa^2$.
Hence, Definition 4916 is consistent with Definition 3020.

4918. Exercise. For each number a:
$a^1 = a$, and
for each positive integer p: $a^{1+p} = aa^p$.

NOTE. This is an important proposition.

4919. Theorem. For any number a and positive integers p, k: $a^p a^k = a^{p+k}$.
Proof. Consider any number a and positive integer k.
$\{p \in Z_+ \mid a^p a^k = a^{p+k}\}$ contains 1   (?)
and contains the successor of each number p therein because
$1 + p$ is a positive integer and
$a^{1+p} a^k = aa^p a^k =_? aa^{p+k} =_? a^{1+(p+k)} = a^{(1+p)+k}$.

4920. Exercises.
 a. For any nonzero number c and positive integer p: $c^p \neq 0$.
 b. For each positive integer p: $0^p = 0$.

Integral Powers

5001. Notation (*for this lesson only*).
The symbol c denotes any given nonzero number.

5002. In the previous lesson we defined, among other things, all positive integral powers of c; i.e., for each positive integer p: we defined c^p, the pth power of c.

We also proved four important propositions: 4918, 4919, 4920a,b.

In this lesson we shall define all nonpositive integral powers of c; i.e., for each nonpositive integer m: we shall define c^m, the mth power of c.

Near the end of this lesson we shall define 0^0, the 0th power of 0.

5003. Now we shall motivate our definition of nonpositive integral powers of c.

We want to insure that the following extension of 4919 be provable.
For any integers i, j: $c^i c^j = c^{i+j}$.

In particular we want to insure that $c^0 c^1 = c^{0+1}$, and
hence that $c^0 = c^{0+1}/c^1 = c^1/c^1 = 1$.

That settles the question of how we should define c^0.
Please keep in mind that $c \neq 0$. (5001)

Furthermore, for each negative integer m, we must also insure
that $c^m c^{-m} = c^{m+(-m)}$ and hence, since $c^{-m} \neq 0$ by 4920a,
we must have $c^m = c^{m+(-m)}/c^{-m} = c^0/c^{-m} = 1/c^{-m}$.

Now we know how we should define negative integral powers of c.
Surely it is interesting to see how our desire to extend 4919 led us to the definition we sought.

239

5004. Definition. For each nonpositive integer m: the mth *power* of c
is 1 if $m = 0$, and
is $1/c^{-m}$ if m is negative.

NOTATION. c^m, read c *to the m*.

NOTE. Recall that $c \neq 0$.

5005. Examples. $c^0 = 1$, $c^{-1} = 1/c$, $c^{-2} = 1/c^2$, $c^{-3} = 1/c^3$.

5006. Theorem. For each integer i: $c^i \neq 0$.

Proof.: in case $0 < i$, then $c^i \neq 0$ by 4920a;
in case $i = 0$, then $c^i = c^0 = 1 \neq 0$;
in case $i < 0$, then $c^i = 1/c^{-i} \neq_? 0$.

5007. Theorem. For each integer i: $c^i c^{-i} = 1$.

Proof.:
in case $0 < i$, then $-i < 0$ and so $c^i c^{-i} = c^i/c^{-(-i)} = c^i/c^i = 1$;
in case $i = 0$, then $c^i c^{-i} = c^0 c^0 = 1 \cdot 1 = 1$;
in case $i < 0$, then $c^i c^{-i} = (1/c^{-i})c^{-i} = 1$.

5008. Corollary. For each integer i: $c^{-i} = 1/c^i$. (5007, 5006)

5009. Theorem. For each integer i: $c^{1+i} = cc^i$.

Proof.: in case $0 < i$, then $c^{1+i} = cc^i$ by 4918;
in case $i = 0$, then $c^{1+i} = c^1 = c \cdot 1 = cc^0 = cc^i$;
in case $i < 0$, then $0 \leq_? -1 - i$ and so
$c^{1+i} = 1/c^{-(1+i)} = c/(cc^{-1-i}) =_? c/c^{1+(-1-i)} = c/c^{-i} = cc^i$.

5010. Theorem. For each integer i: $1^i = 1$.

Proof.

CASE I. i is a nonnegative integer.
$\{i \in Z_0 \mid 1^i = 1\}$ contains 0 and contains the successor of each number i
therein because $(1 + i) \in Z_0$ and $1^{1+i} = 1 \cdot 1^i = 1 \cdot 1 = 1$.

CASE II. i is a negative integer.
$1^i = 1/1^{-i} =_? 1/1 = 1$.

5011. Exercise.

For each integer i: $(-1)^i = \text{parity}(i)$.

5012. By 5011 it follows that

for each even integer i: $(-1)^i = 1$, and
for each odd integer i: $(-1)^i = -1$.

5013. Theorem. For any nonzero numbers c, d and any integer j: $(cd)^j = c^j d^j$.

Proof. Consider any such hypothesized c, d, j.

CASE I. $0 \leq j$.
$\{j \in Z_0 \mid (cd)^j = c^j d^j\}$ contains 0 (?)
and contains the successor of each number j therein because $(1 + j) \in Z_0$
and $(cd)^{1+j} = (cd)(cd)^j = (cd)(c^j d^j) = (cc^j)(dd^j) = c^{1+j} d^{1+j}$.

CASE II. $j < 0$.
$(cd)^j = 1/(cd)^{-j} =_? 1/(c^{-j} d^{-j}) = (1/c^{-j})(1/d^{-j}) = c^j d^j$.

5014. Theorem. For any integers i, j: $c^i c^j = c^{i+j}$.

Proof. Consider any integers i, j.

CASE I. $0 \leq j$.
$\{j \in Z_0 \mid c^i c^j = c^{i+j}\}$ contains 0 (?)
and contains the successor of each number j therein because $(1 + j) \in Z_0$
and $c^i c^{1+j} = c^i c c^j = c c^i c^j = c c^{i+j} = c^{1+(i+j)} = c^{i+(1+j)}$.

CASE II. $j < 0$.
$c^i c^j = (1/c^{-i})(1/c^{-j}) = 1/(c^{-i} c^{-j}) =_? 1/c^{-i+(-j)} = 1/c^{-(i+j)} = c^{i+j}$.

5015. Corollaries.

a. For any integers i, j: $c^i/c^j = c^{i-j}$.
Proof.: $c^i/c^j = c^i c^{-j} = c^{i+(-j)} = c^{i-j}$.

b. For any integers i, j, k: $c^i c^j c^k = c^{i+j+k}$.
Proof.: $c^i c^j c^k = c^i(c^j c^k) = c^i c^{j+k} = c^{i+(j+k)} = c^{i+j+k}$.

5016. Theorem. For any integers i, j: $(c^i)^j = c^{ij}$.

Proof. Consider any integers i, j.

CASE I. $0 \leq j$.
$\{j \in Z_0 \mid (c^i)^j = c^{ij}\}$ contains 0 (?)
and contains the successor of each number j therein because $(1 + j) \in Z_0$
and $(c^i)^{1+j} = (c^i)^1(c^i)^j = c^i c^{ij} = c^{i+ij} = c^{i(1+j)}$.

CASE II. $j < 0$.
$(c^i)^j = 1/(c^i)^{-j} =_? 1/c^{-ij} = c^{ij}$.

5017. Corollaries.

a. For any integers i, j: $(c^i)^j = c^{ij} = (c^j)^i$.

b. For any nonzero numbers c, d and any integer i: $(c/d)^i = c^i/d^i$.
Proof.: $(c/d)^i = (cd^{-1})^i = c^i(d^{-1})^i = c^i d^{-i} = c^i/d^i$.

5018. Exercises.

a. For any positive number b and any integer i: $0 < b^i$.

b. 8^7 is a positive integer.

NOTE. The student knows by now that the author has good reason for including such a simple exercise.

5019. Theorem. For any positive numbers x, y and positive integer p:
$$x < y \Leftrightarrow x^p < y^p.$$

Proof.

PART I($\Rightarrow$).
Consider any positive numbers x, y such that $x < y$.
$\{p \; \epsilon \; Z_+ \mid x^p < y^p\}$ contains 1
and contains the successor of each number p therein because $(1 + p) \; \epsilon \; Z_+$
and $x^{1+p} = xx^p <_? yy^p = y^{1+p}$.

PART II($\Leftarrow$).
Consider any positive numbers x, y and positive integer p such that
$x^p < y^p$. Then neither $x = y$ nor $y < x$.   (?)

5020. Corollaries.

a. For any positive numbers x, y and negative integer n:
$$x < y \Leftrightarrow y^n < x^n.$$
Proof.: $x < y \Leftrightarrow x^{-n} < y^{-n} \Leftrightarrow 1/x^n < 1/y^n \Leftrightarrow y^n < x^n$.

b. For any positive numbers x, y and nonzero integer k:
$$x = y \Leftrightarrow x^k = y^k.$$
Proof. Use 5019 and 5020a.

5021. Theorem. For any number y such that $1 < y$ and any integers i, j:
$$i < j \Leftrightarrow y^i < y^j.$$

Proof.: $i < j \Leftrightarrow 0 < j - i \Leftrightarrow_? 1^{j-i} < y^{j-i} \Leftrightarrow$
$1 < y^j/y^i \Leftrightarrow y^i < y^j$.

5022. Corollaries.

a. For any number x such that $0 < x < 1$ and any integers i, j:
$$i < j \Leftrightarrow x^j < x^i.$$
Proof.: $i < j \Leftrightarrow_? (1/x)^i < (1/x)^j \Leftrightarrow 1/x^i < 1/x^j \Leftrightarrow x^j < x^i$.

b. For any number x such that $0 < x \neq 1$ and any integers i, j:
$$i = j \Leftrightarrow x^i = x^j.$$
Proof. Use 5021 and 5022a.

c. For any number x such that $1 < x$ and any integer p such that $1 < p$:
$1 < x < x^p$.

Proof. 5021 with 1 for i, and p for j, and x for y.

d. For any number x such that $0 < x < 1$ and any integer p such that
$1 < p$: $x^p < x < 1$.

Proof. 5022a with 1 for i, and p for j.

5023. Theorem. *Bernoulli Inequality.*

For any number y such that $-1 < y \neq 0$ and any integer p such that
$1 < p$: $1 + py < (1 + y)^p$.

Proof. Consider any number y such that $-1 < y \neq 0$.

$\{p \in Z_2 \mid 1 + py < (1 + y)^p\}$ contains 2 (?)

and contains the successor of each number p therein because

$(1 + p) \in Z_2$ and $1 + (1 + p)y <_? (1 + y)(1 + py) <_?$

$(1 + y)(1 + y)^p = (1 + y)^{1+p}$.

NOTE. To simplify comparison with Theorem 6511 the author used the hypothesis "p is an integer such that $1 < p$" rather than the equivalent hypothesis "p is an integer such that $2 \leq p$."

5024. Examples.

a. For each integer p exceeding 2: $1 + p < 2^p$.

Proof. 5023 with 1 for y.

b. For each integer p exceeding 2: $2 < [1 + (1/p)]^p$.

Proof.: $2 = 1 + p(1/p) <_? [1 + (1/p)]^p$.

5025. Reminder. In 4916, we defined all positive integral powers of 0.

5026. Reminder. In 4920b, we proved that
for each positive integer p: $0^p = 0$.

5027. Very few writers define 0^0, the 0th power of 0. Some writers carefully explain that they do not define 0^0 and then they unwittingly use it. The author concurs with Landau that it is useful to define 0^0 to be 1.

5028. Definition. The 0th *power* of 0 is 1.

NOTATION. 0^0, read 0 *to the* 0.

NOTE.
We shall soon explain why nobody defines negative integral powers of 0.

5029. By Definitions 5004 and 5028, we know that for each number x: $x^0 = 1$.

5030. Exercises.

a. For each nonnegative integer k: $0^k = 1 - \text{sgn}(k)$.

b. For any number y such that $-1 \leq y$ and any nonnegative integer p:
$1 + py \leq (1 + y)^p$.

5031. Exercises.

PRELIMINARY REMARK. At this stage of our work, a symbol such as x^v is meaningful if and only if at least one of the following conditions is satisfied:

i. x is a nonzero number and $v \in Z$,

ii. $x = 0$ and $v \in Z_0$.

Establish that the following "power" rules are true whenever meaningful.

a. $a^i a^{-i} = 1$.

b. $(ad)^j = a^j d^j$.

c. $a^i a^j = a^{i+j}$.

d. $a^i / a^j = a^{i-j}$.

e. $(a^i)^j = a^{ij}$.

f. $(a/d)^i = a^i / d^i$.

5032. It is impossible to define negative integral powers of 0 and yet preserve 5031a. For consider any negative integer n and suppose that we have defined 0^n. By 5031a, we would then have $0^n 0^{-n} = 1$, and since $0^{-n} = 0$, we would have $0 = 0^n 0^{-n} = 1$.

Positive Integral Roots

5101. Consider any positive integer p and nonnegative number b.
After proving a suitable proposition, we shall define the principal pth root of b to be *the* nonnegative number whose pth power is b.
The principal 2nd root of b will turn out to be $\sqrt{b}$.
First we obtain some preliminary results.

5102. Notation (*for this lesson only*).
The symbol p denotes any given positive integer.

5103. Lemma.

For each positive number c: $\{x \in R_+ \mid x^p < c\}$ has no maximum.

Proof. Consider any positive number c, and let A denote the set indicated.
Consider any number x in A.
It suffices to find a number that is greater than x and in A.
So, it suffices to find a number g such that $0 < g < 1$ and $(x/g)^p < c$ because x/g would be greater than x and in A.   (?)

Noting that
$0 < g < 1$ and $(x/g)^p < c \Leftarrow$
$0 < g < 1$ and $x^p/c < g^p \Leftarrow$
$0 < g < 1$ and $x^p/c < [1 + (g - 1)]^p \Leftarrow_?$
$0 < g < 1$ and $x^p/c < 1 + p(g - 1) \Leftarrow$
$0 < g < 1$ and $(1/p)(x^p/c - 1) + 1 < g$,

and noting that $0 < (1/p)(x^p/c - 1) + 1 < 1$,   (?)

we may choose for g any number strictly between
$(1/p)(x^p/c - 1) + 1$ and 1.

5104. Lemma.
For each positive number c: $\{x \in R_+ \mid c < x^p\}$ has no minimum.

Proof. Consider any positive number c, and let E denote the set indicated.

Consider any number x in E.
It suffices to find a number that is less than x and in E.
So, it suffices to find a number h such that $0 < h < 1$ and $c < (hx)^p$
because hx would be less than x and in E.   (?)

Noting that
$0 < h < 1$ and $c < (hx)^p \;\Leftarrow$
$0 < h < 1$ and $c/x^p < h^p \;\Leftarrow$
$0 < h < 1$ and $c/x^p < [1 + (h - 1)]^p \;\Leftarrow_?$
$0 < h < 1$ and $c/x^p < 1 + p(h - 1) \;\Leftarrow$
$0 < h < 1$ and $(1/p)(c/x^p - 1) + 1 < h,$

and noting that $0 < (1/p)(c/x^p - 1) + 1 < 1,$ (?)

we may choose for h any number strictly between
$(1/p)(c/x^p - 1) + 1$ and 1.

5105. Theorem. For each positive number c:
there is precisely one positive number whose pth power is c.

Proof. Consider any positive number c.

AT MOST ONE. Use 5020b.

AT LEAST ONE.
Consider the sets A, E introduced in 5103 and 5104.
A is nonempty because it contains $(1/2)\min(1, c)$.   (?)
E is nonempty because it contains $c + 1$.   (?)
Furthermore, A precedes E.   (?)
So there is a number u between A, E.
u is positive because it exceeds A.
Since A has no maximum, u is not in A and so $c \leqq u^p$.
Since E has no minimum, u is not in E and so $u^p \leqq c$.
Therefore $u^p = c$.

5106. Exercise. There is precisely one number, namely 0, whose pth power is 0.

5107. Corollary. For each nonnegative number b: there is precisely one
nonnegative number whose pth power is b.   (5105, 5106)

5108. Definition. The *principal pth root* of a nonnegative number b
is the nonnegative number whose pth power is b.

NOTATION. $\sqrt[p]{b}$, read *principal pth root of b*.

NOTE. Each number whose pth power is b is called a pth root of b. Soon
we shall define odd positive integral roots of negative numbers.

5109. Immediate consequences.

a. For each nonnegative number b: $(\sqrt[p]{b})^p = b$.   (5108)

b. For any nonnegative number b and any number y:
$\sqrt[p]{b} = y \iff [0 \le y \text{ and } y^p = b]$.   (5108)

5110. Examples.

a. $\sqrt[3]{8} = 2$ because $0 \le 2$ and $2^3 = 8$.

b. $\sqrt[p]{1} = 1$ because $0 \le 1$ and $1^p = 1$.

c. $\sqrt[p]{0} = 0$ because $0 \le 0$ and $0^p = 0$.

5111. Exercises.

a. For each positive number c: $0 < \sqrt[p]{c}$.

b. For each nonnegative number b: $\sqrt[1]{b} = b$.

c. For each nonnegative number b: $\sqrt[2]{b} = \sqrt{b}$.

d. For any positive number c and any integer j: $\sqrt[p]{c^j} = (\sqrt[p]{c})^j$.

e. For each positive number c:
$\sup\{x \, \epsilon \, R_+ \,|\, x^p < c\} = \sqrt[p]{c} = \inf\{x \, \epsilon \, R_+ \,|\, c < x^p\}$.
HINT. Use 4507.

5112. Theorem. For any odd positive integer n and negative number u:
there is precisely one number, namely the negative number $-\sqrt[n]{-u}$,
whose nth power is u.

Proof.: $-\sqrt[n]{-u}$ is such a number because
$(-\sqrt[n]{-u})^n = (-1)(\sqrt[n]{-u})^n = (-1)(-u) = u$, and
there is at most one such number because for any numbers x, y such that
$x^n = u$ and $y^n = u$:
$x <_? 0$, $y <_? 0$, and since $(-x)^n = (-1)^n x^n = (-1)^n y^n = (-y)^n$,
we have $-x =_? -y$, and so $x = y$.

5113. Definition. For any odd positive integer n and negative number u:
the nth *root* of u is the negative number whose nth power is u.

NOTATION. $\sqrt[n]{u}$, read nth *root of* u.

5114. Corollary. For any odd positive integer n and negative number u:
$\sqrt[n]{u} = -\sqrt[n]{-u}$.   (5113, 5112)

5115. Examples.

   a. $\sqrt[3]{-8} = -\sqrt[3]{-(-8)} = -\sqrt[3]{8} = -2.$

   b. $\sqrt[3]{-1} =_? -\sqrt[3]{1} = -1.$

5116. Exercises.

   a. For each number x: $\sqrt[1]{x} = x.$

   b. For any even positive integer m and negative number u: there is no (real) number whose mth power is u.

Rational Powers

5201. In this lesson we shall define and investigate rational powers of positive numbers. Our work will be substantially simplified by adopting the next convention.

5202. Notation (*for this lesson only*). For each rational r:
the symbol $\bar{r}$, read r bar, denotes the least positive integer whose product with r is integral.

NOTE. This notation is justified by 4803.

5203. Examples.

a. $\bar{3} = 1$.
Furthermore, for each integer n: $\bar{n} = 1$.

b. $\overline{4/10} = 5$.

5204. It is important to keep in mind that for each rational r:
$\bar{r}$ is a positive integer and $r\bar{r}$ is integral.

5205. Consider any positive number b and any rational r.
We wish to define b^r, the rth power of b.
To motivate our definition, we offer the following remarks.

First note that $\sqrt[\bar{r}]{b^{r\bar{r}}}$ has already been defined.   (5108)

In case r is integral, we have $\sqrt[\bar{r}]{b^{r\bar{r}}} = \sqrt[1]{b^r} = b^r$.

Even if r is not integral, we shall see that b^r should equal $\sqrt[\bar{r}]{b^{r\bar{r}}}$.

Among other things, we want to insure that the following be provable.

> i. $0 < b^r$.
>
> ii.   For each rational s: $(b^r)^s = b^{rs}$.

By i, b^r must be positive, and by ii, $(b^r)^{\bar{r}}$ must equal $b^{r\bar{r}}$; hence, by 5109b with $\bar{r}$ for p, $b^{r\bar{r}}$ for b, and b^r for y, we must have $\sqrt[\bar{r}]{b^{r\bar{r}}} = b^r$.

Now we are ready to define b^r.

5206. Definition. For any positive number b and any rational r: the rth *power* of b is $\sqrt[\bar{r}]{b^{r\bar{r}}}$.

NOTATION. b^r, read b *to the* r.

NOTE. This definition is consistent with Definitions 4916 and 5004; i.e., if r is integral, then the above definition yields for b^r the same number as does 4916 or 5004, whichever applies.

5207. Examples.

a. $7^{4/6} = \sqrt[3]{7^2}$ because $\overline{4/6} = 3$ and $(4/6)(\overline{4/6}) = 2$.

b. $7^{2/3} = \sqrt[3]{7^2}$ because $\overline{2/3} = 3$ and $(2/3)(\overline{2/3}) = 2$.

5208. Exercise.

For each rational r: $1^r = 1$.

5209. Theorem. For any positive number b and any rational r: $0 < b^r$.

Proof.: $b^{r\bar{r}}$ is positive, and so by 5111a, $\sqrt[\bar{r}]{b^{r\bar{r}}}$ is positive.

5210. Theorem. For any positive number b and any integers i, m, j, n such that $0 < m$, $0 < n$, and $i/m = j/n$: $\sqrt[m]{b^i} = \sqrt[n]{b^j}$.

Proof.: $0 < \sqrt[m]{b^i}$, $0 < \sqrt[n]{b^j}$, and $(\sqrt[m]{b^i})^{mn} = [(\sqrt[m]{b^i})^m]^n = [b^i]^n = b^{in} = b^{jm} = [b^j]^m = [(\sqrt[n]{b^j})^n]^m = (\sqrt[n]{b^j})^{mn}$,
and so by 5020b, $\sqrt[m]{b^i} = \sqrt[n]{b^j}$.

NOTE. This theorem could have been proved in the previous lesson.

5211. Theorem. For any positive number b and any integers i, m such that $0 < m$: $b^{i/m} = \sqrt[m]{b^i}$.

Proof.: let n denote $\overline{i/m}$ and let j denote $(i/m)n$; then n is a positive integer, j is an integer, $i/m = j/n$, $b^{i/m} =_? \sqrt[n]{b^j}$, and by 5210, $\sqrt[n]{b^j} = \sqrt[m]{b^i}$.

5212. Corollary. For any positive number b and positive integer p: $b^{1/p} = \sqrt[p]{b}$.

Proof.: $b^{1/p} = \sqrt[p]{b^1} = \sqrt[p]{b}$.

NOTE. In case $p = 2$, we have $b^{1/2} = \sqrt[2]{b} = \sqrt{b}$.

5213. Exercise.

For any positive number b and any integers j, n such that $0 < n$: $b^{j/n} = (b^j)^{1/n} = (b^{1/n})^j$.

5214. Theorem. For any positive number b and any rationals r, s: $(b^r)^s = b^{rs}$.

Proof. Consider any such hypothesized b, r, s.
There are integers i, m, j, n such that
$0 < m, \ \ 0 < n, \ \ r = i/m, \ \ s = j/n$.
Let c denote b^r.
Then $(c^s)^n = (c^{j/n})^n = [(c^j)^{1/n}]^n = c^j$.
So, $[(b^r)^s]^{nm} = [(c^s)^n]^m = (c^j)^m = (c^m)^j = [(b^r)^m]^j = [(b^{i/m})^m]^j =_?$
$(b^i)^j = b^{ij}$, and hence
$(b^r)^s = \sqrt[nm]{b^{ij}} = b^{ij/nm} = b^{rs}$.

5215. Theorem. For any positive number b and any rational r: $b^r b^{-r} = 1$.

Proof.: $(b^r b^{-r})^{\bar{r}} = (b^r)^{\bar{r}}(b^{-r})^{\bar{r}} = b^{r\bar{r}} b^{-r\bar{r}} = b^0 = 1$,
and so $b^r b^{-r} = \sqrt[\bar{r}]{1} = 1$.

5216. Exercises.

a. For any positive numbers b, c and any rational r: $(bc)^r = b^r c^r$.

b. For any positive numbers b, g and any rational r: $(b/g)^r = b^r/g^r$.

c. For any positive number b and any rationals r, s: $b^r b^s = b^{r+s}$.

d. For any positive number b and any rationals r, s: $b^r/b^s = b^{r-s}$.

5217. Theorem. For any positive numbers x, y and positive rational r:
$x < y \Leftrightarrow x^r < y^r$.
Proof.: $x < y \Leftrightarrow_? x^{r\bar{r}} < y^{r\bar{r}} \Leftrightarrow (x^r)^{\bar{r}} < (y^r)^{\bar{r}} \Leftrightarrow_? x^r < y^r$.

5218. Corollaries.

a. For any positive numbers x, y and negative rational t:
$x < y \Leftrightarrow y^t < x^t$.
Proof.: $x < y \Leftrightarrow y^{-1} < x^{-1} \Leftrightarrow (y^{-1})^{-t} < (x^{-1})^{-t} \Leftrightarrow y^t < x^t$.

b. For any positive numbers x, y and any nonzero rational u:
$x = y \Leftrightarrow x^u = y^u$.   (5217, 5218a)

5219. Theorem. For any number y such that $1 < y$ and any rationals r, s:
$r < s \Leftrightarrow y^r < y^s$.
Proof.: $r < s \Leftrightarrow 0 < s - r \Leftrightarrow_? 1^{s-r} < y^{s-r} \Leftrightarrow$
$1 < y^s/y^r \Leftrightarrow y^r < y^s$.

5220. Corollaries.

a. For any number x such that $0 < x < 1$ and any rationals r, s:
$r < s \Leftrightarrow x^s < x^r$.
Proof.: $r < s \Leftrightarrow_? (1/x)^r < (1/x)^s \Leftrightarrow 1/x^r < 1/x^s \Leftrightarrow x^s < x^r$.

b. For any number x such that $0 < x \neq 1$ and any rationals r, s:
$r = s \Leftrightarrow x^r = x^s$. (5219, 5220a)

5221. Our next major objective is Theorem 5225; first we obtain two preliminary results.

5222. Lemma. For any numbers a, b such that $1 < b$:
there is a positive integer p such that $a < b^p$.

Proof. Suppose not. Then there are numbers a, b such that $1 < b$ and for each positive integer p: $b^p \leq a$.

So, $\{b^n \mid n \in Z_+\}$ has a supremum, say t, which is positive. (?)
Then, for each positive integer n: $b^n = b^{n+1}/b \leq t/b < t$. (?)
Therefore, t/b is an upper bound of the set. Contradiction. (?)

5223. Exercise.

For any numbers a, w greater than 1:
there is a positive integer p such that $1 < a^{1/p} < w$.

5224. The next theorem is extremely important for our work in the next lesson; an understanding of its proof requires patience and concentration.

5225. Theorem. For any numbers h, k, v such that $h < k$, $0 < k$, $0 < v \neq 1$:
there is a rational s such that $h < v^s < k$.

Proof. Consider any such hypothesized h, k, v.
Either $1 < v$ or $0 < v < 1$.

CASE I. $1 < v$.
Let T denote $\{v^r \mid r$ is rational and $v^r < k\}$.
It suffices to prove that h does not exceed T. (?)

Suppose that h exceeds T.
T is bounded above by k, and T is nonempty because by 5222 there is a positive integer i such that $1/k < v^i$ and so $v^{-i} < k$ and hence $v^{-i} \in T$.
Therefore T has a supremum, say c, and $0 < c \leq h < k$. (?)
By 5223, there is a positive integer p such that $1 < v^{1/p} < k/c$,
and so $cv^{-1/p} <_? c$.
Since $cv^{-1/p}$ is less than sup T (i.e., c), $cv^{-1/p}$ is less than some member of T, say v^w.
Then, $c < v^{w+1/p} = v^w v^{1/p} \leq cv^{1/p} < k$. (?)
Thus we have reached the contradiction that $v^{w+1/p}$, which is in T, (?) is greater than sup T.

CASE II. $0 < v < 1$.
Then $1 < 1/v$, and so by CASE I (with $1/v$ for v), there is a rational z such that $h < (1/v)^z < k$, and so $h < v^{-z} < k$,
and since $-z$ is rational, we are done.

LESSON **53**

Real Powers

5301. In the previous lesson we defined rational powers of positive numbers. However, we have not yet defined irrational powers of positive numbers; e.g., we have not yet defined $2^{\sqrt{3}}$, the $\sqrt{3}$th power of 2.

There are many ways of defining irrational powers of positive numbers; in this lesson the author will use the definition that he believes to be the simplest. First we shall do some preliminary work.

5302. Notation (*for this lesson only*).
The symbol b denotes any given positive number;
the symbol t denotes any given number;
the symbol A denotes $\{b^x \mid x \text{ is rational and } x < t\}$;
the symbol C denotes $\{b^y \mid y \text{ is rational and } t < y\}$.

NOTE. Of course, A and C depend on b, t.

5303. Exercises.

a. A and C are nonempty and consist entirely of positive numbers.

b. If $0 < b < 1$, then C precedes A.

c. If $1 < b$, then A precedes C.

NOTE. If $b = 1$, then $A = \{1\} = C$. (?)

5304. Theorem. There is precisely one number between A, C.

Proof. Either $b = 1$ or $b \neq 1$.

CASE I. $b = 1$.
Then $A = \{1\} = C$, and so 1 is the number between A, C.

253

CASE II. $b \neq 1$.

At least one.
A, C are nonempty, and either A precedes C or C precedes A,   (?)
and so by 4109, there is at least one number between A, C.

At most one.
Suppose there are numbers $w < z$ that are between A, C.
Then by 5225, there is a rational s such that $w < b^s < z$.   (?)
So by 5225, there is a rational u such that $w < b^u < b^s$.
Thus, $w < b^u < b^s < z$.
Since b^u is neither in A nor in C, $u = t$.   (?)
Since b^s is neither in A nor in C, $s = t$.
Hence $u = s$. Contradiction.   (?)

NOTE I. This proposition is true even if t is irrational; nowhere in the proof did we assume that t is rational.

NOTE II. The number between A, C is clearly positive.

5305. Exercise. If t is rational, then the number between A, C is b^t.

5306. Proposition 5305 provides the motivation for our definition of irrational powers of b: if t is irrational, we shall define the tth power of b to be the number between A, C.

5307. Definition. If t is irrational, then the tth *power of b* is the number between A, C.

NOTATION. b^t, read b *to the t.*

NOTE. b is positive of course.

5308. Thus, if t is irrational, then b^t is defined to be the number between the following sets:

$\{b^x \mid x$ is rational and $x < t\}$, $\{b^y \mid y$ is rational and $t < y\}$.

E.g., $2^{\sqrt{3}}$ is the number between the following sets:

$\{2^x \mid x$ is rational and $x < \sqrt{3}\}$, $\{2^y \mid y$ is rational and $\sqrt{3} < y\}$.

5309. Now we have defined all real powers of positive numbers.

5310. Immediate consequence. b^t is the number between A, C; and this is true whether t is rational or irrational.   (5305, 5307)

5311. Reminder. The symbol b denotes any given positive number, and the symbol t denotes any given number.

5312. Immediate consequences.

   a. $0 < b^t$. See 5304(NOTE II).

   b. $1^t = 1$. (?)

   c. If $1 < b$, then $\sup A = b^t = \inf C$. (5303c, 5310, 4507)

   d. If $0 < b < 1$, then $\sup C = b^t = \inf A$. (?)

   e. For any rationals x, y such that t is between x, y:
b^t is between b^x, b^y. (?)

5313. Theorem. If $1 < b$, then for any numbers u, v: $u < v \Leftrightarrow b^u < b^v$.

   Proof. Assume $1 < b$, and consider any numbers u, v.

   PART I($\Rightarrow$). If $u < v$, then there are rationals r, s such that
$u < r < s < v$, and so
$b^u = \sup\{b^x \mid x \text{ is rational and } x < u\} \leq_? b^r < b^s \leq_?$
$\inf\{b^y \mid y \text{ is rational and } v < y\} = b^v$.

   PART II($\Leftarrow$). Use PART I.

5314. Exercises.

   a. If $0 < b < 1$, then for any numbers u, v:
$u < v \Leftrightarrow b^v < b^u$.
HINT. Proof similar to proof of 5313.

   b. If $b \neq 1$, then for any numbers u, v:
$u = v \Leftrightarrow b^u = b^v$.

5315. Theorem. $(b^{-1})^{-t} = b^t$.

   Proof. $(b^{-1})^{-t}$ is the number between
$\{(b^{-1})^x \mid x \text{ is rational and } x < -t\}$,
$\{(b^{-1})^y \mid y \text{ is rational and } -t < y\}$,

   and these sets are equal respectively to
$\{b^{-x} \mid -x \text{ is rational and } t < -x\}$,
$\{b^{-y} \mid -y \text{ is rational and } -y < t\}$,

   and these sets are in turn equal respectively to C, A.

5316. Exercise. $(b^{-1})^t = b^{-t}$.

5317. Theorem. For any numbers u, v: $b^u b^v = b^{u+v}$.

Proof. Consider any numbers u, v.

CASE I. $b = 1$.
Obvious in view of 5312b.

CASE II. $1 < b$.
First we shall prove that $b^u b^v \leq b^{u+v}$;
then we shall prove that $b^{u+v} \leq b^u b^v$.

Consider any rational w less than v.
Then for each rational x less than u: $b^x = b^{x+w} b^{-w} < b^{u+v} b^{-w}$.   (?)
So, $b^u = \sup\{b^x \mid x$ is rational and $x < u\} \leq b^{u+v} b^{-w}$.   (?)
Therefore, $b^w \leq b^{u+v}/b^u$.   (?)
So, $b^v = \sup\{b^w \mid w$ is rational and $w < v\} \leq b^{u+v}/b^u$.   (?)
Hence, $b^u b^v \leq b^{u+v}$.

Now we prove that $b^{u+v} \leq b^u b^v$.

Consider any rational z greater than v.
Then for each rational y greater than u: $b^{-z} b^{u+v} < b^{-z} b^{y+z} = b^y$.
So, $b^{-z} b^{u+v} \leq \inf\{b^y \mid y$ is rational and $u < y\} = b^u$.
Hence, $b^{u+v}/b^u \leq b^z$.
Therefore, $b^{u+v}/b^u \leq \inf\{b^z \mid z$ is rational and $v < z\} = b^v$.
So, $b^{u+v} \leq b^u b^v$.

CASE III. $0 < b < 1$.
$b^u b^v = (b^{-1})^{-u}(b^{-1})^{-v} = (b^{-1})^{-(u+v)} = b^{u+v}$.   (?)

5318. Exercises.

a. $b^t b^{-t} = 1$.

b. For any numbers u, w: $b^u/b^w = b^{u-w}$.

5319. Theorem. For any positive numbers a, c: $(ac)^t = a^t c^t$.

Proof. Consider any positive numbers a, c.

CASE I. $1 < a$ and $1 < c$.
Then $1 < ac$.
For each rational x less than t: $(ac)^x = a^x c^x < a^t c^t$.   (?)
So, $(ac)^t \leq_? a^t c^t$.
For each rational y greater than t: $a^t c^t < a^y c^y = (ac)^y$.
So, $a^t c^t \leq_? (ac)^t$.
Therefore $(ac)^t = a^t c^t$.

CASE II. $a < 1$ and $c < 1$.
$(ac)^t = [(ac)^{-1}]^{-t} = (a^{-1}c^{-1})^{-t} = (a^{-1})^{-t}(c^{-1})^{-t} = a^t c^t$.   (?)

CASE III. $a = 1$ or $c = 1$. Obvious.

CASE IV. $a < 1$ and $1 < c$.

Subcase i. $ac < 1$.
$$a^t c^t = [(ac)^{-1}c]^{-t}c^t = [(ac)^{-1}]^{-t}c^{-t}c^t = (ac)^t. \quad (?)$$

Subcase ii. $ac = 1$.
$$a^t c^t = a^t(a^{-1})^t = a^t a^{-t} = 1 = 1^t = (ac)^t.$$

Subcase iii. $1 < ac$.
$$a^t c^t = a^t[a(ac)^{-1}]^{-t} = a^t a^{-t}[(ac)^{-1}]^{-t} = (ac)^t. \quad (?)$$

CASE V. $1 < a$ and $c < 1$.
This is merely CASE IV with a and c interchanged.

5320. Exercise.

For any positive numbers a, d: $(a/d)^t = a^t/d^t$.

5321. Theorem. For any positive numbers x, y and positive number r:
$x < y \Leftrightarrow x^r < y^r$.

Proof. Consider any positive numbers x, y, r.

PART I($\Rightarrow$). If $x < y$, then $1 < y/x$ and there is a rational z such that
$0 < z < r$ and so $1 = 1^z < (y/x)^z < (y/x)^r = y^r/x^r$
and hence $x^r < y^r$. (?)

PART II($\Leftarrow$). Use PART I.

5322. Corollaries.

a. For any positive numbers x, y and negative number s:
$x < y \Leftrightarrow y^s < x^s$.
Proof.:
$x < y \Leftrightarrow y^{-1} < x^{-1} \Leftrightarrow (y^{-1})^{-s} < (x^{-1})^{-s} \Leftrightarrow y^s < x^s$.

b. For any positive numbers x, y and any nonzero number u:
$x = y \Leftrightarrow x^u = y^u$.
Proof. Use 5321, 5322a.

5323. Exercise.

If $1 < b$ and $0 < t$, then
$b^t = \sup\{b^x \mid x \text{ is rational and } 0 < x < t\}$.

NOTE. We shall exploit this proposition in the proof of the next theorem.

5324. Theorem. For any numbers u, v: $(b^u)^v = b^{uv}$.

Proof. Consider any numbers u, v.

First we consider the situation when $1 < b$.

CASE I. $0 < u$ and $0 < v$.
First we shall prove that $(b^u)^v \leq b^{uv}$.
Consider any rational x such that $0 < x < u$.
Then for each rational z such that $0 < z < v$:
$b^x = (b^{xz})^{1/z} <_? (b^{uv})^{1/z}$, and so
$b^u = \sup\{b^x \mid x \text{ is rational and } 0 < x < u\} \leq (b^{uv})^{1/z}$, and
hence $(b^u)^z \leq_? b^{uv}$.
So, $(b^u)^v = \sup\{(b^u)^z \mid z \text{ is rational and } 0 < z < v\} \leq b^{uv}$.

Now we prove that $b^{uv} \leq (b^u)^v$.
Consider any rational y such that $u < y$.
Then for each rational w such that $v < w$:
$(b^{uv})^{1/w} < (b^{yw})^{1/w} = b^y$, (?), and so
$(b^{uv})^{1/w} \leq \inf\{b^y \mid y \text{ is rational and } u < y\} = b^u$, and
hence $b^{uv} \leq (b^u)^w$.
So, $b^{uv} \leq \inf\{(b^u)^w \mid w \text{ is rational and } v < w\} = (b^u)^v$.

CASE II. $u = 0$ or $v = 0$.   Obvious.

CASE III. $u < 0$ and $0 < v$.
$b^{uv} = 1/b^{-uv} = 1/(b^{-u})^v = (1/b^{-u})^v = (b^u)^v$.   (?)

CASE IV. $0 < u$ and $v < 0$.
$b^{uv} = 1/b^{-uv} = 1/(b^u)^{-v} = (b^u)^v$.   (?)

CASE V. $u < 0$ and $v < 0$.
$b^{uv} = b^{(-u)(-v)} = (b^{-u})^{-v} = (1/b^u)^{-v} = 1/(b^u)^{-v} = (b^u)^v$.

That concludes our consideration of the situation when $1 < b$.

When $b = 1$, the theorem is obvious.

Lastly we consider the situation when $0 < b < 1$.
$1 < b^{-1}$, and so $(b^u)^v = [(b^{-1})^{-u}]^v = (b^{-1})^{-uv} = b^{uv}$.

5325. We know that $0^0 = 1$ and that for each positive integer p: $0^p = 0$.
However, we have not yet defined all positive powers of 0.

5326. Definition. For each positive number t: the tth *power* of 0 is 0.

NOTATION. 0^t, read 0 *to the t*.

NOTE.   We do not define negative powers of 0.

5327. We have defined the following powers of numbers:

all real powers of positive numbers,
all nonnegative real powers of 0,
all integral powers of negative numbers.

Thus, if the symbol g denotes a number,
then the symbol g^w is meaningful if and only if

$$\text{either } (0 < g \text{ and } w \in R)$$
$$\text{or} \quad (g = 0 \text{ and } w \in R_0)$$
$$\text{or} \quad (g < 0 \text{ and } w \in Z).$$

5328. We conclude this lesson by mentioning that the following are true whenever meaningful.

a. $a^u a^v = a^{u+v}$.

b. $a^u / a^v = a^{u-v}$.

c. $(ac)^u = a^u c^u$.

d. $(a/c)^u = a^u / c^u$.

e. $(a^u)^v = a^{uv} = (a^v)^u$.

Logarithms

5401. Notation (*for this lesson only*).

The symbol b denotes any given positive number distinct from 1;

the symbol c denotes any given positive number;

the symbol F denotes $\{x \mid b^x < c\}$;

the symbol G denotes $\{y \mid c < b^y\}$.

5402. Exercises.

a. F and G are nonempty.

b. If $1 < b$, then F precedes G.

c. If $0 < b < 1$, then G precedes F.

5403. Lemma. There is precisely one number between F, G.

Proof.

AT LEAST ONE.
This follows immediately by 5402 and 4109.

AT MOST ONE.
Suppose there are numbers $r < u$ that are between F, G.
There are numbers h, k such that $r < h < k < u$.
Since h is neither in F nor in G, $b^h = c$.
Since k is neither in F nor in G, $b^k = c$.
So $b^h = b^k$ and hence $h = k$. Contradiction.

5404. Theorems.

a. The number between F, G, call it w, is such that $b^w = c$.

Proof. We shall prove that b^w is neither less than nor greater than c.

Suppose $b^w < c$.

By 5225, there is a number s such that $b^w < b^s < c$.

Either $0 < b < 1$ or $1 < b$.

In case $0 < b < 1$, then $s < w$ which is impossible because $s \in F$ and w precedes F. (?)

In case $1 < b$, then $w < s$ which is impossible because $s \in F$ and w exceeds F.

Similarly, one can prove that b^w is not greater than c.

b. There is precisely one number u such that $b^u = c$.

Proof.

AT LEAST ONE. (5404a)

AT MOST ONE. For any numbers r, s such that $b^r = c$ and $b^s = c$: $b^r = b^s$ and so $r = s$.

5405. Definition. For any positive number b distinct from 1 and any positive number c: the *logarithm of c to the base b* (or simply, the base b logarithm of c) is the number w such that $b^w = c$.

NOTATION. $\log_b c$, read as *log of c to base b* or as *base b log of c*.

NOTE I. Briefly, $\log_b c$ is the power to which b must be raised to yield c.

NOTE II. $\log_b c$ is the number between F, G.

NOTE III. In the study of the real number system we do not define $\log_a h$ for $a \leq 0$ or $a = 1$ or $h \leq 0$.

5406. Examples.

a. $\log_5 5 = 1$ because $5^1 = 5$.

b. $\log_5 1 = 0$ because $5^0 = 1$.

c. $\log_5 (1/5) = -1$ because $5^{-1} = 1/5$.

d. $\log_{\sqrt{3}} 3 = 2$ because $(\sqrt{3})^2 = 3$.

e. $\log_3 \sqrt{3} = 1/2$.

f. For each number t: $\log_b (b^t) = t$. (?)

5407. Immediate consequences.

   a. $b^{\log_b c} = c.$ (5405)

   b. For each number z: $z = \log_b c \Leftrightarrow b^z = c.$ (5405)

5408. Exercises.

   a. If $1 < b$, then sup $F = \log_b c = \inf G$.
      If $0 < b < 1$, then sup $G = \log_b c = \inf F$.

   b. $\log_b c = -\log_{1/b} c$.

   c. For each number u: $c^u = b^{u \cdot \log_b c}$.

5409. Theorem. For any positive numbers u, v: $\log_b (uv) = \log_b u + \log_b v$.

   Proof.: $uv = b^{\log_b u} \cdot b^{\log_b v} = b^{\log_b u + \log_b v}$,
   and so $\log_b (uv) = \log_b u + \log_b v$.

5410. Theorem. For each number u: $\log_b (c^u) = u \cdot \log_b c$.

   Proof.: $c^u = b^{u \cdot \log_b c}$.

5411. Corollary. For any positive numbers u, z: $\log_b (u/z) = \log_b u - \log_b z$.

   Proof.: $\log_b (u/z) = \log_b (uz^{-1}) = \log_b u + \log_b (z^{-1}) =$
   $\log_b u + (-1)\log_b z$.

5412. Exercises.

   a. For each nonzero number v: $\log_b (v^2) = 2 \cdot \log_b |v|$.

   b. For each number a such that $0 < a \neq 1$: $(\log_a b)(\log_b c) = \log_a c$.
     NOTE. If $c = a$, we have $(\log_a b)(\log_b a) = 1$.

5413. Theorem. If $1 < b$, then for any positive numbers u, v:
   $u < v \Leftrightarrow \log_b u < \log_b v$.

   Proof.: $u < v \Leftrightarrow b^{\log_b u} < b^{\log_b v} \Leftrightarrow \log_b u < \log_b v$.

5414. Corollary. If $1 < b$, then for each positive number u:
   $1 < u \Leftrightarrow 0 < \log_b u$, and
   $u < 1 \Leftrightarrow \log_b u < 0$.

   Proof. Use 5413 and the fact that $\log_b 1 = 0$.

5415. Exercise.

   If $0 < b < 1$, then for any positive numbers u, v:
   $u < v \Leftrightarrow \log_b v < \log_b u$.

5416. Corollary. If $0 < b < 1$, then for each positive number u:

$1 < u \Leftrightarrow \log_b u < 0$, and

$u < 1 \Leftrightarrow 0 < \log_b u$.

Proof. Use 5415.

5417. Corollary. For any positive numbers u, v:

$u = v \Leftrightarrow \log_b u = \log_b v$.

Proof. Use 5413 and 5415.

5418. Exercise.

For any numbers u, v such that $1 < u < v$: $u^u < v^v$.

Real Functions

5501. Before undertaking this lesson the student should have studied Lessons 19, 20, 21.

5502. Exercises.

a. $\{(x, 4 - 2x) \in [R \times R] \mid 1 \le x \le 2\}$ is onto $\{w \mid 0 \le w \le 2\}$.

b. $\{(n, (-1)^{n+1}) \in [R \times R] \mid n \in Z\} =$
$\{(n, -\text{parity}(n)) \in [R \times R] \mid n \in Z\}$.

5503. When using the brace notation to describe a set of number pairs, we shall henceforth drop the symbol $\in [R \times R]$ that precedes the vertical stroke $\mid$.

E.g., we shall write $\{(x, 4 - 2x) \mid 1 \le x \le 2\}$ instead of
$\{(x, 4 - 2x) \in [R \times R] \mid 1 \le x \le 2\}$.

The symbol $\{(x, 4 - 2x) \mid 1 \le x \le 2\}$ should be read thus:
the set of all number pairs $(x, 4 - 2x)$ such that $1 \le x \le 2$.

5504. Consider any functions F, G whose union is a function.
The union of F, G, i.e., $F \cup G$, is frequently described as the function, say H, such that

$$H(x) = \begin{cases} F(x) & \text{if } x \in \text{domain } F \\ G(x) & \text{if } x \in \text{domain } G \end{cases}.$$

5505. Example. The union of

$$\{(x, 2x) \mid 0 \le x \le 1\}, \quad \{(x, 4 - 2x) \mid 1 \le x \le 2\}$$

is a function (?) that may be described as the function, say H, such that

$$H(x) = \begin{cases} 2x & \text{if } 0 \le x \le 1 \\ 4 - 2x & \text{if } 1 \le x \le 2 \end{cases}.$$

5506. Exercise.

Find a function that has the same domain and range but is not one-one. (See 2008.)

5507. Definition. A *real function* is any function each of whose values is a (real) number.

NOTE I. This definition stipulates nothing about the nature of the arguments of a real function.

NOTE II. A real function is obviously any function that is into R.

5508. Examples. Each of the following is a real function.

a. $\emptyset$.

b. $\{((u, v), u + v) \mid u \in R \text{ and } v \in R\}$.   (the addition function)

c. $\{((u, \text{Ike}), 3u) \mid u \in Q\}$.

d. $\{(\text{Ike}, \sqrt{7})\}$.

e. $\{(\text{Ike}, \sqrt{2}), (3, 5), (\text{Earth}, -7)\}$.

f. $\{(x, x^2) \mid x \in Z_3\}$.

g. $\{(x + 3, 5 - 7x) \mid x \in R_+\}$.

h. $\{(x, |x|) \mid x \in Z\}$.

5509. The following function is not real: $\{(2, 1), (3, \text{Ike})\}$.

5510. Immediate consequence. For any real function G and any function F: $G \circ F$ is a real function.

5511. Exercise.

If possible, find a real function H such that domain H is a real function and the domain of domain H is a real function.

5512. Although $\{(x, x) \mid x \in R\}$ is one of the most important real functions, mathematicians have not yet agreed on a symbol for it; we shall use the symbol I because it is the one most frequently used.

5513. Notation. The symbol I denotes $\{(x, x) \mid x \in R\}$.

NOTE. Thus, I is the set of all number pairs whose first and second components are equal.

5514. Example. $I|Z_{2,4} = \{(2, 2), (3, 3), (4, 4)\}$.   (See 2014.)

5515. Immediate consequences.

  a. I is an identity function.   (2004)

  b. I is on R onto R; i.e.,
     domain $I = R$, and range $I = R$.

  c. For each number x: $I(x) = x$.

  d. I is one-one.

  e. $I^{-1} = I$.   (See 2103.)

  f. For each function F whose range is a subset of R: $I \circ F = F$;
     i.e., for each real function F: $I \circ F = F$.

  g. For each function F whose domain is a subset of R: $F \circ I = F$.

5516. Notation. For each number c: the author uses the symbol $\hat{c}$,
     read c *con*, to denote the constant, real function $\{(x, c) \mid x \in R\}$.   (2002)

5517. Examples.

  a. $\hat{2} = \{(x, 2) \mid x \in R\}$.

  b. $\hat{2} \circ \hat{3} = \hat{2}$.

  c. For any number c and real function F on R: $\hat{c} \circ F = \hat{c}$.

5518. Definitions.

  a. A *positive, real function* is any real function each of whose values is
     positive, i.e., a positive, real function is any function into R_+.

  b. A *nonnegative, real function* is any real function each of whose values is
     nonnegative; i.e., a nonnegative, real function is any function into R_0.

5519. Notation. For each positive integer p: the symbol I^p denotes the real
     function $\{(x, x^p) \mid x \in R\}$.

  NOTE. For each positive integer p: I^p is called the pth power function;
     of course, other power functions may also be defined.

5520. Examples.

  a. $I^1 = \{(x, x^1) \mid x \in R\} = I$.

  b. $I^2 = \{(x, x^2) \mid x \in R\}$.

  c. $I^3 = \{(x, x^3) \mid x \in R\}$.

  d. $I^3(-2) = -8$.

5521. Theorem. For any positive integers p, n: $I^p \circ I^n = I^{pn}$.

Proof.:

$I^p \circ I^n =$

$\{(x, [I^p \circ I^n](x)) \mid x \in \text{domain } I^n \text{ and } I^n(x) \in \text{domain } I^p\} =_?$

$\{(x, I^p(x^n)) \mid x \in R\} =$

$\{(x, (x^n)^p) \mid x \in R\} =$

$\{(x, x^{pn}) \mid x \in R\} =$

I^{pn}.

5522. Exercises.

a. I^3 is one-one.

b. I^2 is not one-one.

c. $[I^2|R_0]$ is one-one.

d. Which of the following are true?

   i. $I^2 \circ \hat{3} = \hat{9}$.

   ii. $\hat{3} \circ I^2 = \hat{9}$.

   iii. $\hat{3} \circ I^2 = \hat{3}$.

5523. Notation. For any real function F and positive integer p:
the symbol F^p denotes the real function $I^p \circ F$.

5524. Examples.

a. $\{(\text{Ike}, 3)\}^2 = I^2 \circ \{(\text{Ike}, 3)\} = \{(\text{Ike}, 9)\}$.

b. $\hat{2}^3 = I^3 \circ \hat{2} = \hat{8}$.

5525. Immediate consequence. For any real function F and positive integer p:
$F^p = \{(x, [F(x)]^p) \mid x \in \text{domain } F\}$.   (5523, 5519)

5526. Notation. $\sqrt{I}$ denotes $\{(x, \sqrt{x}) \mid x \in R_0\}$.

NOTE. $\sqrt{I}$ is called the square root function; its domain is R_0.

5527. Example. $\sqrt{I}(4) = 2$.

5528. Exercise.

Which of the following are true?

   i. $\sqrt{I} \circ \hat{9} = \hat{3}$.

   ii. $\hat{9} \circ \sqrt{I} = \hat{9}$.

5529. Theorem. $\sqrt{I} = \{(x^2, x) \mid x \in R_0\}$.

Proof. For any things a, b:
$(a, b) \in \sqrt{I} \Leftrightarrow$
$a \in R_0$ and $b = \sqrt{a} \Leftrightarrow_?$
$b \in R_0$ and $a = b^2 \Leftrightarrow$
$(a, b) \in \{(x^2, x) \mid x \in R_0\}$.

5530. Exercises.

  a. $[I^2 | R_0]^{-1} = \sqrt{I}$.

  b. $[I^2 \circ \sqrt{I}] \subset [\sqrt{I} \circ I^2]$. See 1926NOTE.

5531. Notation. For each real function F:
the symbol $\sqrt{F}$ denotes the real function $\sqrt{I} \circ F$.

5532. Examples.

  a. $\sqrt{\hat{9}} = \sqrt{I} \circ \hat{9} = \hat{3}$.

  b. $\sqrt{\emptyset} = \sqrt{I} \circ \emptyset = \emptyset$.

5533. Immediate consequence. For each real function F:
$\sqrt{F} = \{(x, \sqrt{F(x)}) \mid x \in \text{domain } F \text{ and } 0 \leq F(x)\}$.

5534. Exercise.

Find domain $\sqrt{\{(x, x^3 - x) \mid x \in R\}}$.

Arithmetic of Real Functions

5601. Definition. The *product* of a number r by a real function F is the real function $\{(x, r \cdot F(x)) \mid x \in \text{domain } F\}$.

NOTATION. $[rF]$, read r *times F*.

NOTE I. $\text{domain}[rF] = \text{domain } F$,
and for each argument t of F: $[rF](t) = r \cdot F(t)$.

NOTE II. Outermost brackets will often be omitted.

5602. Examples.

a. $3I = \{(x, 3x) \mid x \in R\}$.

b. $[3I](2) = 6$.

c. $(-2)I^3 = \{(x, -2x^3) \mid x \in R\}$.

d. $(-3)\sqrt{I} = \{(x, -3\sqrt{x}) \mid x \in R_0\}$.

e. $2\hat{3} = \hat{6}$.

f. $2\emptyset = \emptyset$.

5603. Immediate consequence.
For any numbers r, s and real function F: $r[sF] = (rs)F$.

5604. Definition. The *negative* of a real function F is the real function $\{(x, -F(x)) \mid x \in \text{domain } F\}$.

NOTATION. $[-F]$, read as *the negative of F* or as *minus F*.

NOTE. $\text{domain}[-F] = \text{domain } F$, and
for each argument t of F: $[-F](t) = -F(t)$.

269

5605. Examples.

    a. $-I = \{(x, -x) \mid x \in R\} = (-1)I.$

    b. $-\hat{3} = -\{(x, 3) \mid x \in R\} = \{(x, -3) \mid x \in R\} = \widehat{-3}.$

    c. $[-I^2](3) = -9.$

5606. Immediate consequence.
For each real function F: $-[-F] = F$ and $(-1)F = -F.$

5607. We know that there is precisely one number x such that $-x = x$.
However, there are many real functions F such that $-F = F$;
e.g., each of the following three real functions has this property:
$\emptyset$, $\{(1, 0)\}$, $\{(1, 0), (3, 0)\}$.

5608. Exercise.
For each real function F such that $-F \subseteq F$: every value of F is 0.
QUERY. Does it also follow that $-F = F$?

5609. Definition. A *common argument* of two or more functions is any thing
that is an argument of each of them.

5610. Example. 3 is a common argument of $\hat{7}$, $\sqrt{I}$;
but -3 is not a common argument of these functions.

5611. Definition. For any real functions F, G:

    the *sum* of F and G is the real function
    $\{(x, F(x) + G(x)) \mid x$ is a common argument of F, $G\}$
    and is denoted by the symbol $[F + G]$;

    the *difference* between F and G is the real function
    $\{(x, F(x) - G(x)) \mid x$ is a common argument of F, $G\}$
    and is denoted by the symbol $[F - G]$;

    the *product* of F and G is the real function
    $\{(x, F(x) \cdot G(x)) \mid x$ is a common argument of F, $G\}$
    and is denoted by the symbol $[FG]$;

    the *quotient* of F by G is the real function
    $\{(x, F(x)/G(x)) \mid x$ is a common argument of F, G and $G(x) \neq 0\}$
    and is denoted by the symbols $[F/G]$, $\left[\dfrac{F}{G}\right].$

5612. *Remarks on the previous definition.*

    The domain of $F + G$, $F - G$, FG is domain $F \cap$ domain G.

    If F, G have no common arguments,
    then $F + G$, $F - G$, FG are empty.

For each common argument t of F, G:
$[F + G](t) = F(t) + G(t)$,
$[F - G](t) = F(t) - G(t)$,
$[FG](t) = F(t) \cdot G(t)$.

The domain of F/G consists of all common arguments x of F, G such that $G(x) \neq 0$; if there is no such argument, then F/G is empty.

For each argument t of F/G: $[F/G](t) = F(t)/G(t)$.

NOTE. Since F and G are sets, the symbol $[F - G]$ also denotes the deletion of F by G. (See 1718.) However, it will usually be quite clear from the context whether we are dealing with the difference between real functions or the deletion of one set by another set.

5613. Examples.

a. Let H denote $\{(1, 3), (2, 5), (4, 9), (7, 4)\}$,
and let K denote $\{(0, 1), (2, 1), (7, 2), (4, 0), (5, 3)\}$.
$H + K = \{(2, 6), (4, 9), (7, 6)\}$.
$H - K = \{(2, 4), (4, 9), (7, 2)\}$.
$HK = \{(2, 5), (4, 0), (7, 8)\}$.
$H/K = \{(2, 5), (7, 2)\}$.

b. $\hat{6} + \hat{3} = \hat{9}$, $\hat{2} - \hat{5} = \widehat{-3}$, $\hat{2}\hat{3} = \hat{6}$, $\hat{6}/\hat{3} = \hat{2}$.

c. $[\hat{3} + 5I^2] - 2I^3 = \{(x, 3 + 5x^2 - 2x^3) \mid x \in R\}$.

d. $II^2 = I^3$.

e. $\sqrt{I}\,\sqrt{I} = I|R_0$.

f. $\hat{3}/\hat{0} = \emptyset$.

5614. Theorem. For any real functions F, G, H and numbers r, s:
$F + G = G + F$,
$FG = GF$,
$[F + G] + H = F + [G + H]$,
$[FG]H = F[GH]$,
$F - G = F + [-G]$,
$F[G + H] = FG + FH$,
$F[G/H] = [FG]/H$,
$rF = \hat{r}F$, $1F = F$,
$r[G + H] = rG + rH$,
$r[G - H] = rG - rH$,
$[rG]H = r[GH]$,
$r[G/H] = [rG]/H$,
$(r + s)F = rF + sF$.
Proof. Straightforward.

5615. Exercise.

Which of the following are true?

i.   For each real function F: $F - F = \hat{0}$.
ii. For each real function F: $F - F = \hat{0}|\text{domain } F$.
iii. For each real function F whose domain is a subset of R:
     $F - F = \hat{0}|\text{domain } F$.
iv. For each number r: $\hat{r}/\hat{r} = \hat{1}$.
v. $[I^2 - \hat{1}]/[I - \hat{1}] = I + \hat{1}$.
vi. $[I^2 - \hat{1}]/[I - \hat{1}] = [I + \hat{1}]|\{x \mid x \neq 1\}$.

5616. The reader is reminded that the symbols Z_1, Z_+ both denote the set of all positive integers; henceforth we shall favor the symbol Z_1.

5617. Exercises.

a. Find two real one-one functions whose sum is not one-one.

b. $[I + \hat{2}]|Z_1$ is one-one and on Z_1 onto Z_3.

c. For any real functions F, G and any set S:
$[FG]|S = F[G|S] = [F|S][G|S]$,
and $[F + G]|S = F + [G|S] = [F|S] + [G|S]$.

5618. Notation.

$[F + G + H]$ stands for $F + [G + H]$,
$[E + F + G + H]$ stands for $E + [F + G + H]$,

$[FGH]$ stands for $F[GH]$,
$[EFGH]$ stands for $E[FGH]$.

5619. Theorem. For any real functions F, G and any function H:
$[F + G] \circ H = [F \circ H] + [G \circ H]$.

Proof. Consider any such hypothesized F, G, H.
Let A denote $[F + G] \circ H$, and let B denote $[F \circ H] + [G \circ H]$.

It suffices to prove that domain $A =$ domain B and that
for each argument t of A: $A(t) = B(t)$.

domain $A =$
$\{x \mid x \in \text{domain } H \text{ and } H(x) \in \text{domain}[F + G]\} =$
$\{x \mid x \in \text{domain } H \text{ and } H(x) \text{ is a common argument of } F, G\} =$
$\{x \mid x \in \text{domain } H \text{ and } H(x) \in \text{domain } F\} \cap$
$\quad \{x \mid x \in \text{domain } H \text{ and } H(x) \in \text{domain } G\} =$
$\text{domain}[F \circ H] \cap \text{domain}[G \circ H] =$
domain B.

For each argument t of A: $A(t) = [[F + G] \circ H](t) =$
$[F + G](H(t)) = F(H(t)) + G(H(t)) = [F \circ H](t) + [G \circ H](t) =$
$[[F \circ H] + [G \circ H]](t) = B(t)$.

5620. The following proposition can be proved in the same manner as 5619.

For any real functions F, G and any function H:
$$[FG] \circ H = [F \circ H][G \circ H].$$

5621. Exercises.

a. *Disprove.* For any real functions K, F, G:
$$K \circ [F + G] = [K \circ F] + [K \circ G].$$

b. *Disprove.* For any real functions K, F, G:
$$K \circ [FG] = [K \circ F][K \circ G].$$

5622. Notation. $|I|$ denotes the real function $\{(x, |x|) \mid x \in R\}$.

NOTE I. $|I|$ is called the absolute value function.

NOTE II. For each number t: $|I|(t) = |t|$.

5623. Examples.

a. $|I| \circ \widehat{-3} = \hat{3}$.

b. $I^2 \circ |I| = I^2$.

c. $\sqrt{I^2} =$
$\sqrt{I} \circ I^2 =$
$\{(x, [\sqrt{I} \circ I^2](x)) \mid x \in \text{domain } I^2 \text{ and } I^2(x) \in \text{domain } \sqrt{I}\} =_?$
$\{(x, \sqrt{x^2}) \mid x \in R\} =$
$\{(x, |x|) \mid x \in R\} =$
$|I|$.

5624. Notation. For each real function F:
the symbol $|F|$ denotes the real function $|I| \circ F$.

5625. Examples.

a. $|\{(\text{Ike}, -2), \ (-3, -4), \ (-5, 1)\}| = \{(\text{Ike}, 2), \ (-3, 4), \ (-5, 1)\}$.

b. $|\widehat{-3}| = |I| \circ \widehat{-3} = \hat{3}$. (5623a)

5626. Immediate consequences.

a. For each real function F: $|F| = \{(x, |F(x)|) \mid x \in \text{domain } F\}$.

b. For each real function F: $\sqrt{F^2} = |F|$.

5627. Exercise.

Let L denote $\hat{3} + |I - \hat{3}|$. Prove that for any numbers x, y:
$L(x + y) \leq L(x) + L(y)$ and $L(x) = L(6 - x)$.

The Sum of a Finite Number-Sequence

5701. Definition. A *finite number-sequence* (or *finite sequence of numbers*) is any real function whose domain consists of all integers between two integers.

NOTE. A real function F is a finite number-sequence iff there are integers $b \leqq w$ such that F is on $Z_{b,w}$.

CAUTION. This definition gives us no license to use in isolation the expressions *finite, number-sequence, sequence, finite sequence.*

5702. Examples. Each of the following is a finite number-sequence.

a. $\{(-3, \sqrt{2})\}$.

b. $\{(7, -\sqrt{2})\}$.

c. $\{(-2, 5), (-1, \sqrt{3})\}$.

d. $\{(0, 4), (-2, 5), (1, 0), (-1, \sqrt{3})\}$.

e. $I^2 | Z_{0,5}$.

f. $I | Z_{-9,7}$.

g. $\hat{2} | Z_{-1,9}$.

5703. Examples. None of the following is a finite number-sequence.

$\{(2, 1), (3, 2), (5, 3)\}$. (?)

$I | Z_0$. (?)

$\emptyset$. (?)

$[\hat{3}/I] | Z_{-2,5}$. (?)

5704. Immediate consequence. For any integers $b \leq w$ and real function H over $Z_{b,w}$: $H|Z_{b,w}$ is a finite number-sequence. (See 1915b.)

5705. Definition. For each finite number-sequence F:
the *initial value* of F is the number that F assigns to its least argument, and
the *last value* of F is the number that F assigns to its greatest argument.

5706. Examples.

a. The initial value of $I^2|Z_{-3,2}$ is 9 and its last value is 4.

b. The initial value of $\{(3, \sqrt{2})\}$ is $\sqrt{2}$ and its last value is $\sqrt{2}$.

c. The initial value of $\{(-2, -6), (-1, 5), (0, \sqrt{2}), (1, -6)\}$ is -6 and its last value is -6.

5707. Definitions.

a. A *finite sequence of nonnegative numbers* is
any finite number-sequence each of whose values is nonnegative.

b. A *finite sequence of positive numbers* is
any finite number-sequence each of whose values is positive.

5708. Examples.

a. The functions described in 5702a,c,d,e,g are finite sequences of nonnegative numbers.

b. The functions described in 5702a,c,g are finite sequences of positive numbers.

5709. The purpose of this lesson is to provide a precise definition of the sum (of all values) of a finite number-sequence. In a subsequent lesson we shall discuss certain traditional notations used in the theory of finite number-sequences.

5710. *Note for the teacher.* The usual recursive definition of the sum of a finite number-sequence must be preceded by a theorem that justifies definition by recursion. Since such a theorem is beyond the grasp of many undergraduates, the author uses a different method that is both rigorous and conceptually simple. Teachers who believe that the justification theorem is a simple matter will be interested in reading the last paragraph of Martin Davis' review (*Scripta Mathematica*, Volume XXV, No. 4, p. 337) of Paul Halmos' excellent book *Naive Set Theory*.

5711. The following discussion will help the student to understand Definition 5712.

Let F denote $\{(-2, 3/7),\ (-1, 1),\ (0, -2/7),\ (1, 6/7)\}$, and let G denote $\{(-2, 3/7),\ (-1, 10/7),\ (0, 8/7),\ (1, 2)\}$.

The following propositions may easi'y be verified.

G is on $Z_{-2,1}$ which is the domain of F.

$G(-2) = F(-2)$; i.e., G and F have the same initial value.

For each integer j such that $-2 < j \leq 1$: $G(j) = F(j) + G(j - 1)$.

Note that the last value of G equals $F(-2) + F(-1) + F(0) + F(1)$.

5712. Definition. A *sum accumulator* of (or for) a finite number-sequence, say F on $Z_{b,w}$, is any finite number-sequence G such that

a. G is on $Z_{b,w}$,

b. $G(b) = F(b)$,

c. for each integer j such that $b < j \leq w$: $G(j) = F(j) + G(j - 1)$.

5713. Examples.

a. In the discussion at 5711, G is a sum accumulator of F.

b. $\{(3, \sqrt{7})\}$ is a sum accumulator of $\{(3, \sqrt{7})\}$.
Note that requirement 5712c is vacuously satisfied.

c. For any integer b and real function H over $Z_{b,b}$:
$H|Z_{b,b}$ is a sum accumulator of $H|Z_{b,b}$.

d. $\{(2, 5), (3, 9)\}$ is a sum accumulator of $\{(2, 5), (3, 4)\}$.

e. $\{(1, 0), (2, 5), (3, 7)\}$ is not a sum accumulator of $\{(1, 0), (2, 1), (3, 6)\}$.

5714. Soon we shall prove that for each finite number-sequence there is precisely one sum accumulator thereof. To dispel the student's belief that such a proposition is trivial, we offer the next exercise.

5715. Exercise.
Let k denote the positive integer 8^7.
Prove that there is at least one sum accumulator of $[2I - \hat{1}]|Z_{1,k}$.

HINT. Try $I^2|Z_{1,k}$ and use restricted induction. (See 4017.)

5716. Surely the student knows by now that some intuitively obvious propositions are annoyingly difficult to prove.

5717. Theorem. For each finite number-sequence there is precisely one sum accumulator thereof.

Proof.

AT MOST ONE.

Suppose not.

Then there are integers $a \leq n$, a real function U on $Z_{a,n}$, and two distinct sum accumulators G, H of U.

Since $G \neq H$ and domain $G = Z_{a,n}$ = domain H, there is an integer between a, n to which G and H assign distinct numbers.

So there is a least integer i between a, n such that $G(i) \neq H(i)$.

Since $G(a) =_? H(a)$, we have $i \neq a$.

Therefore $a < i \leq n$.

Hence, $G(i) = U(i) + G(i - 1) =_? U(i) + H(i - 1) = H(i)$.

Contradiction.

AT LEAST ONE.

Consider any integer b. Let S denote

$\{n \in Z_b \mid$ for each real function on $Z_{b,n}$
         there is at least one sum accumulator thereof$\}$.

It suffices to prove that S is hereditary from b.   (?)

S contains b.   (?)

Now consider any number m in S.

We shall prove that $m + 1$ is in S.

Surely $(m + 1) \in Z_b$. In fact $b < m + 1$.

Lastly, for each real function F on $Z_{b,m+1}$:

there is a sum accumulator V of $F|Z_{b,m}$,   (?), and then

$V \cup \{(m + 1, F(m + 1) + V(m))\}$ is a sum accumulator of $F|Z_{b,m+1}$,

and so $m + 1$ is in S.

5718. Examples. Let k denote 8^7.

a. $I^2|Z_{1,k}$ is *the* sum accumulator of $[2I - \hat{1}]|Z_{1,k}$.

Proof. By 5715 we know that $I^2|Z_{1,k}$ is a sum accumulator of $[2I - \hat{1}]|Z_{1,k}$, and by 5717 we know there is no other.

b. To prove there is a sum accumulator of $[5I^6 - 4I^3 + \widehat{\sqrt{2}}]|Z_{1,k}$, we need not submit a formula (that would be rather hard to do); all we need do is quote Theorem 5717.

5719. Definition. The *sum* (of all values) of a finite number-sequence is the last value of its sum accumulator.

5720. Examples.

    a. The sum of $\{(2, -\sqrt{5})\}$ is $-\sqrt{5}$ because $-\sqrt{5}$ is the last value of $\{(2, -\sqrt{5})\}$ which is the sum accumulator of $\{(2, -\sqrt{5})\}$.

    b. Let k denote 8^7. The sum of $[2I - \hat{1}]|Z_{1,k}$ is k^2 because k^2 is the last value of $I^2|Z_{1,k}$ which is the sum accumulator of $[2I - \hat{1}]|Z_{1,k}$.

5721. The reader is reminded of the author's definition which states that a function F is *over* a set A provided that $A \subseteq \text{domain } F$.

5722. Notation. For any integers $b \leq w$ and real function H over $Z_{b,w}$:

    the symbol $\displaystyle\sum_b^w H$ denotes the sum of the finite number-sequence $H|Z_{b,w}$.

NOTE I. The symbol $\displaystyle\sum_b^w H$ is rendered thus: sigma H from b to w.

NOTE II. In Lesson 62 we shall introduce traditional methods of denoting the sum of a finite number-sequence.

5723. It is important to keep in mind that a symbol such as $\displaystyle\sum_a^n F$ is meaningful if and only if a is an integer, n is an integer, $a \leq n$, and F is a real function over $Z_{a,n}$.

5724. Examples.

    a. $\displaystyle\sum_2^2 \{(2, -\sqrt{5})\} = -\sqrt{5}$. (See 5720a.)

    b. Let k denote 8^7. Then $\displaystyle\sum_1^k [2I - \hat{1}] = k^2$. (See 5720b.)

    c. $\displaystyle\sum_2^3 \hat{4} = 8$. (?)

    d. $\displaystyle\sum_1^3 \{(1/2, 7),\ (0, -3),\ (1, 4),\ (2, -1),\ (3, 2)\} = 5$. (?)

5725. Theorem. For any integers $b \leq w$ and real function F over $Z_{b,w}$:

$$\sum_b^w [F|Z_{b,w}] = \sum_b^w F.$$

Proof.: by 5722 with $[F|Z_{b,w}]$ for H, the symbol $\sum\limits_{b}^{w} [F|Z_{b,w}]$ denotes

the sum of $[F|Z_{b,w}]|Z_{b,w}$; since $[F|Z_{b,w}]|Z_{b,w} = [F|Z_{b,w}]$,

the symbol $\sum\limits_{b}^{w} [F|Z_{b,w}]$ denotes the sum of $[F|Z_{b,w}]$, i.e., denotes $\sum\limits_{b}^{w} F$.

5726. Next we prove two important theorems.

5727. Theorems.

a. For any integer b and real function H over $Z_{b,b}$: $\sum\limits_{b}^{b} H = H(b)$.

Proof.: $H(b)$ is the last value of $H|Z_{b,b}$ which is the sum accumulator of $H|Z_{b,b}$.

b. For any integers $b \leq m$ and real function H over $Z_{b,m+1}$:

$$\sum_{b}^{m+1} H = H(m + 1) + \sum_{b}^{m} H.$$

Proof. Consider any such hypothesized b, m, H.
Let G denote the sum accumulator of $H|Z_{b,m}$.
Then $G \cup \{(m + 1, H(m + 1) + G(m))\}$ is the sum accumulator of $H|Z_{b,m+1}$. (?)

So, $\sum\limits_{b}^{m+1} H = H(m + 1) + G(m) = H(m + 1) + \sum\limits_{b}^{m} H.$ (?)

5728. Example. $\sum\limits_{-1}^{2} I^2 = 6.$

Proof I. $\{(-1, 1), (0, 1), (1, 2), (2, 6)\}$ is the sum accumulator of $I^2|Z_{-1,2}$.

Proof II (using 5727). $\sum\limits_{-1}^{2} I^2 = I^2(2) + \sum\limits_{-1}^{1} I^2 = 4 + I^2(1) + \sum\limits_{-1}^{0} I^2 =$

$5 + I^2(0) + \sum\limits_{-1}^{-1} I^2 = 5 + I^2(-1) = 6.$

5729. Example. For each real function F over $Z_{1,3}$:

$$\sum_{1}^{3} F = F(1) + F(2) + F(3).$$

Proof.: $\sum\limits_{1}^{3} F = F(3) + \sum\limits_{1}^{2} F = F(3) + F(2) + \sum\limits_{1}^{1} F =$

$F(3) + F(2) + F(1).$

5730. Example. For each positive integer n: $\sum_1^n I = n(1 + n)/2$.

Proof. $\left\{ n \epsilon Z_1 \,\middle|\, \sum_1^n I = n(1 + n)/2 \right\}$

contains 1 because $1 \epsilon Z_1$ and $\sum_1^1 I = I(1) = 1 = 1(1 + 1)/2$,

and contains the successor of each number j therein because $(j + 1) \epsilon Z_1$

and $\sum_1^{j+1} I = I(j + 1) + \sum_1^j I =_? (j + 1) + j(1 + j)/2 =$

$(j + 1)[1 + (j + 1)]/2$.

5731. Exercises.

a. $\sum_0^4 [2I - \hat{3}] = 5$. Please use 5727.

b. For each positive integer n: $\sum_1^n [2I - \hat{1}] = n^2$.

c. For each positive integer n: $\sum_1^n I^2 = n(n + 1)(2n + 1)/6$.

5732. Whence came the formulas in 5730, 5731b,c? Soon we shall know.

$$\sum$$

5801. Review. In 5701 we defined what is meant by a finite number-sequence, and in 5719 we defined the sum (of all values) of a finite number-sequence.

For any integers $b \leq w$ and real function H over $Z_{b,w}$:

we agreed (5722) to denote the sum of $H|Z_{b,w}$ by the symbol $\displaystyle\sum_{b}^{w} H$,

and we proved (5725) that $\displaystyle\sum_{b}^{w} [H|Z_{b,w}] = \sum_{b}^{w} H$.

In 5727 we proved the following important propositions.

a. For any integer b and real function H over $Z_{b,b}$: $\displaystyle\sum_{b}^{b} H = H(b)$.

b. For any integers $b \leq m$ and real function H over $Z_{b,m+1}$:

$$\sum_{b}^{m+1} H = H(m + 1) + \sum_{b}^{m} H.$$

In this lesson we shall prove many propositions involving Σ.

5802. Theorem. For any integers $a \leq n$: $\displaystyle\sum_{a}^{n} \hat{1} = n - a + 1$.

Proof. Consider any integer a.

$\left\{ n \in Z_a \,\middle|\, \displaystyle\sum_{a}^{n} \hat{1} = n - a + 1 \right\}$ contains a (?) and

contains the successor of each number i therein because $(i + 1) \in Z_a$ and

$$\sum_{a}^{i+1} \hat{1} = \hat{1}(i + 1) + \sum_{a}^{i} \hat{1} =_? 1 + (i - a + 1) = (i + 1) - a + 1.$$

5803. Example. $\displaystyle\sum_{-3}^{4} \hat{1} = 4 - (-3) + 1 = 8$.

5804. Corollary. For each positive integer n: $\displaystyle\sum_{1}^{n} \hat{1} = n$.   (5802 with 1 for a)

5805. Theorem. *Generalized distributive law.*

For any integers $a \leq n$, number r, and real function F over $Z_{a,n}$:

$$\sum_{a}^{n} [rF] = r \sum_{a}^{n} F.$$

Proof. Consider any integer a.

$\left\{ n \, \epsilon \, Z_a \,\middle|\, \text{for any number } r \text{ and real function } F \text{ over } Z_{a,n} \right.$:

$$\sum_{a}^{n} [rF] = r \sum_{a}^{n} F \Bigg\}$$

contains a (?)
and contains the successor of each number i therein because $(i + 1) \, \epsilon \, Z_a$,
and for any number r and real function F over $Z_{a,i+1}$:

$$\sum_{a}^{i+1} [rF] = [rF](i + 1) + \sum_{a}^{i} [rF] = r \cdot F(i + 1) + r \sum_{a}^{i} F =$$

$$r\left[F(i + 1) + \sum_{a}^{i} F \right] = r \sum_{a}^{i+1} F.$$

5806. Example. $\displaystyle\sum_{-2}^{5} 8I^2 = 8 \sum_{-2}^{5} I^2$.

5807. Corollaries.

a. For any integers $a \leq n$ and real function F over $Z_{a,n}$:

$$\sum_{a}^{n} [-F] = -\sum_{a}^{n} F.$$

Proof. 5805 with -1 for r.

b. For any integers $a \leq n$ and any number r:

$$\sum_{a}^{n} \hat{r} = r(n - a + 1).$$

Proof.: $\displaystyle\sum_{a}^{n} \hat{r} = \sum_{a}^{n} [r\hat{1}] = r \sum_{a}^{n} \hat{1} = r(n - a + 1).$

c. For any integers $a \leq n$: $\displaystyle\sum_{a}^{n} \hat{0} = 0$.

Proof. 5807b with 0 for r.

5808. Exercise.

Let us define an infinitesimal to be any nonzero number c such that for each positive integer p: $\left| \sum_{1}^{p} \hat{c} \right| < 1$.

Prove that there are no infinitesimals.

5809. Theorem. For any integers $a \leqq n$ and real functions F, G over $Z_{a,n}$:

$$\sum_{a}^{n} [F + G] = \sum_{a}^{n} F + \sum_{a}^{n} G.$$

Proof. Consider any integer a.

$\left\{ n \in Z_a \middle| \text{ for any real functions } F, G \text{ over } Z_{a,n}: \right.$

$$\left. \sum_{a}^{n} [F + G] = \sum_{a}^{n} F + \sum_{a}^{n} G \right\}$$

contains a (?)
and contains the successor of each number i therein because $(i + 1) \in Z_a$ and for any real functions F, G over $Z_{a,i+1}$:

$$\sum_{a}^{i+1} [F + G] =$$

$$[F + G](i + 1) + \sum_{a}^{i} [F + G] =$$

$$F(i + 1) + G(i + 1) + \sum_{a}^{i} F + \sum_{a}^{i} G =$$

$$\sum_{a}^{i+1} F + \sum_{a}^{i+1} G.$$

5810. Exercises.

a. For any integers $a \leqq n$, numbers u, v, and real functions F, G over $Z_{a,n}$:

$$\sum_{a}^{n} [uF + vG] = u \sum_{a}^{n} F + v \sum_{a}^{n} G.$$

b. For any integers $a \leqq n$ and real functions F, G, H over $Z_{a,n}$:

$$\sum_{a}^{n} [F + G + H] = \sum_{a}^{n} F + \sum_{a}^{n} G + \sum_{a}^{n} H.$$

5811. Theorem. *Extended associative law of addition.*

For any integers $a \le b < n$ and real function F over $Z_{a,n}$:

$$\sum_a^n F = \sum_a^b F + \sum_{b+1}^n F.$$

Proof. Consider any integers $a \le b$.

$\left\{ n \in Z_{b+1} \;\middle|\; \text{for each real function } F \text{ over } Z_{a,n} \right.$:

$$\sum_a^n F = \sum_a^b F + \sum_{b+1}^n F \bigg\}$$

contains $b + 1$ (?) and
contains the successor of each number i therein because $(i + 1) \in Z_{b+1}$
and for each real function F over $Z_{a,i+1}$:

$$\sum_a^{i+1} F = F(i + 1) + \sum_a^i F = F(i + 1) + \sum_a^b F + \sum_{b+1}^i F =$$

$$\sum_a^b F + \sum_{b+1}^{i+1} F.$$

5812. There is also a generalized associative law of addition that we shall neither state nor prove; it is rather difficult to state correctly and is not needed for our work in this book.

5813. Exercises.

a. For any integers $a < n$ and real function F over $Z_{a,n}$:

$$\sum_a^n F = F(a) + \sum_{a+1}^n F.$$

b. For any integers $a < i < n$ and real function F over $Z_{a,n}$:

$$\sum_a^n F = \left(\sum_a^{i-1} F \right) + F(i) + \sum_{i+1}^n F.$$

5814. Consider any real function G over $Z_{4,7}$.

Let us compare $G|Z_{4,7}$ with $\left[G \circ [I - \hat{2}] \right]|Z_{6,9}$.

$G|Z_{4,7} = \{(4, G(4)), \ (5, G(5)), \ (6, G(6)), \ (7, G(7))\}$.

$\left[G \circ [I - \hat{2}] \right]|Z_{6,9} = \{(6, G(4)), \ (7, G(5)), \ (8, G(6)), \ (9, G(7))\}$.

Note the translation (or shift) of arguments. It should not surprise us that any such shift leaves the sum of values unchanged.

5815. Theorem. *Translation.*

For any integers $b \leq m$, real function G over $Z_{b,m}$, and integer c:

$$\sum_b^m G = \sum_{b+c}^{m+c} \left[G \circ [I - \hat{c}] \right].$$

Proof. Consider any integer b.

$$\left\{ m \in Z_b \,\middle|\, \text{for any real function } G \text{ over } Z_{b,m}, \text{ and any integer } c: \right.$$

$$\left. \sum_b^m G = \sum_{b+c}^{m+c} \left[G \circ [I - \hat{c}] \right] \right\}$$

contains b (?)
and contains the successor of each number j therein because $(j + 1) \in Z_b$
and for any real function G over $Z_{b,j+1}$ and any integer c:

$$\sum_b^{j+1} G = G(j + 1) + \sum_b^j G =$$

$$\left[G \circ [I - \hat{c}] \right](j + 1 + c) + \sum_{b+c}^{j+c} \left[G \circ [I - \hat{c}] \right] =$$

$$\sum_{b+c}^{j+1+c} \left[G \circ [I - \hat{c}] \right]. \quad (?)$$

5816. Examples.

a. $\displaystyle\sum_4^8 I^3 = \sum_6^{10} \left[I^3 \circ [I - \hat{2}] \right] = \sum_6^{10} [I - \hat{2}]^3.$

b. $\displaystyle\sum_4^8 [I^2 + \hat{1}]^3 = \sum_6^{10} \left[[I^2 + \hat{1}]^3 \circ [I - \hat{2}] \right] = \sum_6^{10} [I^2 - 4I + \hat{5}]^3.$

5817. Corollary.   For any integers $b \leq m$, real function G over $Z_{b,m}$, and

integer p: $\displaystyle\sum_b^m G = \sum_{b-p}^{m-p} \left[G \circ [I + \hat{p}] \right].$

Proof. 5815 with $-p$ for c.

5818. Example. $\displaystyle\sum_5^8 \sqrt{I} = \sum_3^6 \left[\sqrt{I} \circ [I + \hat{2}] \right] = \sum_3^6 \sqrt{I + \hat{2}}.$

5819. Corollary.   For any integers $b \leq m$ and real function G over $Z_{b,m}$:

$$\sum_b^m G = \sum_1^{m-b+1} \left[G \circ [I + \hat{b} - \hat{1}] \right].$$

Proof. 5817 with $b - 1$ for p.

5820. Examples.

a. $\displaystyle\sum_{5}^{10} I^3 = \sum_{1}^{6} [I^3 \circ [I + \hat{5} - \hat{1}]] = \sum_{1}^{6} [I + \hat{4}]^3.$

b. $\displaystyle\sum_{5}^{10} [I + \hat{2}]^3 = \sum_{1}^{6} \left[[I + \hat{2}]^3 \circ [I + \hat{5} - \hat{1}]\right] = \sum_{1}^{6} [I + \hat{6}]^3.$

5821. Theorem. *Telescope.*

For any integers $a \leqq n$ and real function F over $Z_{a,n+1}$:

$$\sum_{a}^{n} \left[[F \circ [I + \hat{1}]] - F\right] = F(n + 1) - F(a).$$

Proof.: in case $a = n$, the conclusion is obvious;   (?)

in case $a < n$, then

$$\sum_{a}^{n} \left[[F \circ [I + \hat{1}]] - F\right] = \sum_{a}^{n} [F \circ [I + \hat{1}]] - \sum_{a}^{n} F =?$$

$$\sum_{a+1}^{n+1} F - \sum_{a}^{n} F = F(n + 1) + \sum_{a+1}^{n} F - \left[F(a) + \sum_{a+1}^{n} F\right] =$$

$$F(n + 1) - F(a).$$

NOTE. The following is not a proof of this theorem.   (?)

$$\vdots \ \sum_{a}^{n} \left[[F \circ [I + \hat{1}]] - F\right] = \sum_{a}^{n} [F \circ [I + \hat{1}]] - \sum_{a}^{n} F =$$

$$\sum_{a+1}^{n+1} F - \sum_{a}^{n} F = F(n + 1) + \sum_{a+1}^{n} F - \left[F(a) + \sum_{a+1}^{n} F\right] =$$

$$F(n + 1) - F(a).$$

5822. Example. $\displaystyle\sum_{3}^{7} \left[[\sqrt{I} \circ [I + \hat{1}]] - \sqrt{I}\right] = \sqrt{8} - \sqrt{3}.$

5823. Example. In 5730 we proved the following proposition.

For each positive integer n: $\displaystyle\sum_{1}^{n} I = n(1 + n)/2.$

Now we shall use 5821 to prove this proposition and simultaneously to derive the formula.

First note that $I^2 \circ [I + \hat{1}] = I^2 + 2I + \hat{1}.$

Proof.: $2 \sum_{1}^{n} I = \sum_{1}^{n} 2I = \sum_{1}^{n} \left[[I^2 \circ [I + \hat{1}]] - I^2 - \hat{1} \right] =$

$\sum_{1}^{n} \left[[I^2 \circ [I + \hat{1}]] - I^2 \right] - \sum_{1}^{n} \hat{1} = I^2(n+1) - I^2(1) - n = n(1+n).$

NOTE. In 6006 we shall present another derivation-type proof of this proposition.

5824. Exercises.

a. For any integers $a \leq m$: $\sum_{a}^{m} I = (m - a + 1)(a + m)/2.$

NOTE. Please fashion your proof after the proof in 5823.

b. Derive a simple formula for $\sum_{a}^{n} [\hat{u} + vI]$.

HINT. Use 5810a, 5807b, 5824a.

NOTE. Proposition 5731b may be obtained by choosing 1 for a, -1 for u, 2 for v.

c. Derive a simple formula for $\sum_{1}^{n} I^2$.

HINT. $I^3 \circ [I + \hat{1}] = I^3 + 3I^2 + 3I + \hat{1}.$

5825. In Lesson 60 we shall resume our study of Σ.

Permutations

5901. In this lesson we introduce the idea of a permutation as it is used by modern algebraists.

5902. Definition. A *permutation* is any one-one function whose domain and range are equal.

5903. Examples. Each of the following is a permutation:

$\{(5, 5)\}$,

$\{(1, \sqrt{2}), (\sqrt{2}, 1)\}$,

$\{(-1, 1), (0, 0), (1, -1)\}$,

$\{(4, 6), (6, 9), (9, 4)\}$,

$\{(\sqrt{2}, 0), (0, \sqrt{2}), (-3, -3)\}$,

$\{(\text{Moon, Sun}), (\text{Sun, Moon})\}$,

I,

$\emptyset$.

5904. By 5506 we know that a function whose domain and range are equal is not necessarily a permutation.

5905. To prove that a function P is a permutation we must prove that

i. for any distinct arguments x, y of P: $P(x) \neq P(y)$,

ii. domain P = range P.

5906. Example. $5I - \hat{2}$ is a permutation.

Proof. Let P denote $5I - \hat{2}$.

i. For any distinct arguments x, y of P:
$P(x) = 5x - 2 \neq 5y - 2 = P(y)$.

ii. Since domain $P = R$, it suffices to prove that $R = $ range P.
Obviously, range $P \subseteq R$.
Lastly, $R \subseteq$ range P because each member x of R equals $P((x + 2)/5)$
which is in range P.

5907. Lemma. For any integers $a \leq n$: $[\hat{n} + \hat{a} - I]|Z_{a,n}$ is a permutation.

Proof. Consider any integers $a \leq n$ and let P denote $[\hat{n} + \hat{a} - I]|Z_{a,n}$.

i. For any distinct arguments i, k of P:
$P(i) = n + a - i \neq n + a - k = P(k)$.

ii. Since domain $P = Z_{a,n}$, it suffices to prove that $Z_{a,n} = $ range P.
$Z_{a,n} \subseteq$ range P because each member i of $Z_{a,n}$ equals $P(n + a - i)$
which is in range P. (?)
Range $P \subseteq Z_{a,n}$ because for each member of range P, say $P(j)$ where
$j \in Z_{a,n}$: $P(j)$ equals $n + a - j$ which is in $Z_{a,n}$. (?)

NOTE. We know now that $[\hat{n} + \hat{a} - I]|Z_{a,n}$ is onto $Z_{a,n}$.

5908. We know that a permutation is on the set it is onto. For reasons soon
to appear we shall usually emphasize the *onto* feature rather than the *on*
feature.

E.g., we emphasize the fact that $5I - \hat{2}$ is a permutation onto R, and
we emphasize the fact that $[\hat{3} + \hat{1} - I]|Z_{1,3}$ is a permutation onto $Z_{1,3}$.

5909. Exercises.

a. $I^2|R_0$ is a permutation onto R_0.

b. The inverse of each permutation is a permutation.

c. For any permutations V, W onto a set S: $V \circ W$ is a permutation onto S.
HINT. 2027, 2028.

5910. Consider any function F and any permutation P onto domain F.
What do we obtain when we compose F with P?
We obtain a function whose domain equals domain F and whose
range equals range F; (?)
i.e., domain $[F \circ P] = $ domain F, and range $[F \circ P] = $ range F.

However, $F \circ P$ is not necessarily equal to F;
e.g., choose $\{(1, 7), (2, 4)\}$ for F and $\{(1, 2), (2, 1)\}$ for P.

5911. The following discussion will help the student to understand Definition 5913.

Let F denote
$$\{(-5, \sqrt{2}),\ (-4, 0),\ (-3, \sqrt{2}),\ (-2, 7),\ (-1, \sqrt{2}),\ (0, 7),\ (1, -9)\}.$$
F is a finite number-sequence whose domain is $Z_{-5,1}$.

Let P denote
$$\{(-5, 1),\ (-4, -2),\ (-3, -4),\ (-2, 0),\ (-1, -5),\ (0, -3),\ (1, -1)\}.$$
P is a permutation onto domain F.

Let G denote $F \circ P$.

$$G = \{(-5, -9),\ (-4, 7),\ (-3, 0),\ (-2, 7),\ (-1, \sqrt{2}),\ (0, \sqrt{2}),\ (1, \sqrt{2})\}.$$
Domain $G =$ domain F, and range $G =$ range F.

Soon we shall say that G is a rearrangement of F. Informally we may assert that the values of F and G occur with the same frequency. (Count them.)

5912. Exercise. Consider the function F and the permutation P discussed in 5911. Find a permutation T onto domain F such that
$$T \neq P \quad \text{and} \quad F \circ T = F \circ P.$$
Find a permutation V onto domain F such that
$$V \neq P \quad \text{and} \quad F \circ V \neq F \circ P.$$

5913. Definition. A finite number-sequence G is a *rearrangement* of a finite number-sequence F provided there is a permutation P onto domain F such that $G = F \circ P$.

5914. Example. Referring to 5911, we see that G is a rearrangement of F. By 5912 we know that composing F with different permutations that are onto domain F may or may not yield different rearrangements of F.

5915. Exercises.

a. $\{(-2, 0),\ (-1, \sqrt{3}),\ (0, 7),\ (1, 5),\ (2, \sqrt{3}),\ (3, 5)\}$ is a rearrangement of $\{(-2, \sqrt{3}),\ (-1, 5),\ (0, 5),\ (1, \sqrt{3}),\ (2, 7),\ (3, 0)\}$.

b. Each finite number-sequence is a rearrangement of itself.

c. For any finite number-sequences G, F such that G is a rearrangement of F: F is a rearrangement of G.

d. For any finite number-sequences H, G, F such that H is a rearrangement of G and G is a rearrangement of F: H is a rearrangement of F.

e. *Disprove.* For any integers $a \leq n$ and any real functions F, G that are on $Z_{a,n}$ and have the same range: $\sum_{a}^{n} F = \sum_{a}^{n} G$.

Σ (continued)

6001. According to the next theorem the sum of a finite number-sequence equals the sum of each rearrangement thereof. Most students consider this theorem to be obvious, but probably not one in ten thousand could prove it. The proof we shall use is based on the elegant proof that appears in *Fundamental Concepts of Algebra* by Claude Chevalley.

6002. Theorem. *Generalized commutative law of addition.*

The sum of a finite number-sequence equals the sum of each rearrangement thereof.

Proof. Consider any integer a.

It suffices to prove that the following set, call it S, is hereditary from a:

$$\left\{ n \in Z_a \;\middle|\; \text{for any real function } F \text{ over } Z_{a,n} \text{ and any permutation } P \right.$$

$$\left. \text{onto } Z_{a,n} \colon \sum_a^n [F \circ P] = \sum_a^n F \right\}.$$

S contains a.　(?)

Consider any number n in S. We shall prove that $(n + 1) \in S$.

Clearly $(n + 1) \in Z_a$; furthermore, $a < n + 1$.

Consider any real function F over $Z_{a,n+1}$ and
any permutation P onto $Z_{a,n+1}$.

We must prove that $\displaystyle\sum_a^{n+1} [F \circ P] = \sum_a^{n+1} F$.

Since P is on $Z_{a,n+1}$ onto $Z_{a,n+1}$,
there is an integer k in $Z_{a,n+1}$ such that $P(k) = n + 1$.

Either $k = n + 1$　or　$k = a$　or　$a < k \leqq n$.

CASE I. $k = n + 1$.

Then $P|Z_{a,n}$ is a permutation onto $Z_{a,n}$ (?) and so

$$\sum_a^{n+1} [F \circ P] =$$

$$[F \circ P](n + 1) + \sum_a^n [F \circ P] =$$

$$F(n + 1) + \sum_a^n \left[F \circ [P|Z_{a,n}] \right] =_?$$

$$F(n + 1) + \sum_a^n F =$$

$$\sum_a^{n+1} F. \qquad \text{So } (n + 1) \in S, \text{ and we are done with CASE I.}$$

NOTE. We know now that for any permutation V onto $Z_{a,n+1}$ such that

$$V(n + 1) = n + 1 : \sum_a^{n+1} [F \circ V] = \sum_a^{n+1} F.$$

CASE II. $k = a$.

Then $P(a) = P(k) = n + 1$.

Let Y denote the following function:

$$Y(i) = \begin{cases} P(i + 1) & \text{if } i \in Z_{a,n} \\ n + 1 & \text{if } i = n + 1 \end{cases}.$$

Y is a permutation onto $Z_{a,n+1}$ (?) and $Y(n + 1) = n + 1$.

By the above NOTE, we have $\sum_a^{n+1} [F \circ Y] = \sum_a^{n+1} F$.

Furthermore, $\left[P \circ [I + \hat{1}] \right]|Z_{a,n} =_? Y|Z_{a,n}$. So

$$\sum_a^{n+1} [F \circ P] =$$

$$[F \circ P](a) + \sum_{a+1}^{n+1} [F \circ P] =_?$$

$$[F \circ Y](n + 1) + \sum_a^n \left[[F \circ P] \circ [I + \hat{1}] \right] =$$

$$[F \circ Y](n + 1) + \sum_a^n \left[F \circ \left[P \circ [I + \hat{1}] \right]|Z_{a,n} \right] =$$

$$[F \circ Y](n + 1) + \sum_a^n \left[F \circ [Y|Z_{a,n}] \right] =$$

$$[F \circ Y](n + 1) + \sum_{a}^{n} [F \circ Y] =$$

$$\sum_{a}^{n+1} [F \circ Y] =$$

$$\sum_{a}^{n+1} F. \qquad \text{So } (n + 1) \in S, \text{ and we are done with CASE II.}$$

CASE III. $a < k \leq n$.
Let W denote the following function:

$$W(i) = \begin{cases} P(i) & \text{if } i \in Z_{a,k-1} \\ P(i + 1) & \text{if } i \in Z_{k,n} \\ n + 1 & \text{if } i = n + 1 \end{cases}.$$

W is a permutation onto $Z_{a,n+1}$ (?) and $W(n + 1) = n + 1$.
By the above NOTE again, we have $\sum_{a}^{n+1} [F \circ W] = \sum_{a}^{n+1} F$.
Furthermore, $P|Z_{a,k-1} = W|Z_{a,k-1}$, and
$[P \circ [I + \hat{1}]]|Z_{k,n} = W|Z_{k,n}$. So

$$\sum_{a}^{n+1} [F \circ P] =$$

$$\left(\sum_{a}^{k-1} [F \circ P] \right) + [F \circ P](k) + \sum_{k+1}^{n+1} [F \circ P] =?$$

$$\left(\sum_{a}^{k-1} [F \circ W] \right) + [F \circ W](n + 1) + \sum_{k}^{n} [[F \circ P] \circ [I + \hat{1}]] =?$$

$$\left(\sum_{a}^{k-1} [F \circ W] \right) + [F \circ W](n + 1) + \sum_{k}^{n} [F \circ W] =$$

$$\sum_{a}^{n+1} [F \circ W] =$$

$$\sum_{a}^{n+1} F. \qquad \text{Hence } (n + 1) \in S, \text{ and we are done.}$$

6003. The reader should note that in 6002 we proved the following.

For any integers $a \leq m$, real function F over $Z_{a,m}$, and

permutation P onto $Z_{a,m}$: $\sum_{a}^{m} [F \circ P] = \sum_{a}^{m} F$.

6004. Example. Consider any real function F over $Z_{4,7}$.

We know that $[\hat{7} + \hat{4} - I]|Z_{4,7}$, call it P, is a permutation onto $Z_{4,7}$.

So by 6003, $\displaystyle\sum_4^7 [F \circ P] = \sum_4^7 F$;

thus, $\displaystyle\sum_4^7 [[F \circ P]|Z_{4,7}] = \sum_4^7 [F|Z_{4,7}]$.

Now note that

$[F \circ P]|Z_{4,7} = \{(4, F(7)), \ (5, F(6)), \ (6, F(5)), \ (7, F(4))\}$, whereas

$F|Z_{4,7} = \{(4, F(4)), \ (5, F(5)), \ (6, F(6)), \ (7, F(7))\}$.

This example suggests the next corollary.

6005. Corollary. *Reversal of values.*

For any integers $a \leq m$ and real function F over $Z_{a,m}$:

$$\sum_a^m [F \circ [\hat{m} + \hat{a} - I]] = \sum_a^m F.$$

Proof. Use 6003 with $[\hat{m} + \hat{a} - I]|Z_{a,m}$ for P.

6006. Example. We use 6005 to prove that $\displaystyle\sum_1^n I = n(1 + n)/2$.

For each positive integer n:

$$2\sum_1^n I = \sum_1^n I + \sum_1^n I = \sum_1^n I + \sum_1^n [I \circ [\hat{n} + \hat{I} - I]] =$$

$$\sum_1^n I + \sum_1^n [\hat{n} + \hat{I} - I] =_? \sum_1^n [\hat{I} + \hat{n}] = \sum_1^n (1 + n)\hat{I} =$$

$$(1 + n)\sum_1^n \hat{I} = (1 + n)n.$$

NOTE. The idea behind this derivation was discovered by Gauss when he was in grammar school.

6007. The author hopes that the apparent obviousness of the next lemma will not diminish the student's enjoyment of its proof.

6008. Lemma. For any positive integers m, p such that there is a one-one function on $Z_{1,m}$ onto $Z_{1,p}$: $m = p$.

Proof.

It suffices to prove that the following set, call it S, is hereditary from 1:

$\{m \in Z_1 \mid$ for each positive integer p such that there is a one-one function on $Z_{1,m}$ onto $Z_{1,p}$: $m = p\}$.

First we prove that 1 is in S.

Consider any positive integer p such that there is a one-one function, say F, on $Z_{1,1}$ onto $Z_{1,p}$.
Then F^{-1} is a one-one function on $Z_{1,p}$ onto $Z_{1,1}$.
Hence $F^{-1}(1) = 1$ and $F^{-1}(p) = 1$.
So $1 =_? p$. Therefore $1 \in S$.

Now we prove that S is hereditary.

Consider any number k in S.
Then $(k + 1) \in Z_1$. In fact, $2 \leq k + 1$.

Consider any positive integer q such that there is a one-one function, say G, on $Z_{1,k+1}$ onto $Z_{1,q}$.
It suffices to prove that $k + 1 = q$.

First we note that $1 < q$, for otherwise we would have $1 = q$ and then we would have $G(1) = 1$ and $G(k + 1) = 1$ and so 1 would equal $1 + k$, which is impossible.   (?)

Either $G(k + 1) = q$ or $1 \leq G(k + 1) < q$.   (?)

CASE I. $G(k + 1) = q$.
Then $G|Z_{1,k}$ is a one-one function on $Z_{1,k}$ onto $Z_{1,q-1}$,
and so $k =_? q - 1$, and hence $k + 1 = q$.

CASE II. $1 \leq G(k + 1) < q$.
Then $G(k + 1) \in Z_{1,q-1}$ and $G^{-1}(q) \in Z_{1,k}$.   (?)

Let H denote the result obtained from G by
deleting the two number pairs $(k + 1, G(k + 1))$, $(G^{-1}(q), q)$ and
annexing the number pair $(G^{-1}(q), G(k + 1))$.

Then H is a one-one function on $Z_{1,k}$ onto $Z_{1,q-1}$.   (?)
So $k =_? q - 1$ and hence $k + 1 = q$.

6009. Theorem. For any integers $b \leq u$ and integers $c \leq n$ such that there is a one-one function on $Z_{b,u}$ onto $Z_{c,n}$: $u - b = n - c$.

Proof. Consider any such hypothesized b, u, c, n.
Then there is a one-one function F on $Z_{b,u}$ onto $Z_{c,n}$.

Let E denote $[I + \hat{b} - \hat{1}]|Z_{1,u-b+1}$.
Then E is a one-one function on $Z_{1,u-b+1}$ onto $Z_{b,u}$.

Let G denote $[I - \hat{c} + \hat{1}]|Z_{c,n}$.
Then G is a one-one function on $Z_{c,n}$ onto $Z_{1,n-c+1}$.

Hence $G \circ F \circ E$ is a one-one function on $Z_{1,u-b+1}$ onto $Z_{1,n-c+1}$.
So by 6008, $u - b + 1 = n - c + 1$ and hence $u - b = n - c$.

NOTE. The proofs of 6008 and 6009 were devised by Dr. H. R. Rouse of Tufts University.

6010. Many propositions in this lesson may be considered a special case of the next theorem.

6011. Theorem. For any integers $c \leq n$, real function G over $Z_{c,n}$, integers $b \leq u$, and one-one function T on $Z_{b,u}$ onto $Z_{c,n}$:

$$\sum_{b}^{u}[G \circ T] = \sum_{c}^{n} G.$$

Proof. Consider any such hypothesized c, n, G, b, u, T.
By 6009, $u - b = n - c$.
Let C denote $[I + \hat{c}]\|Z_{0,n-c}$.
Then C is a one-one function on $Z_{0,n-c}$ onto $Z_{c,n}$,
and $[G \circ C]$ is a real function over $Z_{0,n-c}$.
Let B denote $[I + \hat{b}]\|Z_{0,u-b}$.
Then B is a one-one function on $Z_{0,u-b}$ onto $Z_{b,u}$. Furthermore,
$C^{-1} \circ T \circ B$ is a one-one function on $Z_{0,n-c}$ onto $Z_{0,n-c}$.   (?)
Hence $C^{-1} \circ T \circ B$ is a permutation onto $Z_{0,n-c}$. So

$$\sum_{c}^{n} G =_? \sum_{0}^{n-c} [G \circ C] =_1$$

$$\sum_{0}^{n-c}\left[[G \circ C] \circ [C^{-1} \circ T \circ B]\right] =_? \sum_{0}^{n-c} [G \circ T \circ B] =$$

$$\sum_{0}^{u-b} [G \circ T \circ B] =_? \sum_{b}^{u} [G \circ T].$$

Reference 1. Use 6003 with 0 for a, $n - c$ for m, $G \circ C$ for F, $C^{-1} \circ T \circ B$ for P.

6012. Theorem.
The sum of any finite sequence of nonnegative numbers is nonnegative.

Proof. Consider any integer a.

$$\left\{n \in Z_a \;\middle|\; \text{for each nonnegative, real function } F \text{ on } Z_{a,n} \colon\; 0 \leq \sum_{a}^{n} F\right\}$$

contains a (?)
and contains the successor of each number i therein because $(i + 1) \in Z_a$,
and for each nonnegative, real function F on $Z_{a,i+1}$:

$$\sum_{a}^{i+1} F = F(i + 1) + \sum_{a}^{i} F \geq_? 0 + 0 = 0.$$

6013. Corollaries.

a. The sum of any finite sequence of positive numbers is positive.

Proof. Consider any finite sequence of positive numbers, say F on $Z_{a,n}$. Either $a = n$ or $a < n$.

In case $a = n$, then $\sum\limits_{a}^{n} F = \sum\limits_{a}^{a} F = F(a) > 0$;

in case $a < n$, then $0 < F(n)$ and $0 \leq_? \sum\limits_{a}^{n-1} F$, and so

$$0 < F(n) + \sum\limits_{a}^{n-1} F = \sum\limits_{a}^{n} F.$$

b. For any integers $a \leq n$ and real functions G, H over $Z_{a,n}$ such that each integer j in $Z_{a,n}$ satisfies $G(j) \leq H(j)$: $\sum\limits_{a}^{n} G \leq \sum\limits_{a}^{n} H$.

Proof.: $[H - G] | Z_{a,n}$ is a finite sequence of nonnegative numbers, and so

$$0 \leq \sum\limits_{a}^{n} [[H - G] | Z_{a,n}] = \sum\limits_{a}^{n} [H - G] = \sum\limits_{a}^{n} H - \sum\limits_{a}^{n} G.$$

c. For any integers $a \leq n$ and real functions G, H over $Z_{a,n}$ such that each integer j in $Z_{a,n}$ satisfies $G(j) < H(j)$: $\sum\limits_{a}^{n} G < \sum\limits_{a}^{n} H$.

Proof.: $[H - G] | Z_{a,n}$ is a finite sequence of positive numbers, and so

$$0 < \sum\limits_{a}^{n} [[H - G] | Z_{a,n}] = \sum\limits_{a}^{n} H - \sum\limits_{a}^{n} G.$$

6014. Exercises.

a. For any integers $a \leq n$ and real function F on $Z_{a,n}$: $\left| \sum\limits_{a}^{n} F \right| \leq \sum\limits_{a}^{n} |F|$.

b. For any positive integer n and real function F over $Z_{0,n}$:

$$|F(0)| - \sum\limits_{1}^{n} |F| \leq \left| \sum\limits_{0}^{n} F \right|.$$

NOTE. Both of these propositions can be proved without induction.

The Product of a Finite Number-Sequence

6101. In this lesson we shall define and investigate the product (of all values) of a finite number-sequence.

6102. Definition. A *product accumulator* of (or for) a finite number-sequence, say F on $Z_{b,w}$, is any finite number-sequence G such that

G is on $Z_{b,w}$,

$G(b) = F(b)$,

for each integer j such that $b < j \leqq w$: $G(j) = F(j) \cdot G(j-1)$.

6103. Examples.

a. $\{(1, 1), (2, 2), (3, 6)\}$ is a product accumulator of $I|Z_{1,3}$.

b. For any integer b and real function H over $Z_{b,b}$:
$H|Z_{b,b}$ is a product accumulator of $H|Z_{b,b}$.

6104. Theorem. For each finite number-sequence there is precisely one product accumulator thereof.

Proof. Similar to proof of 5717.

6105. Corollary. For any integer b and real function H over $Z_{b,b}$:
$H|Z_{b,b}$ is the product accumulator of $H|Z_{b,b}$.

6106. Definition. The *product* (of all values) of a finite number-sequence is the last value of its product accumulator.

6107. Example. The product of $I|Z_{1,3}$ is 6.

Proof. 6 is the last value of $\{(1, 1), (2, 2), (3, 6)\}$ which is the product accumulator of $I|Z_{1,3}$. (6103a)

6108. Notation. For any integers $b \leq w$ and real function H over $Z_{b,w}$:

the symbol $\prod\limits_{b}^{w} H$ denotes the product of $H|Z_{b,w}$.

NOTE I. The symbol $\prod\limits_{b}^{w} H$ is rendered thus: pi of H from b to w.

NOTE II. In the next lesson we shall introduce traditional methods of denoting the product of a finite number-sequence.

6109. Example. $\prod\limits_{1}^{3} I = 6$. (6108, 6107)

6110. It is important to keep in mind that a symbol such as $\prod\limits_{a}^{n} F$ is meaningful if and only if a is an integer, n is an integer, $a \leq n$, and F is a real function over $Z_{a,n}$.

6111. Theorem. For any integers $b \leq w$ and real function F over $Z_{b,w}$:

$$\prod\limits_{b}^{w} [F|Z_{b,w}] = \prod\limits_{b}^{w} F.$$

Proof. Similar to proof of 5725.

6112. Exercises.

a. For any integer b and real function H over $Z_{b,b}$: $\prod\limits_{b}^{b} H = H(b)$.

b. For any integers $b \leq m$ and real function H over $Z_{b,m+1}$:

$$\prod\limits_{b}^{m+1} H = H(m + 1) \cdot \prod\limits_{b}^{m} H.$$

6113. Theorem. For any number r and any integers $a \leq n$: $\displaystyle\prod_a^n \hat{r} = r^{n-a+1}$.

Proof. Consider any number r and any integer a.

$\left\{ n \in Z_a \,\middle|\, \displaystyle\prod_a^n \hat{r} = r^{n-a+1} \right\}$ contains a (?) and contains the successor of

each number i therein because $(i + 1) \in Z_a$ and

$$\prod_a^{i+1} \hat{r} = \hat{r}(i + 1) \cdot \prod_a^{i} \hat{r} =_? rr^{i-a+1} = r^{(i+1)-a+1}.$$

6114. Corollaries.

a. For any integers $a \leq n$: $\displaystyle\prod_a^n \hat{1} = 1$.

b. For any number r and positive integer n: $\displaystyle\prod_1^n \hat{r} = r^n$.

NOTE. If this lesson had come before Lesson 49, we could have defined

r^n to be $\displaystyle\prod_1^n \hat{r}$. This would have spared us the chore (in Lesson 49) of

developing the idea of *productor for a number*.

c. For any integers $a \leq n$: $\displaystyle\prod_a^n \hat{0} = 0$.

6115. Theorem. For any integers $a \leq n$ and real function F on $Z_{a,n}$:

$$\prod_a^n F = 0 \iff \text{some value of } F \text{ is } 0.$$

Proof. Consider any integer a.

$\left\{ n \in Z_a \,\middle|\, \text{for each real function } F \text{ on } Z_{a,n}: \right.$

$$\left. \prod_a^n F = 0 \iff \text{some value of } F \text{ is } 0 \right\}$$

contains a (?) and contains the successor of each number i therein because
$(i + 1) \in Z_a$ and for each real function F on $Z_{a,i+1}$:

$$\prod_a^{i+1} F = 0 \iff$$

$$F(i + 1) \cdot \prod_a^{i} F = 0 \iff_?$$

$F(i + 1) = 0$ or some value of $F|Z_{a,i}$ is $0 \iff$

some value of F is 0.

6116. Exercise. Prove or disprove the proposition obtained from 6115 by replacing *on* by *over*.

6117. Exercises.

a. For any integers $a \leq n$ and real functions F, G over $Z_{a,n}$:

$$\prod_a^n [FG] = \prod_a^n F \cdot \prod_a^n G.$$

b. For any integers $a \leq n$ and real function H over $Z_{a,n}$ such that no value of $H|Z_{a,n}$ is 0: $\displaystyle \prod_a^n [\hat{1}/H] = 1 \Big/ \prod_a^n H.$

6118. Corollary. For any integers $a \leq n$ and real functions F, H over $Z_{a,n}$ such that no value of $H|Z_{a,n}$ is 0: $\displaystyle \prod_a^n [F/H] = \left(\prod_a^n F \right) \Big/ \left(\prod_a^n H \right).$

Proof.: $\displaystyle \prod_a^n [F/H] = \prod_a^n [F[\hat{1}/H]] = \left(\prod_a^n F \right) \left(\prod_a^n [\hat{1}/H] \right) =$? $\left(\prod_a^n F \right) \Big/ \left(\prod_a^n H \right).$

6119. The following propositions can be proved in a manner similar to that used for their $\sum$ counterparts.

a. For any integers $a \leq n$ and real functions F, G, H over $Z_{a,n}$:

$$\prod_a^n [FGH] = \prod_a^n F \cdot \prod_a^n G \cdot \prod_a^n H.$$

b. *Extended associative law of multiplication.*
For any integers $a \leq b < n$ and real function F over $Z_{a,n}$:

$$\prod_a^n F = \prod_a^b F \cdot \prod_{b+1}^n F.$$

NOTE. There is also a generalized associative law of multiplication.

c. For any integers $a < n$ and real function F over $Z_{a,n}$:

$$\prod_a^n F = F(a) \cdot \prod_{a+1}^n F.$$

d. For any integers $a < i < n$ and real function F over $Z_{a,n}$:

$$\prod_a^n F = \left(\prod_a^{i-1} F \right) \cdot F(i) \cdot \prod_{i+1}^n F.$$

e. *Translation.* For any integers $b \leq m$, real function G over $Z_{b,m}$, and integer c:

$$\prod_b^m G = \prod_{b+c}^{m+c} \left[G \circ [I - \hat{c}] \right] = \prod_{b-c}^{m-c} \left[G \circ [I + \hat{c}] \right].$$

f. For any integers $b \leq m$ and real function G over $Z_{b,m}$:

$$\prod_b^m G = \prod_1^{m-b+1} \left[G \circ [I + \hat{b} - \hat{1}] \right].$$

g. *Telescope.* For any integers $a \leq n$ and real function F such that F is over $Z_{a,n+1}$ and no value of $F|Z_{a,n}$ is 0:

$$\prod_a^n \left[\left[F \circ [I + \hat{1}] \right] / F \right] = F(n + 1)/F(a).$$

h. *Generalized commutative law of multiplication.*
The product of a finite number-sequence equals the product of every rearrangement thereof.

i. For any integers $a \leq m$, real function F over $Z_{a,m}$, and permutation P onto $Z_{a,m}$:

$$\prod_a^m [F \circ P] = \prod_a^m F.$$

j. *Reversal of values.* For any integers $a \leq m$ and real function F over $Z_{a,m}$:

$$\prod_a^m [F \circ [\hat{m} + \hat{a} - I]] = \prod_a^m F.$$

k. For any integers $c \leq n$, real function G over $Z_{c,n}$, integers $b \leq u$, and one-one function T on $Z_{b,u}$ onto $Z_{c,n}$:

$$\prod_b^u [G \circ T] = \prod_c^n G.$$

6120. Exercises.

a. For any integers $a \leq n$, number r, and real function F over $Z_{a,n}$:

$$\prod_a^n [rF] = r^{n-a+1} \cdot \prod_a^n F.$$

NOTE. In particular, $\prod_a^n [-F] = (-1)^{n-a+1} \cdot \prod_a^n F.$

b. For each integer n exceeding 2: $\prod_2^n [\hat{1} - \hat{1}/I] = 1/n.$

HINT. $\hat{1} - \hat{1}/I =_? [I - \hat{1}]/I.$

6121. Exercise.

For any integers $a \leq n$ and any real functions G, H over $Z_{a,n}$ such that each integer j in $Z_{a,n}$ satisfies $0 \leq G(j) \leq H(j)$:

$$0 \leq \prod_a^n G \leq \prod_a^n H.$$

6122. Corollaries.

a. The product of any finite sequence of nonnegative numbers is nonnegative.

Proof. Use 6121.

b. The product of any finite sequence of positive numbers is positive.

Proof. Consider any finite sequence of positive numbers, say K on $Z_{a,n}$.

Then $0 \leq_? \prod_a^n K$ and $0 \neq_? \prod_a^n K$.

6123. Exercises.

a. For any integers $a \leq n$ and real functions G, H over $Z_{a,n}$ such that each integer j in $Z_{a,n}$ satisfies $0 \leq G(j) < H(j)$:

$$\prod_a^n G < \prod_a^n H.$$

b. *Prove or disprove.*

For any positive integers m, n and real function F over $Z_{1,m+n}$:

$$\left(\prod_1^m F \right) \left(\prod_1^n F \right) = \prod_1^{m+n} F.$$

c. For any integers $a \leq n$ and real function F over $Z_{a,n}$:

$$\left| \prod_a^n F \right| = \prod_a^n |F|.$$

6124. Notation. For each number b such that $0 < b \neq 1$:

the symbol Log_b denotes the real function $\{(x, \log_b(x)) \mid x \in R_+\}$.

NOTE. Log_b is called the base b logarithmic function.

6125. Theorem. For any number b such that $0 < b \neq 1$, any integers $a \leqq n$, and any positive, real function F over $Z_{a,n}$:

$$\log_b \left(\prod_a^n F \right) = \sum_a^n [\text{Log}_b \circ F].$$

Proof. Consider any number b such that $0 < b \neq 1$, and consider any integer a.

$$\left\{ n \in Z_a \; \middle| \; \text{for each positive, real function } F \text{ over } Z_{a,n} \colon \right.$$

$$\left. \log_b \left(\prod_a^n F \right) = \sum_a^n [\text{Log}_b \circ F] \right\}$$

contains a (?) and contains the successor of each number i therein because $(i + 1) \in Z_a$, and for each positive, real function F over $Z_{a,i+1}$:

$$\log_b \left(\prod_a^{i+1} F \right) =$$

$$\log_b \left(F(i + 1) \cdot \prod_a^i F \right) =$$

$$\log_b (F(i + 1)) + \log_b \left(\prod_a^i F \right) =$$

$$[\text{Log}_b \circ F](i + 1) + \sum_a^i [\text{Log}_b \circ F] =$$

$$\sum_a^{i+1} [\text{Log}_b \circ F].$$

Traditional Notations

6201. In our treatment of finite number-sequences we used the so-called function notation that is gradually finding its way into college textbooks on mathematics. In this lesson we shall discuss certain traditional notations and some of their advantages and disadvantages.

6202. Notation. The value that a function F assigns to an argument x thereof is denoted by the symbol F_x as well as by the symbol $F(x)$.

6203. Examples.

a. $I_2 = 2$.

b. $[I^2 + \hat{3}]_2 = 2^2 + 3 = 7$.

c. $|\hat{1} - I|_3 = |1 - 3| = 2$.

d. For each number x: $I^2_x = x^2$.

e. For each number x: $\hat{2}_x = 2$.

f. For any real function F and argument x thereof: $|F|_x = |F_x|$.

6204. For the reader's convenience we repeat an earlier definition.

6205. Definition. A symbol is said to be *available* in a given context provided that it is not permanently used to denote a particular mathematical thing and does not occur earlier in the context, except possibly as part of a word.

NOTE. A symbol that is available in a given context is called a dummy because any other available symbol would serve equally well.

6206. Remark.

In this book the symbols I, R, Q, Z, e are available in no context.

6207. Notation. For any integers $a \leq p$, any real function F over $Z_{a,p}$, and any available symbol, say λ:

the symbol $\sum\limits_{\lambda=a}^{p} F_\lambda$ denotes the sum of $F|Z_{a,p}$, and

the symbol $\prod\limits_{\lambda=a}^{p} F_\lambda$ denotes the product of $F|Z_{a,p}$.

NOTE. In symbols such as $\sum\limits_{\lambda=a}^{p} F_\lambda$, $\prod\limits_{\lambda=a}^{p} F_\lambda$, the letter λ is a dummy.

In this context the letters a, p are not available; accordingly, none of the following symbols may be used:

$$\sum_{p=a}^{p} F_p, \quad \prod_{p=a}^{p} F_p, \quad \sum_{a=a}^{p} F_a, \quad \prod_{a=a}^{p} F_a.$$

6208. Examples.

a. Each of the following symbols denotes the sum of $I^2|Z_{3,7}$:

$$\sum_{i=3}^{7} I^2{}_i, \quad \sum_{j=3}^{7} I^2{}_j, \quad \sum_{k=3}^{7} I^2{}_k, \quad \sum_{m=3}^{7} I^2{}_m, \quad \sum_{n=3}^{7} I^2{}_n, \quad \sum_{p=3}^{7} I^2{}_p.$$

b. Each of the following symbols denotes the product of $[\hat{5} - I]|Z_{3,7}$:

$$\prod_{i=3}^{7} [\hat{5} - I]_i, \quad \prod_{j=3}^{7} [\hat{5} - I]_j, \quad \prod_{n=3}^{7} [\hat{5} - I]_n.$$

6209. When using symbols such as $\sum\limits_{j=3}^{7} I^2{}_j$, $\prod\limits_{j=3}^{7} I^2{}_j$, it is helpful to think of the dummy j as referring to an unspecified integer between 3 and 7, and so it is natural to replace the symbol $I^2{}_j$ by the symbol j^2 (see 6203d) thereby arriving at the following symbols:

$$\sum_{j=3}^{7} j^2, \quad \prod_{j=3}^{7} j^2.$$

E.g., the sum of $I^2|Z_{3,7}$ may be denoted by each of the following symbols:

$$\sum_{3}^{7} I^2, \quad \sum_{j=3}^{7} I^2{}_j, \quad \sum_{j=3}^{7} j^2.$$

Similarly, the product of $I^2|Z_{3,7}$ may be denoted by each of the following:

$$\prod_{3}^{7} I^2, \quad \prod_{j=3}^{7} I^2{}_j, \quad \prod_{j=3}^{7} j^2.$$

6210. Examples.

a. $\displaystyle\sum_{4}^{6} [I^2 - I + \hat{3}] = \sum_{j=4}^{6} [I^2 - I + \hat{3}]_j = \sum_{j=4}^{6} (j^2 - j + 3).$

b. $\displaystyle\prod_{0}^{7} \sqrt{I} = \prod_{k=0}^{7} [\sqrt{I}]_k = \prod_{k=0}^{7} \sqrt{k}.$

6211. In a symbol such as $\displaystyle\sum_{i=1}^{4} \hat{2}_i$ one naturally replaces the symbol $\hat{2}_i$ by the symbol 2. (See 6203e.)

Such practice leads to results that perplex some students; e.g.,

$$8 = \sum_{i=1}^{4} 2 \quad \text{because} \quad 8 = \sum_{1}^{4} \hat{2} = \sum_{i=1}^{4} \hat{2}_i = \sum_{i=1}^{4} 2.$$

The symbol $\displaystyle\sum_{i=1}^{4} 2$ fails to convey the fact that we are really concerned with the function $\hat{2}$ rather than with the number 2.

6212. To illustrate how these traditional notations are used, we restate the conclusion of various propositions from previous lessons.

5801a. $\displaystyle\sum_{i=b}^{b} H_i = H_b$

5801b. $\displaystyle\sum_{i=b}^{m+1} H_i = H_{m+1} + \sum_{i=b}^{m} H_i$

5804. $\displaystyle\sum_{i=1}^{n} 1 = n$

5805. $\displaystyle\sum_{i=a}^{n} r F_i = r \sum_{i=a}^{n} F_i$

5809. $\displaystyle\sum_{j=a}^{n} (F_j + G_j) = \sum_{j=a}^{n} F_j + \sum_{j=a}^{n} G_j$

5811. $\displaystyle\sum_{i=a}^{n} F_i = \sum_{i=a}^{b} F_i + \sum_{i=b+1}^{n} F_i$

5815. *Translation.* $\displaystyle\sum_{i=b}^{m} G_i = \sum_{i=b+c}^{m+c} \big[G \circ [I - \hat{c}]\big]_i$

NOTE. It is natural to replace $\big[G \circ [I - \hat{c}]\big]_i$ by G_{i-c}. Accordingly, the conclusion of 5815 may be written thus:

$$\sum_{i=b}^{m} G_i = \sum_{i=b+c}^{m+c} G_{i-c}.$$

5821. *Telescope.* $\displaystyle\sum_{j=a}^{n} (F_{j+1} - F_j) = F_{n+1} - F_a$

NOTE. $(F_{j+1} - F_j)$ replaces $\Big[\big[F \circ [I + \hat{1}]\big] - F\Big]_j$

6003. $\displaystyle\sum_{i=a}^{m} F_{P_i} = \sum_{i=a}^{m} F_i$

6119k. $\displaystyle\prod_{i=b}^{u} G_{T_i} = \prod_{i=c}^{n} G_i$

6213. Exercise.

In the spirit of 6212, restate the conclusions of 5730, 5807a, 5807b, 5810a, 5817, 6005, 6011, 6013b, 6117b, 6123c, 6125.

6214. Notation. For any integers $a \leqq n$ and real function F over $Z_{a,n}$:

the symbol $(F_a + \cdots + F_n)$ denotes the number $\displaystyle\sum_{i=a}^{n} F_i$, and

the symbol $(F_a \cdots \cdots F_n)$ denotes the number $\displaystyle\prod_{i=a}^{n} F_i$.

NOTE. Outermost parentheses are often omitted.

6215. Examples.

a. The symbol $I^2{}_3 + \cdots + I^2{}_8$ denotes the number $\displaystyle\sum_{j=3}^{8} j^2$.

b. The symbol $I^2{}_3 \cdots \cdots I^2{}_8$ denotes the number $\displaystyle\prod_{j=3}^{8} j^2$.

c. The conclusion of 6014a may be stated as follows:
$$|F_a + \cdots + F_n| \leqq |F_a| + \cdots + |F_n|.$$

d. The conclusion of 6123c may be stated as follows:
$$|F_a \cdots \cdots F_n| = |F_a| \cdots \cdots |F_n|.$$

6216. The convention in 6214 can lead to perplexing results. E.g.,

$$6 = \sum_{j=-1}^{2} j^2 = I^2_{-1} + \cdots + I^2_{2} = 1 + \cdots + 4,$$

$$10 = \sum_{j=1}^{4} j = I_1 + \cdots + I_4 = 1 + \cdots + 4.$$

Have we proved that $6 = 10$?
No. We have been deceived by our notation.
In such situations we should resort to some other notational device.

6217. The convention in 6214 leads to other perplexing results.
E.g., consider any real function F over $Z_{1,1}$. Then

$$F_1 = \sum_{i=1}^{1} F_i = F_1 + \cdots + F_1.$$

Some students are troubled by the equation $F_1 = F_1 + \cdots + F_1$;
however, this equation is in strict conformity with 6214.

To make matters worse, let us choose I for F.
Then we have $1 = I_1 = I_1 + \cdots + I_1 = 1 + \cdots + 1$.

6218. Despite such perplexing results, the convention in 6214 enables us to state
some propositions perspicuously; e.g., the conclusion of 6005 may be
stated as follows: $F_m + \cdots + F_a = F_a + \cdots + F_m$.

6219. Exercise.

In the spirit of 6218, restate the conclusions of 5801b, 5805, 5811, 5817,
5821, 5823, 6003, 6014b, 6115, 6119d, 6119g.

6220. Conventions.

a. An expression such as
for any n numbers $x_1, \ldots, x_n$
stands for the expression
for any positive integer n and real function x on $Z_{1,n}$.

b. An expression such as
for any m nonnegative numbers $y_1, \ldots, y_m$
stands for the expression
for any positive integer m and nonnegative, real function y on $Z_{1,m}$.

c. An expression such as
for any n positive numbers $w_1, \ldots, w_n$
stands for the expression
for any positive integer n and positive, real function w on $Z_{1,n}$.

d. An expression such as
there are n numbers $x_1, \ldots, x_n$
stands for the expression
there is a positive integer n and a real function x on $Z_{1,n}$.

And so on.

6221. Examples.

a. Proposition 6014a (with 1 for a and x for F) may be stated thus:
for any n numbers $x_1, \ldots, x_n$: $|x_1 + \cdots + x_n| \leq |x_1| + \cdots + |x_n|$.

b. The following proposition is a special case of 6012:
for any n nonnegative numbers $x_1, \ldots, x_n$: $0 \leq x_1 + \cdots + x_n$.

6222. These traditional notations are dangerous only to the extent that they encourage the student to forget that he is dealing with real functions of a certain kind.

Factorization of $x^n - y^n$ and other matters

6301. Notation (*for this lesson only*).
The symbol r denotes any given number, and
the symbol F denotes any given real function.

6302. Notation. In this book the author uses the symbol $[r^F]$ to denote
the real function $\{(v, r^{F(v)}) \mid v \in \text{domain } F \text{ and } F(v) \in Z_0\}$.

NOTE I. If no value of F is in Z_0, then $r^F = \emptyset$.

NOTE II. Domain $r^F = \{v \mid v \in \text{domain } F \text{ and } F(v) \in Z_0\}$.

6303. Examples.

a. $r^I = \{(v, r^{I(v)}) \mid v \in \text{domain } I \text{ and } I(v) \in Z_0\} = \{(v, r^v) \mid v \in Z_0\}$.

b. $0^I = \{(v, 0^v) \mid v \in Z_0\} = \{(0, 1)\} \cup [\hat{0} \mid Z_1]$.

c. $0^F = \{(v, 0^{F(v)}) \mid v \in \text{domain } F \text{ and } F(v) \in Z_0\}$.

d. $0^{I + \hat{2}} = \{(v, 0^{v+2}) \mid v \in R \text{ and } (v + 2) \in Z_0\} = \{(v, 0^{v+2}) \mid v \in Z_{-2}\}$.

e. $2^{\hat{1} + I} = \{(v, 2^{1+v}) \mid (1 + v) \in Z_0\} = \{(v, 2^{1+v}) \mid v \in Z_{-1}\}$.

f. $3^{\hat{2}} = \{(v, 3^2) \mid v \in R\} = \hat{9}$.

g. $(1/2)^{\hat{5} - I} = \{(v, (1/2)^{5-v}) \mid (5 - v) \in Z_0\}$.

h. For each argument v of F such that $F(v) \in Z_0$: $[r^F](v) = r^{F(v)}$.

311

6304. Exercises.

a. $r^F = r^I \circ F$.

b. For each set A: $r^{F|A} = r^F|A$.

c. For each nonnegative integer b: $r^{\hat{b}} = \widehat{r^b}$.

d. *Prove or disprove.* $2[2^I] = 2^{\hat{1}+I}$.

e. For any functions G, H into Z_0: $r^G r^H = r^{G+H}$.

6305. Lemma. For any nonnegative integers b, a, m such that $a \leq m$, and any function H such that $H|Z_{a,m}$ is on $Z_{a,m}$ into Z_0:
$$[r^b r^H]|Z_{a,m} = r^{\hat{b}+H}|Z_{a,m}.$$

Proof.: $[r^b r^H]|Z_{a,m} = [\widehat{r^b} r^H]|Z_{a,m} = [r^{\hat{b}} r^H]|Z_{a,m} = r^{\hat{b}}[r^H|Z_{a,m}] =$
$r^{\hat{b}} r^{H|Z_{a,m}} =_? r^{\hat{b}+[H|Z_{a,m}]} =_? r^{[\hat{b}+H]|Z_{a,m}} = r^{\hat{b}+H}|Z_{a,m}.$

6306. Consider any numbers x, y.

Each of the following propositions is easy to verify.

$$x^1 - y^1 = (x - y)(x^0 y^0) =$$
$$(x - y) \sum_{i=0}^{1-1} x^i y^{1-1-i} = (x - y) \sum_{0}^{1-1} x^I y^{\hat{1}-\hat{1}-I}.$$

$$x^2 - y^2 = (x - y)(x^0 y^1 + x^1 y^0) =$$
$$(x - y) \sum_{i=0}^{2-1} x^i y^{2-1-i} = (x - y) \sum_{0}^{2-1} x^I y^{\hat{2}-\hat{1}-I}.$$

$$x^3 - y^3 = (x - y)(x^0 y^2 + x^1 y^1 + x^2 y^0) =$$
$$(x - y) \sum_{i=0}^{3-1} x^i y^{3-1-i} = (x - y) \sum_{0}^{3-1} x^I y^{\hat{3}-\hat{1}-I}.$$

$$x^4 - y^4 = (x - y)(x^0 y^3 + x^1 y^2 + x^2 y^1 + x^3 y^0) =$$
$$(x - y) \sum_{i=0}^{4-1} x^i y^{4-1-i} = (x - y) \sum_{0}^{4-1} x^I y^{\hat{4}-\hat{1}-I}.$$

$$x^5 - y^5 = (x - y)(x^0 y^4 + x^1 y^3 + x^2 y^2 + x^3 y^1 + x^4 y^0) =$$
$$(x - y) \sum_{i=0}^{5-1} x^i y^{5-1-i} = (x - y) \sum_{0}^{5-1} x^I y^{\hat{5}-\hat{1}-I}.$$

These results suggest the next theorem.

6307. Theorem. For any numbers x, y and positive integer n:

$$x^n - y^n = (x - y) \sum_{i=0}^{n-1} x^i y^{n-1-i}.$$

Proof. Consider any numbers x, y and positive integer n.

In case $n = 1$, then

$$(x - y) \sum_{i=0}^{1-1} x^i y^{1-1-i} = (x - y) \sum_{i=0}^{0} x^i y^{-i} = (x - y)x^0 y^0 = x^1 - y^1.$$

In case $1 < n$, then

$$(x - y) \sum_{i=0}^{n-1} x^i y^{n-1-i} =$$

$$(x - y) \sum_{0}^{n-1} x^I y^{\hat{n}-\hat{1}-I} =$$

$$\sum_{0}^{n-1} y^{\hat{n}-\hat{1}-I}[x^1 x^I] - \sum_{0}^{n-1} x^I [y^1 y^{\hat{n}-\hat{1}-I}] =$$

$$\sum_{0}^{n-1} y^{\hat{n}-\hat{1}-I}[x^1 x^I]|Z_{0,n-1} - \sum_{0}^{n-1} x^I [y^1 y^{\hat{n}-\hat{1}-I}]|Z_{0,n-1} =_1$$

$$\sum_{0}^{n-1} y^{\hat{n}-\hat{1}-I} x^{\hat{1}+I}|Z_{0,n-1} - \sum_{0}^{n-1} x^I [y^1 y^{\hat{n}-\hat{1}-I}]|Z_{0,n-1} =_2$$

$$\sum_{0}^{n-1} y^{\hat{n}-\hat{1}-I} x^{\hat{1}+I}|Z_{0,n-1} - \sum_{0}^{n-1} x^I y^{\hat{n}-I}|Z_{0,n-1} =$$

$$\sum_{0}^{n-1} y^{\hat{n}-\hat{1}-I} x^{\hat{1}+I} - \sum_{0}^{n-1} y^{\hat{n}-I} x^I =_3$$

$$\sum_{1}^{n} y^{\hat{n}-I} x^I - \sum_{0}^{n-1} y^{\hat{n}-I} x^I =$$

$$\left(y^0 x^n + \sum_{1}^{n-1} y^{\hat{n}-I} x^I \right) - \left(y^n x^0 + \sum_{1}^{n-1} y^{\hat{n}-I} x^I \right) =$$

$$x^n - y^n.$$

References.

1. 6305 with x for r, 1 for b, I for H, 0 for a, $n - 1$ for m.
2. 6305 with y for r, 1 for b, $\hat{n} - \hat{1} - I$ for H, 0 for a, $n - 1$ for m.
3. 5815 with 0 for b, $n - 1$ for m, $y^{\hat{n}-\hat{1}-I} x^{\hat{1}+I}$ for G, 1 for c.

QUERY. Why did the author break this proof into two cases?

6308. Exercise.

Supply all the details for the justification of $=_3$ in the proof of 6307.

6309. Corollary. For any nonnegative integers $b \leqq u$:

$$(r - 1) \sum_{i=b}^{u} r^i = r^{u+1} - r^b.$$

Proof.: $(r - 1) \sum_{i=b}^{u} r^i =_1 (r - 1) \sum_{i=0}^{u-b} r^{b+i} =_?$

$$(r - 1) \sum_{i=0}^{u-b} r^b r^i = r^b(r - 1) \sum_{i=0}^{u-b} r^i = r^b(r - 1) \sum_{i=0}^{u-b} r^i 1^{u-b-i} =_2$$

$$r^b(r^{u-b+1} - 1^{u-b+1}) = r^{u+1} - r^b.$$

References.

1. 5817 with b for p, and u for m.
2. 6307 with $u - b + 1$ for n, r for x, 1 for y.

6310. Consider the second equality in the proof of 6309:

$$(r - 1) \sum_{i=0}^{u-b} r^{b+i} = (r - 1) \sum_{i=0}^{u-b} r^b r^i.$$

Traditionally this equality would be justified by asserting that r^{b+i} and r^i denote numbers and hence $r^{b+i} = r^b r^i$ by the usual law of exponents. The author cannot accept such a justification because here the symbols r^{b+i} and r^i do not denote numbers but are part of the notation for the sums of finite number-sequences. The author proposes the following justification for this equality.

$$\sum_{i=0}^{u-b} r^{b+i} = \sum_{i=0}^{u-b} [r^{\hat{b}+I}]_i = \sum_{0}^{u-b} r^{\hat{b}+I} = \sum_{0}^{u-b} r^{\hat{b}+I}|Z_{0,u-b} =_1$$

$$\sum_{0}^{u-b} [r^b r^I]|Z_{0,u-b} = \sum_{0}^{u-b} [r^b r^I] = \sum_{i=0}^{u-b} [r^b r^I]_i = \sum_{i=0}^{u-b} r^b r^i.$$

Reference. 1.6305.

6311. Example. For each positive integer p: $2^p > p$.

Proof.: $2^p > 2^{(p-1)+1} - 2^0 =_? (2 - 1) \sum_{i=0}^{p-1} 2^i \geqq_? \sum_{i=0}^{p-1} 1^i =$

$$\sum_{0}^{p-1} 1^I = \sum_{0}^{p-1} \hat{1} =_1 (p - 1) - 0 + 1 = p.$$

Reference. 1.5802.

6312. Exercise.

For any number x exceeding 2, and any positive integer p: $x^p > p$. Please use 6309.

6313. It is interesting to see how Bernoulli's Inequality (5023) may be obtained from 6309. To this end, consider any number y such that $-1 < y \neq 0$ and any integer p such that $1 < p$. Then

$$(1 + y)^p - 1 = (1 + y)^{(p-1)+1} - (1 + y)^0 =$$

$$((1 + y) - 1) \sum_{i=0}^{p-1} (1 + y)^i = y \sum_{i=0}^{p-1} (1 + y)^i =$$

$$y\left[1 + \sum_{i=1}^{p-1} (1 + y)^i\right] >_? y\left[1 + \sum_{i=1}^{p-1} 1^i\right] = yp,$$

and so $1 + py < (1 + y)^p$.

NOTE. In answering the indicated question, consider the cases $0 < y$ and $-1 < y < 0$.

6314. Corollary. *Sum of a geometric progression.*

For any number t distinct from 1, and any nonnegative integers $b \leq u$:

$$\sum_{i=b}^{u} t^i = \frac{t^{u+1} - t^b}{t - 1}.$$

Proof. 6309.

6315. Examples.

a. $\displaystyle\sum_{i=3}^{7} (\sqrt{2})^i = \frac{(\sqrt{2})^8 - (\sqrt{2})^3}{\sqrt{2} - 1}.$

b. $\displaystyle\sum_{i=0}^{3} 0^i = \frac{0^4 - 0^0}{0 - 1} = 1.$

c. $\displaystyle\sum_{i=0}^{5} (-1)^i = \frac{(-1)^6 - (-1)^0}{(-1) - 1} = 0.$

6316. Exercise.

For each positive integer n: let s_n denote $\displaystyle\sum_{i=1}^{n} (1/2)^i$.

Prove that $\sup\{s_n \mid n \in Z_1\} = 1$.

Binomial Theorem

6401. Definition.

The *factorial* of 0 is 1;

the *factorial* of a positive integer n is $\displaystyle\prod_{i=1}^{n} i$.

NOTATION. $m!$, read m *factorial*.

6402. Examples.

a. $0! = 1$.

b. $1! = \displaystyle\prod_{i=1}^{1} i = 1$.

c. $2! = \displaystyle\prod_{i=1}^{2} i = 1 \cdot 2 = 2$.

d. $3! = \displaystyle\prod_{i=1}^{3} i = 1 \cdot 2 \cdot 3 = 6$.

6403. The next lemma provides a useful formula for the factorial of a nonnegative integer.

6404. Lemma. For each nonnegative integer n: $n! = \displaystyle\prod_{i=0}^{n} (i + 0^i)$;

i.e., $n! = \displaystyle\prod_{0}^{n} [I + 0^I]$.

Proof.: in case $0 = n$, then $\displaystyle\prod_{0}^{0} [I + 0^I] = [I + 0^I]_0 = 1 = 0!$;

in case $0 < n$, then $\displaystyle\prod_{0}^{n} [I + 0^I] = [I + 0^I]_0 \cdot \prod_{1}^{n} [I + 0^I] =$

$\displaystyle\prod_{1}^{n} [I + 0^I]|Z_{1,n} =_? \prod_{1}^{n} I|Z_{1,n} = \prod_{1}^{n} I = n!.$

6405. Theorem. For each nonnegative integer n: $(n + 1)! = (n + 1)(n!)$.

Proof.: $(n + 1)! = \displaystyle\prod_{0}^{n+1} [I + 0^I] = [I + 0^I]_{n+1} \cdot \prod_{0}^{n} [I + 0^I] =$

$(n + 1)(n!).$

6406. Example. $4! = (3 + 1)! = (3 + 1)(3!) = 4(3!) = 4 \cdot 6.$

6407. Exercises.

a. For any nonnegative integer n and positive integer p:

$$(n + p)! = (n!) \cdot \prod_{i=1}^{p} (n + i).$$

b. *Prove or disprove.*
For any nonnegative integers m, n: $(mn)! = (m!)(n!)$.

c. *Prove or disprove.*
For any nonnegative integers m, n: $(m + n)! = m! + n!$.

d. For each nonnegative integer n: $0 < n!$.

e. For each integer n exceeding 4: $2^n < n!$.

6408. Theorem. For any integer k and nonnegative integer m:

$$\prod_{i=0}^{m} (k - i) = \prod_{i=k-m}^{k} i.$$

Proof.: $\displaystyle\prod_{i=k-m}^{k} i = \prod_{k-m}^{k} I = \prod_{k-m}^{k} [[\hat{k} - I] \circ [\hat{k} - I]] =$

$\displaystyle\prod_{k-m}^{k} \left[[\hat{k} - I] \circ [\hat{k} - I]|Z_{k-m,k} \right] =_1 \prod_{0}^{m} [\hat{k} - I] = \prod_{i=0}^{m} (k - i).$

Reference 1. 6119k with $k - m$ for b, k for u, $\hat{k} - I$ for G,
$[\hat{k} - I]|Z_{k-m,k}$ for T, 0 for c, m for n.

6409. Corollary. For each positive integer p: $\displaystyle\prod_{i=0}^{p-1} (p - i) = p!$.

Proof.: $\displaystyle\prod_{i=0}^{p-1} (p - i) =_1 \prod_{i=1}^{p} i = p!$.

Reference 1.   6408 with $p - 1$ for m, p for k.

6410. Notations.

a. For each number r: the symbol $\displaystyle\binom{r}{0}$, read r *above* 0, denotes the number 1.

b. For any number r and positive integer p: the symbol $\displaystyle\binom{r}{p}$, read r *above* p, denotes the number $(1/p!) \displaystyle\prod_{i=0}^{p-1} (r - i)$.

6411. Exercises.

a. For each number r: $\displaystyle\binom{r}{1} = r$.

b. For each nonnegative integer n: $\displaystyle\binom{n}{0} = 1 = \binom{n}{n}$.

c. For any nonnegative integers $n \leq k$: $\displaystyle\binom{k}{n} = k!/(k - n)!(n!)$.

NOTE. It then follows that $\displaystyle\binom{k}{n} = \binom{k}{k - n}$.   (?)

d. For any nonnegative integers $n < k$: $\displaystyle\binom{n}{k} = 0$.

6412. Theorem. For any number r and positive integer p:
$$\binom{r}{p} + \binom{r}{p - 1} = \binom{r + 1}{p}.$$

Proof.: in case $1 = p$, then $\displaystyle\binom{r}{1} + \binom{r}{1 - 1} = r + 1 = \binom{r + 1}{1}$;

in case $1 < p$, then

$$\binom{r}{p} + \binom{r}{p - 1} =$$

$$\left[(1/p!) \prod_{i=0}^{p-1} (r - i) \right] + \left[1/(p - 1)! \right] \prod_{i=0}^{p-2} (r - i) =?$$

$$\left[(1/p!)[r - (p - 1)] \prod_{i=0}^{p-2} (r - i) \right] + (1/p!)p \prod_{i=0}^{p-2} (r - i) =?$$

$$(1/p!)(r + 1) \prod_{i=0}^{p-2} (r - i) = ?$$

$$(1/p!)(r + 1) \prod_{i=1}^{p-1} (r + 1 - i) =$$

$$(1/p!) \prod_{i=0}^{p-1} (r + 1 - i) =$$

$$\binom{r + 1}{p}.$$

6413. Notation. For each number r:

the symbol $\binom{r}{I}$ denotes the function $\left\{ \left(v, \binom{r}{v} \right) \middle| v \in Z_0 \right\}$, and

the symbol $\binom{r}{I - \hat{1}}$ denotes the function $\left\{ \left(v, \binom{r}{v - 1} \right) \middle| v \in Z_1 \right\}$.

6414. Corollaries.

a. For each number r: $\binom{r}{I} \circ [I - \hat{1}] = \binom{r}{I - \hat{1}}$.

b. For any number r and positive integer n:

$$\left[\binom{r}{I} + \binom{r}{I - \hat{1}} \right] \middle| Z_{1,n} = \binom{r + 1}{I} \middle| Z_{1,n}.$$

6415. Consider any numbers x, y.
Each of the following propositions is easy to verify.

$$(x + y)^0 = 1 = \binom{0}{0} x^0 y^0 = \sum_{i=0}^{0} \binom{0}{i} x^{0-i} y^i.$$

$$(x + y)^1 = x + y =$$
$$\binom{1}{0} x^1 y^0 + \binom{1}{1} x^0 y^1 = \sum_{i=0}^{1} \binom{1}{i} x^{1-i} y^i.$$

$$(x + y)^2 = x^2 + 2xy + y^2 =$$
$$\binom{2}{0} x^2 y^0 + \binom{2}{1} x^1 y^1 + \binom{2}{2} x^0 y^2 = \sum_{i=0}^{2} \binom{2}{i} x^{2-i} y^i.$$

$$(x + y)^3 = x^3 + 3x^2 y + 3xy^2 + y^3 =$$
$$\binom{3}{0} x^3 y^0 + \binom{3}{1} x^2 y^1 + \binom{3}{2} x^1 y^2 + \binom{3}{3} x^0 y^3 = \sum_{i=0}^{3} \binom{3}{i} x^{3-i} y^i.$$

These results suggest the next theorem.

6416. Theorem. *Binomial theorem.*

For any nonnegative integer n and any numbers x, y:

$$(x + y)^n = \sum_{i=0}^{n} \binom{n}{i} x^{n-i} y^i.$$

Proof. Consider any nonnegative integer n and any numbers x, y.

In case $0 = n$, then $(x + y)^0 = 1 = \binom{0}{0} x^0 y^0 = \sum_{i=0}^{0} \binom{0}{i} x^{0-i} y^i.$

Now consider the case that $0 < n$. Then $1 \leq n$.

Let S denote $\left\{ n \in Z_1 \,\middle|\, (x + y)^n = \sum_{i=0}^{n} \binom{n}{i} x^{n-i} y^i \right\}.$

S contains 1. (?)

Lastly we prove that S is hereditary.

Consider any number n in S. Then $(n + 1) \in Z_1$, and

$(x + y)^{n+1} =$

$(x + y)(x + y)^n =$

$(x + y) \sum_{i=0}^{n} \binom{n}{i} x^{n-i} y^i =$

$\sum_{i=0}^{n} \binom{n}{i} x^{n+1-i} y^i + \sum_{i=0}^{n} \binom{n}{i} x^{n-i} y^{i+1} = ?$

$\sum_{i=0}^{n} \binom{n}{i} x^{n+1-i} y^i + \sum_{i=1}^{n+1} \binom{n}{i-1} x^{n+1-i} y^i =$

$\left[\binom{n}{0} x^{n+1} y^0 + \sum_{i=1}^{n} \binom{n}{i} x^{n+1-i} y^i \right] +$

$\qquad\qquad \left[\binom{n}{n} x^0 y^{n+1} + \sum_{i=1}^{n} \binom{n}{i-1} x^{n+1-i} y^i \right] =$

$x^{n+1} + y^{n+1} + \sum_{i=1}^{n} \left[\binom{n}{i} + \binom{n}{i-1} \right] x^{n+1-i} y^i = ?$

$\binom{n+1}{0} x^{n+1} + \binom{n+1}{n+1} y^{n+1} + \sum_{i=1}^{n} \binom{n+1}{i} x^{n+1-i} y^i = ?$

$\sum_{i=0}^{n+1} \binom{n+1}{i} x^{n+1-i} y^i.$ \qquad Hence $(n + 1) \in S$.

6417. For any integers i, n such that $0 \leq i \leq n$:

the number $\binom{n}{i}$ is called a *binomial coefficient*.

Some Useful Inequalities

6501. To simplify our work in this lesson, let us define a *normal sequence* to be any finite sequence of positive numbers whose product is 1, and let us use the symbol n to denote any given integer that exceeds 2.

6502. Exercises.

a. For each constant, normal sequence V on $Z_{1,n}$: $\displaystyle\sum_1^n V = n$.

b. For each nonconstant, normal sequence W on $Z_{1,2}$: $\displaystyle\sum_1^2 W > 2$.

6503. Lemma. For each nonconstant, normal sequence W on $Z_{1,n}$: $\displaystyle\sum_1^n W > n$.

Proof. Let S denote

$$\left\{ p \in Z_2 \,\middle|\, \text{for each nonconstant, normal sequence } W \text{ on } Z_{1,p}: \sum_1^p W > p \right\}.$$

It suffices to prove that S is hereditary from 2.
S contains 2. (6502b)
To prove that S is hereditary, consider any number p in S.
Then $(p + 1) \in Z_2$.
Consider any nonconstant, normal sequence W on $Z_{1,p+1}$.
Then at least one value of W, say W_j, is less than 1, and
at least one value of W, say W_k, is greater than 1. (?)
The integers j, k are between 1, $p + 1$ and are distinct.
Let T denote the result obtained from W by
deleting the two number pairs $(j,\ W_j)$, $(k,\ W_k)$,
annexing the two number pairs $(j,\ W_j W_k)$, $(k,\ W_{p+1})$,
and deleting the number pair $(p + 1,\ W_{p+1})$.

321

Then T is a normal sequence on $Z_{1,p}$.   (?)

Of course, T might be constant.   (?)   We have

$$\sum_1^{p+1} W = \left(\sum_1^p T\right) - W_j W_k + W_j + W_k \geq_? p - W_j W_k + W_j + W_k =$$

$$(p + 1) + (W_k - 1)(1 - W_j) >_? p + 1.$$

Hence $(p + 1) \epsilon S$.

6504. Corollary. For each normal sequence W on $Z_{1,n}$:

$$W \text{ is constant } \Leftrightarrow \sum_1^n W = n.$$

Proof. 6502a, 6503.

6505. Next we prove a very important theorem.

6506. Theorem.

For each nonconstant, finite sequence of positive numbers F on $Z_{1,n}$:

$$\left(\prod_1^n F\right)^{1/n} < (1/n) \sum_1^n F.$$

Proof. Consider any such hypothesized F and let u denote $\left(\prod_1^n F\right)^{1/n}$.

Then $\left[\prod_1^n (1/u)F\right]^{1/n} =_? 1$, and so $\prod_1^n (1/u)F = 1$, and hence

$(1/u)F$ is a nonconstant, normal sequence on $Z_{1,n}$ (?)   and therefore

$$n < \sum_1^n (1/u)F, \text{ and so } u < (1/n) \sum_1^n F.$$

NOTE. The number $\left(\prod_1^n F\right)^{1/n}$ is called *the geometric mean of F*;

the number $(1/n) \sum_1^n F$ is called *the arithmetic mean of F*.

6507. Corollary. For each finite sequence of positive numbers F on $Z_{1,n}$:

$$F \text{ is constant } \Leftrightarrow \left(\prod_1^n F\right)^{1/n} = (1/n) \sum_1^n F.$$

Proof. Consider any finite sequence of positive numbers F on $Z_{1,n}$.

PART I($\Leftarrow$). Use 6506.

PART II($\Rightarrow$). If F is constant, then all its values are equal to a positive number c, and so

$$\left(\prod_1^n F\right)^{1/n} = \left(\prod_1^n \hat{c}\right)^{1/n} = (c^n)^{1/n} = c = (1/n)\sum_1^n \hat{c} = (1/n)\sum_1^n F.$$

6508. We shall conclude our work by proving four related propositions that provide important extensions of Bernoulli's Inequality (5023).

Students who wish to pursue further the subject of inequalities are referred to *An Introduction to Inequalities* by Beckenbach and Bellman.

6509. Theorem. For any number y such that $-1 < y \neq 0$ and any number r such that $0 < r < 1$: $(1 + y)^r < 1 + ry$.

Proof. Consider any such hypothesized y, r.
Either r is rational or r is irrational.

CASE I. r is rational.
Then there are integers m, p such that $1 \leq m < p$ and $r = m/p$.

Let F denote the following function: $F(i) = \begin{cases} 1 + y & \text{if } i \in Z_{1,m} \\ 1 & \text{if } i \in Z_{m+1,p} \end{cases}$.

Then F is a nonconstant, finite sequence of positive numbers on $Z_{1,p}$, and so,

$$(1 + y)^r = (1 + y)^{m/p} = [(1 + y)^m]^{1/p} = ?$$

$$\left(\prod_1^p F\right)^{1/p} <_1 (1/p)\sum_1^n F = (1/p)\left[\sum_1^m F + \sum_{m+1}^p F\right] = ?$$

$$(1/p)[m(1 + y) + (p - m)(1)] = 1 + ry.$$

Reference. 1.6506.

CASE II. r is irrational.
Either $-1 < y < 0$ or $0 < y$.

Subcase i. $-1 < y < 0$.
Then $0 < 1 + y < 1$.
There is a rational u such that $0 < r < u < 1$.
Then $0 < r/u < 1$.
Consider any rational v such that $0 < v < r/u < 1$.
Then $(1 + y)^{r/u} < (1 + y)^v < 1 + vy$. (?)
So $[(1 + y)^{r/u} - 1]/y > v$.
Hence $[(1 + y)^{r/u} - 1]/y \geq r/u$. (?)
Then $(1 + y)^{r/u} \leq 1 + (r/u)y$, and so
$(1 + y)^r \leq [1 + (r/u)y]^u <_? 1 + u(r/u)y = 1 + ry$.

Subcase ii. $0 < y$.

Then $1 < 1 + y$.

There is a rational u such that $0 < r < u < 1$.

Then $0 < r/u < 1$.

Consider any rational v such that $0 < r/u < v < 1$.

Then $(1 + y)^{r/u} < (1 + y)^v < 1 + vy$. (?)

So $[(1 + y)^{r/u} - 1]/y < v$, and hence $[(1 + y)^{r/u} - 1]/y \leq r/u$. (?)

Then $(1 + y)^{r/u} \leq 1 + (r/u)y$, and so

$(1 + y)^r \leq [1 + (r/u)y]^u <_? 1 + u(r/u)y = 1 + ry$.

6510. Corollary. For any number y such that $-1 < y$ and any number r such that $0 < r < 1$: $\quad y = 0 \iff (1 + y)^r = 1 + ry$.

Proof. ($\Rightarrow$) is obvious, and ($\Leftarrow$) follows by 6509.

6511. Theorem. For any number x such that $-1 < x \neq 0$ and any number s such that $1 < s$ or $s < 0$: $\quad 1 + sx < (1 + x)^s$.

Proof. Consider any such hypothesized x, s.

CASE I. $1 < s$.

Either $1 + sx \leq 0$ or $0 < 1 + sx$.

In event $1 + sx \leq 0$, then the desired conclusion is obvious because its right side is positive.

In event $0 < 1 + sx$, then $-1 < sx$, and so by 6509 with sx for y and $1/s$ for r, we have $(1 + sx)^{1/s} < 1 + (1/s)sx = 1 + x$,

and so $1 + sx < (1 + x)^s$.

CASE II. $s < 0$.

Either $1 + sx \leq 0$ or $0 < 1 + sx$.

In event $1 + sx \leq 0$, the desired conclusion is obvious.

Lastly, consider the event that $0 < 1 + sx$.

There is an integer p such that $0 < -s/p < 1 < p$. (?)

So by 6509, $0 < (1 + x)^{-s/p} < 1 + (-s/p)x$.

Hence $(1 + x)^{s/p} > 1/[1 + (-s/p)x] > 1 + (s/p)x > 0$. (?)

So, $1 + sx = 1 + p[(s/p)x] <_1 [1 + (s/p)x]^p <_? (1 + x)^s$.

Reference 1.   5023 with $(s/p)x$ for y.

6512. Corollary. For any number x such that $-1 < x$ and any number s such that $1 < s$ or $s < 0$:

$x = 0 \iff 1 + sx = (1 + x)^s$.

Proof. ($\Rightarrow$) is obvious, and ($\Leftarrow$) follows by 6511.

Selected Bibliography

BATES, G. E., and KIOKEMEISTER, F. L., *The Real Number System*. Boston: Allyn and Bacon, Inc., 1960.

BEAUMONT, R. A., and PIERCE, R. S., *The Algebraic Foundations of Mathematics*. Reading, Mass.: Addison-Wesley Publishing Company, Inc., 1963.

BECKENBACH, E., and BELLMAN, R., *An Introduction to Inequalities*. New York: Random House, Inc., 1961.

CHEVALLEY, C., *Fundamental Concepts of Algebra*. New York: Academic Press, Inc., 1956.

COHEN, L. W., and EHRLICH, G., *The Structure of the Real Number System*. Princeton, N. J.: D. Van Nostrand Company, Inc., 1963.

COOLEY, J. C., *A Primer of Formal Logic*. New York: The Macmillan Company, 1942.

CROUCH, R., and WALKER, E., *Introduction to Modern Algebra and Analysis*. New York: Holt, Rinehart and Winston, Inc., 1962.

DEDEKIND, R., *Essays on the Theory of Numbers*, trans. by W. W. Beman. La Salle, Illinois: The Open Court Publishing Company, 1901.

DUBISCH, R., *The Nature of Number: An Approach to Basic Ideas of Modern Mathematics*. New York: The Ronald Press Company, 1952.

FEFERMAN, S., *The Number Systems: Foundations of Algebra and Analysis*. Reading, Mass.: Addison-Wesley Publishing Company, Inc., 1964.

HALMOS, P. R., *Naive Set Theory*. Princeton, N. J.: D. Van Nostrand Company, Inc., 1960.

HAMILTON, N. T., and LANDIN, J., *Set Theory: The Structure of Arithmetic*. Boston: Allyn and Bacon, Inc., 1961.

HENKIN, L., SMITH, W., VARINEAU, V., and WALSH, M., *Retracing Elementary Mathematics*. New York: The Macmillan Company, 1962.

KERSHNER, R. B., and WILCOX, L. R., *The Anatomy of Mathematics*. New York: The Ronald Press Company, 1950.

LANDAU, E., *Differential and Integral Calculus*. New York: Chelsea Publishing Company, 1951.

LANDAU, E., *Foundations of Analysis*, translated by F. Steinhardt. New York: Chelsea Publishing Company, 1951.

MOSTOW, G. D., SAMPSON, J. H., and MEYER, J.-P., *Fundamental Structures of Algebra*. New York: McGraw-Hill Book Company, Inc., 1963.

OLMSTED, J. M. H., *The Real Number System*. New York: Appleton-Century-Crofts, 1962.

ROBERTS, J. B., *The Real Number System in an Algebraic Setting*. San Francisco: W. H. Freeman and Company, 1962.

STOLL, R. R., *Set Theory and Logic*. San Francisco: W. H. Freeman and Company, 1963.

SUPPES, P., *Axiomatic Set Theory*. Princeton, N. J.: D. Van Nostrand Company, Inc., 1960.

SUPPES, P., *Introduction to Logic*. Princeton, N. J.: D. Van Nostrand Company, Inc., 1957.

THURSTON, H. A., *The Number-System*. New York: Interscience Publishers, a division of John Wiley & Sons, Inc., 1956.

WAISMANN, F., *Introduction to Mathematical Thinking*. New York: Harper & Brothers, 1959.

WILDER, R. L., *Introduction to the Foundations of Mathematics*. New York: John Wiley & Sons, Inc., 1952.

Glossary of Special Symbols

All references are to sections

Numerical subscripts used with symbols such as **sim**, **ent**, $\Rightarrow$, $\Leftrightarrow$, $>$, $=$, ϵ allude to references listed after the proof.
For further details see 120(NOTE III), 1927c NOTE.

For explanation of subscript question marks, see 226NOTE.
For explanation of (?), see 504NOTE.

$\vdots$	104(NOTE II), 120(NOTE VI)	$\supseteq$	1612	$\doteq$	3327
sim	115, 117	$\subset$	1614, 1613	Z, Z_0, Z_+	3813
$\sim$	204–207	$\cup$	1701	Z_i	3920a
$\Rightarrow$	303, 321	$\cap$	1710	$Z_{i,j}$	3920b
$\Leftarrow$	324	(x, y)	1813	sup	4302
$\Leftrightarrow$	401, 408	$S \times T$	1828	inf	4402
iff	401(NOTE II)	$W(x)$	1920	$[x]$	4602
ent	503, 521a	$V \circ W$	2018	Q, Q_0, Q_+	4807
s.f.	812(NOTE II)	V^{-1}	2103	φ	(*temporary*), 4909
a.s.f.	812(NOTE III)	R	2202	0^0	5028
$\mid$	906, 2014	max	2204c, 3602	$\bar{r}$	(*temporary*), 5202
d-false	1119, 1115	min	2602, 3702	$\log_b c$	5405
d-true	1119, 1106	$\pm$	2615	Log_b	6124
$\neq$	1307, 1309	sgn	2702	I	5513
$\{..\mid..\}$	1502	$\S$	2715	$\hat{c}$	5516
$\{\ \}$	1507, 1527, 1533, 1535	$<$	2902, 2908	$\sum$	5722, 6207
$\emptyset$	1519	$>$	2928	$\prod$	6108, 6207
ϵ	1539a, 1725	$\leqq$	3002, 3004	r^F	6302
$\notin$	1539b	$\geqq$	3033	$m!$	6401
$\subseteq$	1605	$\mid\ \mid$	3101, 5622, 5624	$\binom{r}{p}$	6410
		R_0, R_+	3304		

Index

Date Due

9-2302		
102302		